RONALD D. WYNNE was born in [illegible] Haven, Connecticut, and received his B.A. in Psychology from the University of Maryland and a Ph.D. from Catholic University. He has worked as a research psychologist, a professor at Queens College, and as director of a research branch of the Federal Job Corps. In 1973, he organized his own firm to conduct a variety of research and training projects in drug abuse, alcoholism, special education, and community organization. He is the author of numerous reports and articles, including a book-length contract report for the National Institute on Drug Abuse. Dr. Wynne is currently in private practice in Washington, D.C., specializing in family therapy with substance abusers.

JOËL L. PHILLIPS received his B.A. in History from Georgetown University and an M.A. in Criminal Justice from Nova University in Florida. With Dr. Wynne, he has coauthored numerous technical articles on cocaine, drug abuse, and alcoholism. He is presently a Senior Associate at Metametrics, Inc., a consulting firm specializing in criminal justice, and lives in Sacramento, California.

COCAINE

The Mystique and the Reality

JOËL L. PHILLIPS and
RONALD D. WYNNE, Ph.D.

A DISCUS BOOK/PUBLISHED BY AVON BOOKS

AVON BOOKS
A division of
The Hearst Corporation
959 Eighth Avenue
New York, New York 10019

Published by arrangement with the author
Library of Congress Catalog Card Number: 79-57333
ISBN: 0-380-48678-4

First Discus Printing, April, 1980

Printed in the U.S.A.

OPB 10 9 8 7 6 5 4 3

Thanks are due the following authors/publishers for permission to reprint portions of the text or tables from their publications:

Richard Ashley, *Cocaine: Its History, Uses and Effects*, © 1975 by St. Martin's Press, Inc., New York.

David Lee, *Cocaine Consumer's Handbook*, © 1976 by And/Or Press, San Francisco.

G. R. Gay et al., "An old girl: Flyin' low, dyin' slow, blinded by snow: Cocaine in perspective." From *International Journal of the Addictions* 8(1973): 1036, 1038, 1040, by courtesy of Marcel Dekker, Inc., New York.

G. T. McLaughlin, "Cocaine: The history and regulation of a dangerous drug." From *Cornell Law Review* 58(1973), by permission of Fred B. Rothman and Co., Law Books, S. Hackensack, New Jersey.

David Musto, *The American Disease: Origins of Narcotics Control*, © 1973 by Yale University Press, New Haven.

Wilder Penfield, "Halstead of Johns Hopkins, the man and his problem as described in the secret records of William Osler," from the *Journal of the American Medical Association* 210(1969): 2214-18, © 1969 by the American Medical Association. Permission granted by Dr. William Feindel, literary executor of Dr. Penfield's estate.

Pittigrilli, *Cocaine*, © 1974 by And/Or Press, San Francisco.

R. W. Post, "Cocaine psychoses: A continuum model." From *American Journal of Psychiatry* 132(1975): 225-31, © 1975 by the American Psychiatric Association. Reprinted by permission.

Richard Woodley, *Dealer: Portrait of a Cocaine Merchant*, © 1971 by Richard A. Woodley. Reprinted by permission of Holt, Rinehart and Winston, Publishers.

Much of the material contained in this publication was prepared under Contract No. ADM-45-74-144 from the National Institute on Drug Abuse. The material contained herein does not necessarily reflect opinions, official policy or the position of the National Institute on Drug Abuse of the Alcohol, Drug Abuse and Mental Health Administration of the U.S. Department of Health, Education and Welfare.

. . . the reason research on cocaine almost ended with Freud and a few of his contemporaries may be moralistic. We fear that if we admit a drug produces pleasure, we will have to take responsibility for an ensuing epidemic of abuse. Freud, like most who have taken cocaine, said it produces a uniquely pleasant euphoria, so that the danger of abuse is obviously very high. This failure to learn more about cocaine is striking in this age of renewed interest in drugs that alter thought and behavior.

—Robert Byck, ed., *Cocaine Papers by Sigmund Freud*

TABLE OF CONTENTS

* ASTERISKS DENOTES BOXED MATERIAL.

PREFACE

This volume provides a comprehensive summary of historical, scientific, and popular information on cocaine and coca, statistical data concerning the use and abuse of cocaine, an overview of pertinent federal and state laws and recent legal developments, and the results of a field study of current street myths and rituals involving cocaine. In its original form, and with its two companion volumes—Phillips and Wynne, *A Cocaine Bibliography—Nonannotated*, published as No. 8 in the National Institute on Drug Abuse's Research Issue Series, DHEW Publication No. (ADM) 75-203, 1975; and Wynne Associates et al., *Cocaine—Summaries of Psychosocial Research*, published as No. 18 in the same series, DHEW Publication No. (ADM) 77-391, 1976)—this book constituted the final report of contract ADM 45-74-144, The Facts and Myths of Human Cocaine Use and Abuse, between Wynne Associates of Washington, D.C., and the Division of Research, National Institute on Drug Abuse, ADAMHA, DHEW. Together, the three volumes are a major basic reference source for those interested in the study of cocaine and its effects.

ORGANIZATION OF THIS VOLUME

Appendix A presents a chronological overview of key events in the history of coca and cocaine and provides a quick summary of many of the topics in this book, which is divided into four parts plus an annotated bibliography.

Part I deals with the use of coca, past and present, and

summarizes the development of its popularity through the centuries of Indian migration, during the heyday of the Inca Empire, and after the Spanish conquest.

Part II begins with the introduction of coca to Europe, the early study and experimentation with cocaine after its isolation as coca's psychoactive ingredient, and the rapidly growing popularity of the drug throughout the world in the latter part of the nineteenth century, which gave rise to many of the myths about the drug that are still prevalent today. The counterreactions to this popularity are discussed, which culminated in the passage of regulatory legislation in many countries, and the long eclipse of cocaine, from the 1920s into the 1960s. The patent-medicine industry and a number of artistic efforts dealing with cocaine are discussed.

Part III is a largely technical section which attempts to summarize most of what is known about the pharmacology, physiology, biochemistry, and toxicology of cocaine. This section includes summaries of the first controlled studies of cocaine's effects on humans, done very recently, as well as suggestions for needed research in these areas.

Part IV—the core of the book, in terms of the primary purpose of our contract with NIDA—focuses on the socio-psychological aspects of cocaine use and abuse. The chapters in this section draw heavily on the fieldwork. Available statistics on cocaine use are summarized both from the literature and from government sources, followed by an overview of the treatment of cocaine in the popular culture. A discussion of street myths and rituals of use is presented, based largely on our interviews with users. There is a detailed treatment of dealing, smuggling, and the law-enforcement activities directed against them, based primarily on our analysis of statistical information from law-enforcement agencies and interviews with dealers, smugglers, and agency officials. There is a chapter on consumer aspects, discussing common adulterants in street cocaine and a variety of tests consumers can use to protect themselves. Part IV concludes with a tabular summary of present knowledge about the drug.

As a service to the general reader, references within the text are not given in the parenthetical form standard in scientific publications but in less obtrusive superior figures, which refer to the reference lists at the end of each chapter. Full citations for all such references are in the Bibliography.

Joël L. Phillips
Ronald D. Wynne, Ph.D.
Washington, D.C.
1979

ACKNOWLEDGMENTS

This book represents the collaborative efforts of many people. Nonny Soifer played a major role in preparing the bibliographies and conducting background research. She assisted in editing the volume, as did Suzan Wynne. Help in compiling the bibliographies was also provided by Gayle Dakof, Kristine Bruner, Daniel Fischer, and Laura Thompson. Kathy McNaughton gathered and tabulated the considerable data from the Drug Enforcement Administration. Barbara Cobbett, Stephanie Chris, and Martha Dexter creatively typed the various manuscript drafts. Susan Moldow, executive editor of Avon Books, provided great help in reorganizing what had been a government report into a more readable, accessible format.

Special thanks for their contributions are due the following:

Joe Phillips, formerly of the Virginia Bureau of Forensic Medicine, Springfield, helped determine the validity of the major tests now in vogue to determine the presence and/or purity of cocaine street samples.

Dan Waldorf and Sheigla Murphy, drug researchers from the San Francisco area, provided access to the subjects of their own study of cocaine dealing and use, and transcripts of some of their interviews. We had intended to interview the head of the distribution network with which they worked, code-named "Smuggler." The day before our interview was scheduled, an altercation broke out between Smuggler and his partner, which resulted in Smuggler's death by gunfire and the jailing of the partner for first-degree murder.

Michael Aldrich, Ph.D., executive curator of the Fitzhugh Ludlow Memorial Library in San Francisco, the largest (over 10,000 items) private library of rare drug literature in the world, provided copies of previously unavailable books and essays on cocaine.

Michael Starkes, an associate of the Ludlow Memorial Library, prepared abstracts of some of the more important books and documents in his own library and identified many books and movies dealing with cocaine.

Douglas F. Wainer, chief of the Statistical and Data Services Division of the Drug Enforcement Administration, and Eric Rosenquist, chief of this division's Analysis Branch, provided considerable statistical material. Paul Casagrande and Robert Long of the division provided further assistance.

Several special agents of the DEA's Washington, D.C., and New York City field offices, as well as several undercover agents for D.C.-area police departments, provided information about their experiences with cocaine users and dealers, trafficking patterns, arrests and seizures, and many more areas of illicit cocaine use and abuse.

James Woods, Ph.D., Department of Pharmacology, University of Michigan, shared his comprehensive understanding of the field, and Robert Post, M.D. of the National Institute of Mental Health, who has been conducting some of the first well-controlled cocaine research with humans, shared his many insights into the drug's psychoactive effects.

Bruce Ratcliffe, Ph.D., of PharmChem Laboratories, Palo Alto, Calif., editor of *PharmChem Newsletter*, a nationally distributed monthly that presents results of analyses (done in its own labs) of street drug samples from across the country, and historical and scientifically sound pharmacological information concerning drugs with high abuse potential, provided summaries of analyses and insights into the illicit cocaine market. Help was also provided by Marshall Werner.

"Joshua" and other disc jockies at Radio Station WHFS-FM, Bethesda, Md., and at several other D.C.-area stations, broadcast our request for letters from cocaine users concerning their experiences.

Many people responded to these radio requests by taking the time and trouble to write to us.

Many users, dealers, smugglers and others associated with cocaine permitted us to attend their social gatherings, observe their behavior, and interview them about their experiences.

The staffs at the following libraries and information centers from which references and materials were obtained were extremely helpful: American Medical Association; American Pharmaceutical Manufacturers Association; American University; Drug Abuse Council; Drug Enforcement Administration; Fitzhugh Ludlow Memorial Library, San Francisco; Georgetown University; George Washington University (Scientific Communication Division); Library of Congress; National Institute on Drug Abuse; National Library of Medicine; PharmChem Laboratories, Palo Alto, Calif.; Smithsonian Science Information Exchange; and Virginia Bureau of Forensic Science, Springfield.

INTRODUCTION

Much of this book represents our attempts to sort out the "facts" from the "myths"—beliefs that have neither a historical nor a scientific basis in fact. Our desire had been to present the historical, physiological, pharmacological, psychological, economic, legal, and cultural facts, as clearly as possible.

With the recent renewal of interest in the drug, which had been out of the public eye since the 1920s, a number of classic works on coca and cocaine, both scientific and literary, have been reissued. There have also been several attempts to draw together what is known about cocaine into systematic and specialized surveys. The reissues range from new translations of Freud's classic studies of the 1880s to Mortimer's still-fascinating and authoritative 1901 classic on coca and Pitigrilli's melodramatic novel of the dangers of cocaine among the young and sophisticated in the Parisian 1920s.

The surveys include Woods and Downs' review of cocaine physiology and toxicology for the final report of the National Commission on Marijuana and Drug Abuse; McLaughlin's law-review article; several guidebooks to the production, preparation, and enjoyment of the drug; and Ashley's *Cocaine: Its History, Uses and Effects.*

Much literature exists on cocaine, especially in English, Spanish, German, and Portuguese. Our own bibliography, published in 1975, included over 1,800 items, and considerably more has been published in the few years between its publication and the present. But there are tremendous gaps in the literature, especially in the socio-psychological areas. Many of these gaps are due, quite simply, to cocaine's illicit status. The passage in 1914 of the Harrison Narcotics Act and subsequent state and federal legislation made the use of cocaine illegal for other than legitimate medical purposes. Because of the legal situation, however, post–Harrison Act research on cocaine was and continues to be extremely difficult. Questions as to who and how many use cocaine, what quantities are consumed, and other issues concerning its illicit use remain largely speculative. As Richard Ashley's book points out, there are peculiar problems in attempting to study the illicit use of cocaine because "unlike the opiates, cocaine is not a drug which compels the user to desperate measures to replenish his supply."[1] As a result it is difficult to contact ordinary cocaine users, obviously an important research source. Relatively few persons whose primary drug of abuse is reported as cocaine appear in drug treatment facilities. The primary contacts of law-enforcement agencies, which are the source of most available statistics on cocaine use, are with dealers rather than users. Further, the newspapers are of only minimal assistance to those attempting to understand the magnitude of cocaine use and the rituals and beliefs associated with it. Reporters assigned to the "drug beat" are usually generalists and rarely knowledgeable enough not to fall victim to the mythology themselves.[2]

Because of the gaps in the literature and the research difficulties it has been necessary for us to go well beyond the merely scientific in preparing this volume. We attempted here to draw together and systematize available information from the professional, scientific, and lay literatures, from the "street," and from the experiences and knowledge of various levels of experts in the field of substance use and misuse. In addition, we have attempted to resolve a number of inconsistencies noted during the literature review.

The book is directed toward answering such questions as:

- What accounts for the recent resurgence of interest in the drug, after a dormant period of nearly thirty years?
- What is the relationship of cocaine to coca and its use?
- Who uses the drug and how?
- Who distributes it and how?

- How much is being circulated and how much is being removed from circulation through law-enforcement efforts?
- What is a cocaine "high"?
- What are the physiological and pharmacological facts about cocaine?
- What are the most prevalent beliefs about its effects?
- How, if at all, have they changed over time?
- What constitutes cocaine abuse and how is it treated?
- How many abusers are seeking treatment?

Some of the cocaine "myths"

Here is a sampling of views about cocaine as expressed in the literature (1885–1971):

- "[Cocaine] can supply the place of food, make the coward brave, the silent eloquent, free the victims of alcohol and opium habit from their bondage, and, as an anesthetic, render the sufferer insensitive to pain" (an 1885 drug manufacturer's ad).
- "Taken internally, the effect of cocaine is to produce criminals" (1909).
- "No drug on the market seems to have anywhere near such a demoralizing effect upon the human system. The habitual user soon loses all moral courage. Lying and stealing are the least of the crimes he is ready to commit when under the influence, and, in a majority of cases, his nature becomes brutalized and changed for the worse" (1909).
- "The cocaine habit is pronounced by physicians and neurologists to be the most terrible vice ever acquired by a civilized people, in the havoc that it works upon the mental, moral and physical life of a person that acquires it" (1909).
- "The use of 'coke' is probably much more widely spread among Negroes than among whites. 'Heaven dust' they call it. Its use by Negro field hands in the South has spread with appalling swiftness and results. There is little doubt but that every Jew peddler in the South carries the stuff. . . ." (1910).
- "Cocaine is the most insidious of known narcotics—a

drug that wrecks its victim more swiftly and surely than opium" (1911).

- "There is no doubt that this drug is used more than any other by those in the white slave market to corrupt young girls—and bring them into the ranks of prostitution" (1911).
- "Criminals use cocaine to stimulate their courage" (1925).
- "People use daily preparations of cocaine to give them fancied strength for their work" (1925).
- "Latin people think coke is an aphrodisiac" (1969), "*but* cocaine produces a decrease in sexual appetite" (1971).
- "Kids are learning that coke's pretty much like speed" (1970).

Here is a sampling of views about cocaine expressed by users in the course of preparing this book:

- It makes people aggressive, just like speed.
- It enhances sexual performance and feeling.
- When its available, it's almost everybody's drug of choice.
- There's no quality control on the street; coke's always cut with something.
- It's worth every cent you have to pay.
- It's so costly, no one can afford to be a coke junkie.
- It's a dangerous drug and harmful to your brain. It will make you go crazy.

THE FIELDWORK

To carry the scope of this project beyond the literature, we turned to three alternative data sources.

Interviews with users and dealers

Through personal contacts, in both the Washington, D.C., and San Francisco Bay areas, we obtained access to a variety of self-reported cocaine users and dealers who agreed to personal (and essentially informal) interviews. We interviewed, individually and in small groups, approximately a hundred such people. They included persons aged fifteen to fifty-five, of both sexes, several races and nationalities, and a number of occupations, such as university professors, secretaries, singers, mechanics, students, waitresses, and many more, including some who were unemployed.

There was considerable variation in the extent of their experience with cocaine and with other drugs as well. Twenty sold cocaine, though mostly in small amounts. One was a dealer of repute (selling pounds of cocaine at a time). Several had personally smuggled cocaine into this country from South America. We personally observed the use of the drug (or what was purported to be the drug) by approximately forty people, typically in party situations.

With the knowledge and permission of the interviewees, many of the interviews were tape-recorded and later transcribed. The tape recordings themselves, as well as any identifying information from which the interviewees could be identified, have been sent out of the United States, to prevent anyone else from obtaining them.

Letters from users

We solicited "air time," in the form of free public-service announcements, from several FM radio stations in the Washington area that cater to an audience we felt would probably include cocaine users. Listeners were asked to send stories about their personal experiences with cocaine to a post-office box. They were told the letters were for a government-supported research project, and that they should not include any identifying information. The letter to radio stations requesting air time was as follows:

January 28, 1975

> Wynne Associates is a small social science research and consulting firm specializing in evaluation, program development and planning in the fields of drug abuse, alcoholism, community mental health, special education, aging and community organization.
>
> This past year, we were under contract with the National Institute on Drug Abuse to study treatment facilities currently in use to treat nonopiate abuse. Recently, we were granted a contract by NIDA (ADM-45-74-

144) to do a year-long study on The Facts and Myths of Human Cocaine Use/Abuse. The product of the project will be a book to be available to the general public.

The project requires an extensive literature review, with annotations of the 100 most relevant articles and books on cocaine. In addition, NIDA would like us to contact (using their terminology) "street-wise experts" to obtain further information on various street or popular myths, habits, rituals, etc. surrounding the use of cocaine.

It is in this regard that we think your station can help us. We would like you to announce as a public service that a local consulting firm is doing research on the facts and myths of cocaine use/abuse and that this firm needs personal anecdotes and stories on various aspects of cocaine use.

WANTED: COCAINE STORIES

- DEALING (cutting; burns; costs; customers; dealers; etc.)
- DOING (first high stories; combination highs; where do you do it—home or parties, etc.; why do you do it—sex, artistic reasons, feel better, etc.; how do you do it—shoot or snort it, etc.)
- OVERDOING (bad effects; effects from long-term use; what about treatment—detoxification or therapy; etc.)
- SMUGGLING (scoring in South America; passing customs; street deals; etc.)

From the writer we need to know: age, sex, number of times they have done cocaine. However, and we stress this point, WE DO NOT WANT ANY NAMES OR ADDRESSES! All letters are to be sent to an anonymous post office box in Washington [the box number was included in the announcement].

Perhaps you can stress the fact that it is only by getting information from the users—both good and bad—that the truth about cocaine can be known.

We received approximately thirty letters. Most were fairly long, handwritten, and from a group of seemingly creative and intelligent persons. The letters generally highlighted specific incidents concerning cocaine, rather than summarizing the writer's general experience with the drug. Most were "pro-cocaine"; there was only one "horror story." There seemed an even mix of male and female writers. The few who indicated their age stated they were in their early twenties. It is our assumption, given the stations from which cooperation was solicited, that most writers were white.

Interviews with narcotics officials

We conducted informal interviews with sixteen law-enforcement-related officials, federal, state and local, in the Washington, D.C., area. These included two federal administrators, five undercover narcotics agents, one member of a federal drug intelligence-gathering group, two forensic laboratory specialists, and six Drug Enforcement Administration support staffers, including the librarian and several statisticians, who were extremely helpful in providing us access to reports on trafficking, publications, etc. In these interviews we tried to obtain an understanding of the illicit cocaine distribution network: kinds of people involved, smuggling procedures, adulterants, prices, etc. We also solicited views about cocaine use and users from the agents.

A caveat

There are clearly holes in the data we obtained through these informal methods: How do we ascertain the veracity of these stories told to us? Did the writers (and even some of the interviewees) actually use cocaine? If so, how do they know (if they know) that what they used was cocaine and not simply some other drug that was a "white powder with crystals"? What were the dosages consumed by the letter writers? In what settings and under what conditions did they use the drug? And so on.

Obviously, our letter-writing radio-ad respondents and our interviewees may or may not have been doing "the real thing." But it is clear that we obtained considerable provocative information about the attitudes, beliefs, and expectations of a variety of users, and also obtained corroboration of much of what has been written about street myths and use/sales/dealing patterns. At the very least, our findings provide potentially fruitful hypotheses for further research. And, imprecise as this data may be, our "street-wise experts" offered considerable insights into the reasons for what seems to be the ever increasing popularity of cocaine.

REFERENCES

1. Ashley, R., *Cocaine: Its History, Uses and Effects,* (New York: St. Martin's Press, 1975).
2. Bomboy, R., "Major newspaper coverage of drug issues," *Fellows Series Monographs, FS-1,* (Washington, D.C.: Drug Abuse Council, 1974).

Part I

The Story of Coca

CHAPTER 1

THE HISTORY OF COCA USE

Of all the Plants that any soil does bear
This Tree in Fruits the richest does appear,
It bears the best, and bears them all year. . . .
Each leaf is Fruit, and such substantial Fare,
No fruit beside to rival it will dare.
Mov'd with his Country's coming Fate, (whose soil)
Must for her Treasurers be expoted to (spoil)
Our Variocha first this Coca sent,
Endow'd with leaves of wond'rous Nourishment,
Whose Juice Succ'd in, and to the Stomach tak'n
Long Hunger and long Labour can sustain;
From which our faint and weary Bodies And
Mor Succor, more they cheer the dropping Mind,
Than can your Bacchus and your Cretes join'd.

—Crowley, *Book of Plants* (1721)

THE COCA PLANT

Coca shrubs grow wild in much of South America, and it is from the shrub's "delicate tealike leaves"[1] that the alkaloid cocaine is extracted. Although there are over a hundred species of coca shrubs, the leaves of only two are used for chewing: *Erythroxylon coca* (Lamarck), also known commercially as the Huanuco or "Bolivian" leaf, and *Erythroxylon novogranatense* (Morris) Hieronymus, known commercially as the Truxillo or Trujillo or "Peruvian" leaf.[2] The leaves of these two species of coca shrub differ in size and in chemical composition (the level of cocaine that can be extracted from the Peruvian leaf is greater), and they are produced in different areas. These distinctions have more commercial than historical significance, since the literature has not generally indicated the species. (Further information about these points can be found in Chapter 7.)

There has been a more serious confusion, however, between coca and several other plants: cocoa (chocolate), a product of the cacao plant; kola, a product of the African kola tree; and even coco, a product of the coconut palm.[3]

The plant itself is very distinctive. The wild coca shrub often reaches a height of 12 to 18 feet, although the cultivated plant is usually kept to about 6 feet.[4] A plant's productive life is half a century. Coca plants, either through cultivation or spontaneous propagation, have spread "until they are now found in the whole eastern curve of the Andes from the Strait of Magellan to the borders of the Caribbean Sea, growing on the moist sides of the mountains at elevations from 4,500 to 6,000 feet."[5]

A Coca Branch

THE ORIGIN OF THE PRACTICE OF CHEWING COCA LEAVES

Coca was widely used by pre-Columbian South American Indians.[6] There is some evidence indicating that the custom of chewing the leaves of the shrub originated in the Amazonian jungle.[7] As Bejarano indicated, however, the "true origin of the coca leaf chewing habit is lost in the mists of time."[8] Examination of the etymology of the word "coca," or other terms by which the shrub is known, such as *ipada* by the Amazons, *cuca* in Quechua, or *hayo* in Brazil and Venezuela, provides little insight into the origin of its use. Blejer-Prieto and others trace the term to the Aymara *khoka*, which means "the tree."[9] Some think "that the word 'coca' means 'food,' which would be in accordance with the belief that it is a foodstuff."[10]

SOME EARLY MYTHS AND LEGENDS ABOUT THE COCA PLANT

Early South American folklore is replete with stories and legends that account for the appearance of coca on earth. These, in fact, constitute the earliest myths surrounding the use of cocaine—the psychoactive substance of the coca leaf. Most of the coca legends serve a dual function: they established a preternatural origin for the plant—giving it a "divine" status—and they restricted the chewing of the leaves, or at least dictated when the leaves were to be chewed. A Peruvian saying about coca is, "God is a substance."[11]

Probably the earliest-known legend concerning the origin of coca was recorded by investigators of the Viceroy Toledo in 1571 in their *Informacion* of Inca history and customs:

> In answering questions about the shrub, the aged Indians invariably told the same story. From what they had heard, the Indians recalled, before coca was a shrub it was a beautiful woman. Discovered to be an adultress, she was executed, cut in half, and buried as a seed would be planted. From part of her severed body, a shrub, which became known as "macoca" and "cocamana," began to grow and blossom. Only men were permitted to pick its leaves, placing them in their pouches. It was soon learned that the pouches could be opened to take coca only after copulation, which was to be performed in the memory of the beautiful but dismembered adultress.[12]

Gutierrez-Noriega suggested that the emphasis of these legends on sex and sexual perversions was a reflection of the Indians' knowledge of the sexually stimulating properties of coca, which also accounts for coca's original use as an aphrodisiac.[13] At least two present-day tribes in Colombia, the Kogi and Cabaga, "preserve the tradition that coca promotes fertility, at least during the early years of the habit."[14]

Freud and later Osborne cited a legend of the Aymaran tribe in which Khuno, god of snow and storm, angrily burned the land of all vegetation but the boba shrub.[15] In chewing the coca to relieve their hunger, the Indians of the land discovered its euphoric properties, and its ability to help them endure the cold.

Two other legends, both from the Inca period (beginning in the eleventh century), attribute divine origin to the plant. According to one of these legends, the shrub was a gift from the sun god—Inti—who instructed the moon mother, Moma Quilla, to plant the coca in the moist valleys. It was to be used only by the Incas (the rulers, who were descendants of the gods) to give them endurance "to perform their earthly functions."[16]

The second and more famous of these Incan legends involves Manco Capac, the "son of god," founder of the Inca Empire (ca. 1021). According to the legend, he and his sister-wife, Mama Oello, brought the practice of agriculture "into their vast dominions" and made a present to the inhabitants of the coca, "a divine plant which satiates the hungry, strengthens the weak, and causes them to forget their misfortunes."[17]

PRE-INCAN USE OF COCA

Although this famous legend claims that the coca plant was a divine gift of the Incas, there is considerable evidence suggesting the extensive use of coca by pre-Incan tribes.

Certain archaeological artifacts and medical findings indicate pre-Incan use. In 1917, an economic botanist with the U.S. Department of Agriculture uncovered a number of thousand-year-old mummy bundles containing coca leaves, sacks, and the lime containers used by coca chewers.[18] This would be a century or two prior to the founding of the Inca Empire in the early eleventh century. There is also considerable archaelogical evidence, in the form of ceramic pots, that dates the use of coca to the Mochica era of 600–800 A.D.[19]

Bejarano[20] believed that one of the first coca-using tribes was the Archuacos, inhabitants of a country in northwestern South America, possibly in what is Colombia today. Conquered by the fierce Chibchas (who, incidentally, assimilated the coca-chewing custom themselves) and driven south, the Archuacos spread their custom to other tribes, such as the Uras, who lived in what is now northern Bolivia and southern Peru.

Apparently, the spread of coca was such that by the time of the Spanish conquest in the 1500s, it was cultivated far more extensively in Latin America than it is today. Its geographic distribution ranged from the River Plate, separating Argentina and Uruguay, to the islands of the Caribbean. The Indian inhabitants of this vast area either chewed the leaves or used them "as infusions in liquid."[21]

COCA AND THE INCAS

With the consolidation of the Inca Empire came a significant change in the status of coca in the "political and social structure of pre-Spanish Andean society."[22] The Incas not only retained many of the earlier restrictions on the chewing of coca, but increasingly restricted its use as their influence extended throughout the Andes.

The literature offers varying accounts for the restriction of coca's use. Mortimer felt that the limitations of use to only the rulers and religious leaders resulted from shortages in the coca supply during the early part of Incan rule.[23] In part, Mortimer said, the shortages resulted because the conquered Indian tribes held back parts of their crops from the ruling classes. To prevent this occurrence in the future, the rulers claimed their right to all coca crops and the use thereof. A less-plausible explanation provided by Saenz is that the restrictions resulted from an altruistic desire on the part of the Incan rulers to protect the masses from the drug's effects.[24] There is no supporting evidence for this theory, however.

The most frequently given explanation, and the one that seems to make the most sense, is that coca use was restricted for political reasons. The drug was to be an exclusive privilege and right of the rulers and religious leaders and a symbol of their authority and control over the populace. The process of establishing this control, however, was an evolutionary one that became gradually more defined throughout the long history of Incan rule and domination (from the early eleventh to the late sixteenth century).

The Incas had no written language and thus no recorded history, and much of the early history written by the conquering Spaniards was inaccurate. So it is difficult to determine very precisely just when coca became a significant factor in the political and religious structure of the Inca Empire. One speculation is that coca's role became sharply defined during the reign of Inca Toca (ca. 1250–1315), when the empire was greatly expanded and the Incas were exposed to numbers of coca-chewing Indians. The imperialistic expansion continued under the leadership of later Incas, and by the end of the fourteenth century (especially with the conquest of Paucartanslo, a major source of coca production) the Incas had a virtual monopolistic control over the cultivation of the shrub.[25] These coca plantations—*cocales*—became a state monopoly during the reign of Topa Inca (ca. 1471–93), and the use of coca became a prerogative of the ruling class. However, the common classes were permitted to partake of the plant under special circumstances—citizens for meritorious service, soldiers for use during military campaigns, and workers for involvement in public projects.[26]

The religious use of coca began during the reign of Inca Roca (1250–1315) and developed out of the practice of tossing wads of coca leaves at *huacas* (roadside stone dwellings honoring the gods) in the hope that this would guarantee a safe crossing of the Andes.[27] Later it was used by priests who chewed it and/or burned it as incense. "By the end of their empire, coca had become the offering most frequently employed in the numerous sacrifices and superstitious practices of the Incas."[28]

Restrictions on coca's use lessened during the second half of the fifteenth century as the Inca Empire declined. The empire was racked by a series of civil wars that weakened the powers of the ruling classes. To maintain the allegiance of his followers, the emperor Huayana Capas (1493–1527) inaugurated a practice of providing the most loyal of them with a noble title, along with which came the right to cultivate coca plantations. This practice effectively ended the state monopoly over the coca plantations.

With the further collapse of the empire in the fifteenth and sixteenth centuries, coca-chewing permission was extended to all but the lowest classes—the "plebes" or "purics."[29] (These lower classes, however, still constituted the majority of the estimated 10 million population.) The net effect was that by the time of the Spanish conquest of Cuzo by Pizarro's troops in 1536, coca had lost much of its initial significance in the Inca Empire. It was "no longer a symbol of exclusive political authority and social status."[30]

COCA UNDER THE SPANISH CONQUISTADORES

Spanish attitudes toward coca underwent striking changes. The Spaniards initially forbade the use of coca, believing its effect to be a product of a pact with the devil.[31] The first law was passed by Philip II of Spain in October 1573.[32] The conquerors, however, soon realized the huge profit potential in trading coca leaves with the Indians for their gold and silver, and some of the restrictions were lifted.[33]

There is some controversy as to the specific role the Spanish played in the use of coca following the conquest. Zapata-Ortiz felt that coca chewing became widespread after, rather than before, the conquest, because of four factors: considerable decline in the production of foodstuffs as the empire quickly withered; the institution of forced labor by the Spaniards; the large profits involved in trading coca for gold and silver; and the euphoric feeling brought on by the drug, which helped the natives "relieve the hardships of the conquest and subjugation," and thus increased their own desire to chew the leaves.[34]

Several students of the history of the colonial period assert that the Spaniards deliberately used the plant as an instrument of social control "to hold [the natives] more tightly as virtual slaves."[35] On the other hand, Gagliano states:

> The *Leyenda Negra* is quite black enough without adding to it the charge that Spaniards used coca in order to drug the Andean Indians into submission. There is no evidence to prove such an accusation. The moralists who opposed generally did so for reasons other than the

euphoric effects of mastication. Indeed, to claim that the Spaniards even realized that coca contained narcotic properties is to give them credit for knowledge which they did not possess.[36]

REFERENCES

1. Gutierrez-Noriega, C., & Von Hagen, V. W. "The strange case of the coca leaf," *Sci. Monthly*, 1950, *70(2)*, 81–89.
2. Cardenas, M. "Psychological aspects of coca addiction," *Bull. Narc.*, 1952, *4(2)*, 6–9.
3. Gutierrez-Noriega & Von Hagen, 1950, Op. Cit.
4. Maher, J. "Coca—Erythroxylon coca," (Unpublished BNDD document, 1968).
5. Ibid.
6. Gagliano, J. "A Social History of Coca in Peru," Doctoral Dissertation (History), (Georgetown University, Washington, D.C., 1960).
7. Spruce, R. *Notes of a botanist on the Amazon and Andes, being a record of travel . . . During the years 1849–1864,* (ed. and cond. by Alfred R. Wallace). Two Vols. London, 1908.
8. Bejarano, J. "Present state of coca-leaf habit in Columbia," *Bull. Narc.*, 1961, *13(1)*, 1–5.
9. Blejer-Prieto, H. "Coca leaf and cocaine addictions, some historical notes," *Can. Med. Assoc. J.*, 1965, 93, 700–704.
10. Bejarano, J. "Further considerations on the coca habit in Columbia," *Bull. Narc.*, 1952, *4(3)*, 3–19.
11. Lingeman, R. R. *Drugs from A to Z: A dictionary,* (New York: McGraw-Hill, 1969).
12. Gagliano, 1961, Op. Cit.
13. Gutierrez-Noriega, 1950, Op. Cit.
14. Bejarano, 1952, Op. Cit.
15. Freud, S. "On coca." In: R. Byck (ed.), *Cocaine Papers by Sigmund Freud* (tr. S. Edminster), (New York: Stonehill Publishing Co., 1974).
16. Gagliano, 1960, Op. Cit.
17. Mortimer, W. G. *Peru history of coca, the divine plant of the Incas,* (New York: J. H. Vail and Company, 1901.) Reprinted as *History of Coca,* (San Francisco: And/Or Press, 1974).
18. Ashley, 1975, Op. Cit.
19. Drug Enforcement Administration. Report on cocaine users (#BH-003). Conducted by DAWN scientific investigators for the Cocaine Policy Task Force (unpublished). (Washington, D.C.: DEA, July, 1974.)

20. Bejarano, 1952, Op. Cit.
21. Gagliano, 1961, Op. Cit.
22. Ibid.
23. Mortimer, 1901, Op. Cit.
24. Saenz, L. N. *La coca: Estudio medico-social de gran toxicomania Peruana* (Lima: 1938).
25. Gagliano, 1961, Op. Cit.
26. Ibid.
27. Bennett, W. C. "The Andean highlands: An introduction," in *The Andean Civilizations*, Vol. II of *Handbook of South American Indians*, (ed.) J. H. Steward, Smithsonian Institution. Bureau of American Ethnology, Bulletin 143, (6 Vols.), (Washington, D.C.: 1946–50).
28. Gagliano, 1961, Op. Cit.
29. Blejer-Prieto, 1965, Op. Cit.
30. Gagliano, 1961, Op. Cit.
31. Mortimer, 1901, Op. Cit.
32. Leon, L. A. "The disappearance of cocaism in Ecuador," *Bull. Narc., 4(2)*, 21–25.
33. Rowe, J. H. "Inca Culture at the times of the Spanish Conquest," in *The Andean Civilizations*, Vol. II of *Handbook of South American Indians*, (ed.) J. H. Steward, Smithsonian Institution. Bureau of American Ethnology, Bulletin 143, (6 Vols.). Washington, D.C.: 1946–50.
34. Zapata-Ortiz, V. "The problems of the chewing of the coca leaf in Peru," *Bull. Narc.*, 1952, *4*, 26–33.
35. Blejer-Prieto, 1965, Op. Cit.
36. Gagliano, 1961, Op. Cit.

CHAPTER 2

USE AND USES OF COCA

Whereas cocaine addiction is associated with night life, with loose women and their lovers seeking to stimulate sexual desire, the coca chewing habit is ingrained among the Indians, the farmers and miners, who use it to arouse physical energy and to deaden pain, loneliness, hunger and thirst. . . .

—Fernandez, quoted by R. P. Alcala,
"The Coca Question in Bolivia"

Two distinct methods of coca use are practiced by the Indians of the Andes region and those of the western Amazon River region in Brazil, Peru, Ecuador, and Columbia. The Andean method, much better known, involves mixing coca leaves and an alkaline material together into a wad which is held in the cheek and periodically rechewed. The Amazonian method consists of taking coca leaves in a powdered form, working them into a paste, and holding them in the cheek for one to several hours.[1] Here we focus on the Andean method.

MANNER OF USE IN THE ANDES

The chewing of coca is a well-defined practice that has changed very little over the centuries. First, the *coquero* (coca chewer) takes several coca leaves from a *chuspa*, a baglike container. The midribs of each individual leaf are removed, and the leaves, one at a time, are placed in the side of the mouth. More leaves are added until a quid or plug is formed. From a *poporo*, a small gourd usually carried in or attached to the *chuspa*, a limestone substance (*lilipta*) is removed with the use of a small stick and then placed in the mouth with the quid of coca.[2]

The *lilipta* contains potassium, sodium, calcium, magnesium, phosphorus, and some traces of iron and antimony.[3]

The source of the lime varies in different parts of South America, however. Generally it is made from "ashes left after burning certain plants or by burning shells or limestones,"[4] but quicklime is typically used in mining regions.[5]

THE ADDITION OF LIME TO COCA

The literature offers several explanations for the addition of lime to coca: to improve the flavor of the coca, to potentiate the cocaine action, or to release the cocaine alkaloid from the coca quid.

Many scholars have maintained that lime is essential to release the cocaine alkaloid from the coca quid. Chemically, the alkaloid cocaine is released when combined with acids, although "this is not necessary for its extraction by the saliva or absorption by the system."[6] In fact, lime may retard the freeing of cocaine from the leaf. Based on studies performed in 1911 by Hartwich, in which he extracted slightly more cocaine from coca leaves with plain water than with a dilute lime water, the U.N. Commission concluded that lime or another alkaline substance "is added to improve the flavor, or perhaps to promote the flow of saliva or both."[7]

Another theory is that the lime *potentiates* "the neurostimulant, cardiovascular, psychological and metabolic actions of cocaine alkaloids."[8] The most frequent explanation for use of the alkaline substance, however, is that it plays a role in the extraction of cocaine from the quid and also facilitates the absorption by the digestive tract. According to Zapata-Ortiz:

> The cocaine is ingested in its basic form and is transformed in the stomach into hydrochloride. The alkaline substance which is ingested at the same time hinders this transformation by neutralizing the hydrochloric acid in the stomach, thus enabling more of the alkaloids to be absorbed at the level of the intestinal tract.[9]

Summarizing the evidence, Zapata-Ortiz indicated that without the use of alkalines the physiological changes are "retarded or feeble" compared to the reaction when an alkaline is used.[10]

None of the researchers has attempted to explain how the South American natives, with their primitive pharmacological knowledge, ever came to use an alkaline substance with their coca leaves.

ESTIMATED AMOUNT OF COCAINE INGESTED BY HABITUAL COCA CHEWERS

The amount of cocaine ingested by coqueros (the habitual users of coca) can be computed. . . .

It seems fair to say that 60 grams per day (of coca leaves) is . . . a fair average estimate for an adult who is a confirmed user.

The total alkaloid content may be taken as about 0.75 per cent on the average. In Huanuco or Bolivian leaf this total alkaloid is about 80 per cent cocaine, therefore we take 0.6 per cent actual cocaine as an average in these leaves. The average dose of cocaine, according to the United States Dispensatory, is 8 to 16 milligrams. The calculation indicates that the average coquero using Huanuco leaf takes 360 milligrams per day, or 22½ to 45 times the medicinal dose. This is the cocaine he takes into his system every day. If he chews Truxillo leaf, he perhaps gets less true cocaine (unless he chews more leaves); say 15 to 30 times the medicinal dose every day.[11]

From 30–75% of the total alkaloid content is cocaine, according to Woods and Downs.[12]

EXPLANATIONS THAT HAVE BEEN OFFERED FOR THE USE OF COCA

The literature offers a variety of explanations for the use of coca. In the preceding chapter, we described its use as a mechanism of social control (its use being restricted to certain classes, under certain circumstances, etc.), as a religious symbol, and as a medium of exchange. Now we'll examine some others.

As a food substitute

Probably the single most important factor in the spread of the coca-chewing habit among the Indians was the plant's use as a food substitute.[13] The need for a food substitute was a result of the breakdown of the Inca's highly efficient agricultural economy which began during the period of internecine civil war, and was completed by the Spanish conquest. Clearly, this breakdown affected the nutritional quality of the Indian diet.[14]

It is significant to note that while the nutritional level for the Indians was declining, they were also being required to expend greater physical efforts, primarily to work the mines.

> To overcome their constant gnawing hunger and to gain the necessary stamina to work in the mines, the Indians turned to the chewing of coca both as a nutritive substitute and a stimulant. These two motives are interrelated. Chewing the wondrous leaves, the Indians not only could work all day without eating, but they would perform what appeared to be prodigious feats of strength.[15]

Recent nutritional analysis[16] shows that 100 grams of coca leaves contain 305 calories, 18.9 grams of protein, and 46.2 grams of carbohydrates, and satisfies the recommended dietary allowances for calcium, iron, phosphorus, and vitamins A, B, and E. With the 60 grams per day ingested by the average confirmed adult user, this comes to 183 calories per day, plus some vitamins and minerals, hardly evidence to support the view that coca is a good nutritional substitute, especially for hard workers. The fact that coca-chewing Andean Indians apparently eat little and/or do not appear to be hungry is related more to coca's pharmacological properties (as a stimulant) than to its nutritive content.

Of the many factors that contribute to the misconception that coca is a substitute for food, the two major ones are direct consequences of the effect of the released cocaine: anorexia, or loss of appetite, which is one of the properties of stimulants; and anesthesia of the mouth, which causes the sense of taste to disappear.[17]

Near the end of the Napoleonic Wars, there appeared a letter in *Gentlemen's Magazine* in which the writer proposed the use of coca to overcome food scarcities caused in part by Napoleon's blockade:

> Now if professor [Humphry] *Davy* will apply his thoughts to this subject . . . there are thousands who will pour their blessing on him if he will but discover a temporary *anti-famine*, or substitute for food, free from all inconvenience of weight, bulk and expenses; and by which any person might be enabled, like a Peruvian Indian to live and labour in health and spirits, for a month now and then without eating. It would be the greatest achievement. . . .

Actually, the idea of using coca as a nutritive substance during a siege was not new. The historian Unanue tells about an incident in the siege of La Paz in 1771 "when the inhabitants, after a blockade of several months, during a severe winter, ran short of provisions and were compelled to depend wholly upon coca, of which happily there was sufficient to banish hunger and to support fatigue, while enabling the soldiers to bear the intense cold."[18]

As a stimulant

There is some evidence to suggest that coca was used as a stimulant (and also as an analgesic) by both Incan and pre-Incan warriors. Many ceramics, some dating from the ninth century, show warriors with the characteristic bulging cheek of the coca chewer.[19] Apparently the use of coca as a stimulant became a "general habit among the indigenous population of the Andean highlands during the early years of the Spanish conquest."[20] Coca was especially widely used by those natives who labored in the mines, many of which were situated high in the mountains. Thor Heyerdahl speculated that the Peruvian Indians used coca both as a stimulant and for its anorexic effect on their long raft voyages to the South Pacific islands.[21]

Coca and the Andean miners

Much of the literature deals with the question of the role coca chewing plays in the Andean mining industry.[22] A partial review of the literature by Gagliano showed there have been varying estimates of the amounts of coca consumed by Andean miners:[23]

- Poeppig (1835) and Tschudi (1849): from 1 to 1.5 ounces daily (with an occasional miner needing up to 4 ounces a day)
- Markam (1862): from 2 to 3 ounces daily
- Mortimer (1901): from 1 to 2 ounces daily

One viewpoint is that the coca gives the miners the strength and endurance needed to do the hard work of mining at high altitudes. Another view is that the Indian miners turned to the chewing of coca as a food substitute. In fact, these views are interrelated.

Zapata-Ortiz cautioned against romanticizing coca's effect on strength and diet:

> . . . and although it is true that the chewing of coca leaf diminishes fatigue and by exerting a stimulating effect may increase the output of work within the short period of a particular experiment, this result in no way shows that coca addicts are capable of doing more work and achieving a greater output over the protracted period required for their customary tasks and much less that they have a greater capacity for labor than persons who do not consume coca and who receive proper nourishment.[24]

Zapata-Ortiz cites an observation by Gimenez on a group of Andeans who had no need for coca because they were well fed. They worked hard and productively in a copper mine 4,500 meters above sea level in central Argentina.

Hughes reported on the use of coca by miners in 1946:

> In there, in the bowels of the earth, three miles high, it was dark and dank and hot; the dust-laden air was painfully thin. It seemed a miracle that men could work there, work hard and for long hours, day after day, week after week, year after year, until they are worn out.
>
> The company engineer seemed to read our minds. "It's their own fault, that dust," he said. "They won't work with wet drills, so they get silicosis. Just dumb Indians."

"But how do they stand it?" we asked.

"Used to it, I guess," he said, "and they've got their coca."

"Coca?"

"Watch; you'll see."

Just then the gnome-like brown figures laid down their tools, and by the dim lights on their caps made their way to a spot wide and flat enough for squatting.

"It's time for rest and refreshments," explained the engineer.

As the Indians sat down, they silently fumbled with small woven pouches hanging from their belts. But instead of sandwiches and a thermos of coffee, they pulled out handfuls of leaves, dry, gray-green, oval leaves, about two inches long. This they stuffed into their mouths.

"It's *el chacchco*, the hour to chew coca," said the engineer.

Their mouths full of leaves, the Indians next bit into wedges of hard ash, rolling the gritty particles under their tongues. Then they settled back against the rock wall, slowly and deliberately chewing until one cheek bulged as from a huge quid of tobacco.

This was the ancient ritual of chaccuo, the chewing of coca, the miracle, the divine leaf, the green gold of the Andes: comfort and curse of the South American Indian.[25]

The opinion of those familiar with the subject of coca's effect is divided. Some believe that coca is beneficial:

> . . . coca leaves provide the same benefits that aspirin, coffee, tea, stimulants, sedatives and numerous other medications supply in our society.[26]

However, other researchers believe that relying on coca's stimulating effect, in lieu of proper nourishment, is self-defeating. Alcala pointed out:

> How can an ill-nourished body possibly have endurance? What happens is that for a few short years the Indian makes an effort which is out of proportion with his real physical powers, and then becomes a human derelict until his death, which usually occurs at an early age.[27]

As medicine

As a medicinal herb, coca has been used in treating a variety of ailments and diseases. Both Hodge and Saenz comment on coca's use in the past as an analgesic for wounded soldiers.[28] In support of this, there are drawings on vases that depict wounded soldiers with the characteristic bulging cheeks of the coca chewer. Some researchers speculate that coca was used as a painkiller in the difficult and very painful trephining operations in which a hole is cut in the skull.[29]

Much of coca's medicinal applications involved ritual practices by the shaman or medicine man. Many similar practices are continued today. The shamans used (and use) coca in many of their rites, such as divination and ritualistic ceremonies "at the graveside of the deceased."[30] In fact, it still is believed by many of the natives that if the "moribund person was able to perceive the taste of the coca leaves pressed against his mouth, his soul would go to paradise."[31]

Sometimes the patient was instructed to make a gift of coca to the gods, based on the belief that the illness was due to neglect of the rituals of worship. The shamans, in the case of headaches and toothaches, made the patients tie leaves to their foreheads.[32] In cases of extreme pain, shamans advised patients "to chew the leaves as an analgesic."[33] There is also some speculation that due to the invigorating properties of coca leaves, it was also prescribed for illnesses involving the elderly.[34] In these cases, the drug was likely used for its stimulant properties.

As a euphoriant-aphrodisiac

Nicholas Monardes in 1565 (translated into English in 1596) was one of the first chroniclers to mention coca's use as a euphoriant or mind-altering substance. Monardes reported that Indians used a mixture of coca and tobacco leaves to intoxicate themselves, which resulted in their going "out of their wittes," but being very contented.[35]

Bejarano suggested that coca owes most of its esteem to its reputed powers as an aphrodisiac. He mentioned that all the early chroniclers of the Spanish Conquest note "sodomitistic, homosexual and bestial perversions" resulting from the consumption of coca.[36]

As a sexual substitute

According to the culture of the Kogi, a primitive Colombian tribe, the ideal life consists of eating nothing but coca, never sleeping, talking, dancing all night in celebration of their ancestors and abstaining from sexual intercourse. There is a fascinating ceremony in which the young men of the tribe are introduced to the coca habit:

> The young man receives the small gourd of lime with which the coca he chews will be mixed, and he is made to understand that the small receptacle represents a woman. The young man is married to this woman during the ceremony, and perforates the gourd in imitation of the ritual deflowering; the small twig with which he does this symbolizes the penis. The introduction of the twig into the small gourd or receptacle and the gesture of rubbing round the opening are interpreted as the symbolizing of the sexual act, and in their culture this means that all sexual intercourse is to be abandoned, its only manifestations or expression being the symbolic use of coca.[37]

The myth of the Andean man

There are two related and oft-cited beliefs about the use of coca. One is that coca use is necessary for adapting to the great heights of the Andean Mountains, and the other is that the Andean residents are a distinct and separate race, and thus physiologically *need* coca to function.[38] The evidence is not strongly supportive for either belief.

Buck, Sasaki, Hewitt, and Macrae, in a survey of four Peruvian villages, found the use of coca by the adult population to be 72% at 11,500 feet, 28% at 5,600 feet, and 3% at sea level.[39] However, as both Zapata-Ortiz and Cardenas indicated:[40]

- Other South American groups who do not use coca also live at Andean heights.
- Reported groups of users live near sea level.
- Both Peruvian and Anglo newcomers to the Andes do not find it necessary to use coca.
- The Peruvian army consists of many former users who do not find it necessary to use coca when conducting military exercises in the Andean Mountains.

The "myth of the Andean man" is succinctly refuted by Gutierrez-Noriega:

> It is maintained that the acclimatized Andeans are a true "climato-physiological-racial variety." This means that the process of adaptation has reached such an extreme of perfection that it transforms the human being into a new race. . . . It seems to be absurd to assert that the "climato-physiological race," whose inhabitation of the Andes goes back for thousands of years, requires coca alkaloids to enable it to live at great heights, while races which are of much more recent settlement and which theoretically would be less well adapted do not need the drug.[41]

As a means of keeping warm

Both Mortimer and Little indicated that one use of coca by habitual users was to promote a feeling of warmth in the cold Andean climate.[42] In Little's study, 75% of the Indians surveyed responded that their consumption of coca was greater during colder weather. Hanna found some physiological evidence to support this use.[43] Coca has peripheral vasoconstrictive effects. This reduces the amount of heat loss through the extremities and produces a higher central body temperature.

As a measure of distance

It is not certain when the practice started, but coca use led to a measure of distance—the *cocada*—which is the distance traveled during the chewing of a quid of coca. A *cocada* is equivalent to about forty minutes, which translates to about two miles on the level or a mile and a half uphill.[44]

CONTEMPORARY USE AND PRODUCTION OF COCA

It has been estimated that, worldwide, 8 million people currently chew coca leaves.[45] It has been estimated that at least half the Bolivian native population of 5 million are coca users.[46] In Peru, estimates range from 900,000 users (from official figures provided to the UN[47]) to 2 million.[48]

Considerable coca is produced each year in both Peru and Bolivia, although official figures are available only for Peru. According to the National Coca Enterprise of Peru, in 1977 over 17,000 growers were authorized to produce 10,450 tons of coca leaves on 64 square miles of territory. Unofficial estimates, however, are that actual production was over twice that level, with nearly 12,000 tons of leaves entering the market illegally, the bulk of that undoubtedly being converted to illicit cocaine.[49] Estimates submitted to the U.S. Embassy in Bolivia are that 7,700 tons of coca leaves are legally consumed each year and 2,200 tons are legally exported.

That portion of the crop legally exported is sent to Europe and America to produce cocaine for pharmaceutical use. Peru produces some legal cocaine for export, but there are no legal cocaine labs in Bolivia.

So, while researchers continue to debate the effects of coca, South American natives continue a practice that has gone on perhaps for thousands of years. The coca shrub and the habit of chewing its leaves quite clearly remain an "integral part of the Indian's way of life, deeply involved with his traditions, his religion, his work, and his medicine."[50]

REFERENCES

1. Holmstead, B., Lindgren, J., Rivier, L., and Plowman, T., "Cocaine in the blood of coca chewers," *Journal of Ethnopharmacol.*, 1979, *1*, 69–78.
2. Mortimer, W. G., *Peru history of coca, the divine plant of the Incas*, (New York: J. H. Vail and Company, 1901), reprinted as *History of coca*, (San Francisco: And/Or Press, 1974).
3. Zapata-Ortiz, V., "The problems of the chewing of the coca leaf in Peru," *Bull. Narc.*, 1952, *4*, 26–33.
4. Mortimer, 1901, Op. Cit.
5. Gagliano, J. A., "Social History of Coca in Peru," Doctoral Dissertion (History), (Georgetown University, Washington, D.C., 1960).
6. U.N. Economic and Social Council, Commission on Narcotic Drugs, *Study on coca leaves*, Third Session, May, 1948.

7. Ibid.
8. Gutierrez-Noriega, C. and Von Hagen, V. W., "The strange case of the coca leaf," *Sci. Monthly*, 1950, *70(2)*, 81–89.
9. Zapata-Ortiz, 1952, Op. Cit.
10. Ibid.
11. Ibid.
12. Woods, J. H. and Downs, D. A. "The psychopharmacology of cocaine." In: *Drug use in America: Problem in perspective*, Appendix, Vol. I, (Washington, D.C.: U.S. Government Printing Office, 1973), 116–139.
13. Zapata-Ortiz, 1952, Op. Cit.
14. Gagliano, 1960, Op. Cit.
15. Ibid.
16. Duke, J. A., Aulik, D., and Plowman, T., "Nutritional value of coca," *Botanical Museum Leaflets,* Harvard University, 1975, *24*, 113–119.
17. Bejarano, J., "Further considerations on the coca habit in Columbia," *Bull. Narc.*, 1952, *4(3)*, 3–19.
18. Mortimer, 1901, Op. Cit.
19. Saenz, L. N. "La coca: Estudio medico-social de gran toxicomania Peruana," Lima, 1938.
20. Gagliano, 1960, Op. Cit.
21. Heyerdahl, T., *Kon-Tiki, across the Pacific by raft* (trans. F. H. Lyon), (New York: Permabook Edition, 1960).
22. Gagliano, 1960, Op. Cit.
23. Ibid.
24. Zapata-Ortiz, 1952, Op. Cit.
25. Hughes, 1964, Op. Cit.
26. Martin, R. T., "The role of coca in the history, religion and medicine of South American Indians," *Econ. Bot.*, 1970, *24*, 422, 438.
27. Alcala, R. P. "The coca question in Bolivia," *Bull. Narc.*, 1952, *4(2)*, 10–15.
28. Hodge, W. H., "Coca," *National History,* 1947, *56*, 86–93; Saenz, 1938, Op. Cit.
29. Gagliano, 1960, Op. Cit.
30. Ibid.
31. Blejer-Prieto, H., "Coca leaf and cocaine addictions, some historical notes," *Can. Med. Assoc. J.*, 1965, *95*, 700–704.
32. Osborne, H., "Indians of the Andes, Hymaras and Quechuas," London, 1952.
33. Gagliano, 1960, Op. Cit.
34. Ibid.
35. Ibid.
36. Bejarano, 1952, Op. Cit.
37. Ibid.
38. Monge, C., "The need for studying the problem of coca-leaf chewing," *Bull. Narc.*, 1952, *4(4)*.

39. Buck, A. A., Sasaki, T. T., Hewitt, J. J., and Macrae, A. A., "Coca chewing and health: An epidemiologic study among residents of a Peruvian village," *American Journal of Epidem.*, 1968, *88*, 159–177.
40. Zapata-Ortiz, 1952, Op. Cit.; Cardenas, M., "Psychological aspects of coca addiction," *Bull. Narc.*, 1952, *4(2)*, 6–9.
41. Gutierrez-Noriega, 1950, Op. Cit.
42. Mortimer, 1901, Op. Cit.
43. Hanna, J. M., "Coca leaf use in Southern Peru: Some biosocial aspects," *American Anthropol.*, 1974, *76*, 281–296.
44. Mortimer, 1901, Op. Cit.
45. Maher, J., "Coca—Erythroxylon coca," (unpublished BNDD document, 1968).
46. Carroll, E., "Coca: The plant and its use." In: R. C. Petersen, and R. C. Stillman (eds.), *Cocaine: 1977*, Research Monograph Series No. 13, DHEW Publ. No. (ADM) 77–432, (Rockville, Maryland: NIDA, 1977), 47–62.
47. Ibid.
48. Sullivan, W., "U.N. Seeking Curbs on Leaf Chewing," *The New York Times*, September 20, 1964.
49. Ashley, R., "The Fight for Legal Cocaine," *High Times*, June, 1976, *10*, 57–59, 63.
50. Martin, 1970, Op. Cit.

Part II

From Free Enterprise to Government Regulation

CHAPTER 3

DISCOVERY AND INITIAL EXPERIMENTATION

Borne on the wings of two coca leaves, I flew about in the spaces of 77,438 worlds, one more splendid than another. I prefer a life of ten years with coca to one of a hundred thousand without it. It seemed to me that I was separated from the whole world, and I beheld the strangest images, most beautiful in color and in form than can be imagined.

—Paolo Mantegazza, 1859, quoted in W. G. Mortimer, *History of Coca*

INTRODUCTION OF COCA TO EUROPE

Many of the early explorers of the New World brought back with them to Europe descriptions of the coca plant and its effects on the natives. Among them were Ramon Pave in 1495, Tomas Ortiz in 1499, and even the famous explorer Amerigo Vespucci.[1] However, Nicolas Monardes, a Spanish physician, is generally given credit for the first publication on coca and its effect. Published in English in 1596, it was entitled *Joyful Newes out of the Newfound Worlde.*

Joseph de Jussieu, in 1750, was the first botanist to send coca plants to Europe.[2] These plants, preserved in the French Museum of Natural History, were studied by many botanists. In 1783, Lamarck classified the plant as belonging to the family Erythroxylaceae and the genus *Erythroxylon.*[3] However, although many other scientists, explorers and physicians wrote about the coca plant from the sixteenth century onward, it was not until the latter half of the nineteenth century, when cocaine was touted as a "wonder drug," that the plant generated much interest.[4]

The absence of interest in coca may have been due to its lack of adaptability to the European climate and the fact that the leaves deteriorated in the long voyages from South America.[5]

ISOLATION OF COCAINE AS COCA'S PSYCHOACTIVE INGREDIENT

The isolation of cocaine was attempted by many, and there is some dispute as to when and by whom this was first accomplished. Ashley, in an excellent and comprehensive review on the history of cocaine, gives a flavor of the historical confusion that has surrounded this issue (the citations are from his text):

> Two sources give the honor to one Gaedkin in 1844. [Maurer and Vogel, 1967, and Remington's *Pharmaceutical Science*]. Four credit Gaedecke (variously spelled Gaedeke, Gaedche, Gardecke, Gardeke) in 1855 [Becker, 1963; Mortimer, 1901; Taylor, 1965; Woods and Downs, 1973]. Three say that Albert Niemann did it in 1853 [Blum and Associates, 1970; National Clearinghouse for Drug Abuse Information, Report Series 11, 1972; STASH Fact Sheet on Cocaine, 1972], four think it was in 1859 [Clark, 1973; Freud, 1884; McLaughlin, 1973; Mortimer, 1901] and five hold out for 1860 [Brill, 1969; *Encyclopedia Americana*, 1938; Keys, 1963; Taylor, 1965; Woods and Downs, 1973]. . . . The 1844 is probably an error and, given all the ways I've seen Gaedecke's name spelled, the Gaedkin of 1844 may very well be the Gaedecke of 1855.[6]

In any case, the evidence suggests that Gaedecke isolated cocaine in 1855 and named it "erythroxylon" after the plant name. Sometime between 1858 and 1860, Neimann, "perhaps obtaining a purer product," called the alkaloid cocaine.[7]

EARLY EXPERIMENTATION WITH THE DRUG

Though cocaine had been identified, most of the early experimentation—and there was very little conducted—was done with coca infusions. The coca infusion was first mentioned in the Sixth United States Pharmacopoeia of

1880.[8] According to the Pharmacopoeia this infusion contained 0.5 gram of coca alkaloids per 100 cubic centimeters, about 15 milligrams of cocaine per teaspoon. The average dose of cocaine, according to the United States Dispensatory, is from 8 to 16 milligrams.[9]

In the late 1800s, American physicians "were not only investigating the stimulative properties of coca" and coca infusions, but many were prescribing coca preparations for their patients.[10] Searle prescribed coca infusions for patients in sedentary occupations but noted negative side effects—loss of appetite and insomnia. He was one of the first physicians to discuss the successful use of coca in treating opium and morphine addicts, in particular the experiments of Dr. Palmer of the University of Louisville.

In commenting on Palmer's work, Searle made the important distinction that the use of coca infusion (which correctly can be viewed as a cocaine elixir) *was not an exchange of narcotic habits*, because even those who used the infusions for long periods of time could abstain from them without any feelings of distress or discomfort.[11] Implicit in this is the fact that the coca, or cocaine, infusion was seen as a nonaddictive substance.

In England a series of interesting experiments were carried out by Dr. Robert Christison (from 1870 to 1876) and others on coca's stimulant properties. Christison, at that time seventy-eight years old, was able to take hikes of up to 16 miles without fatigue when he used coca.[12] Leehody, another early experimenter, hiked up to 24 miles without experiencing fatigue after ingesting grains of cocaine.[13]

Apparently, the American scientists of this period directed their attention to the psychoactive properties of the drug, while their European counterparts, particularly the English, were concerned with the physiological effects.[14]

FREUD, KOLLER, AND THE DISCOVERY OF COCAINE'S ANESTHETIC PROPERTIES

The extraordinary thing about the discovery of cocaine's anesthetic properties is the length of time it took to surface. In 1862, Schraff noted cocaine's anesthetic or numbing effect when placed on the tip of the tongue.[15] However, "neither the meaning nor the usefulness of this observation was appreciated at the time."[16] In the same paper, given at the Viennese Medical Society, Schraff also described how cocaine narrowed the peripheral arteries and widened the pupils of the eye. He was not the only one to have experimented on the eye with cocaine, as these "facts were commented upon by Montegazza in 1859, De Marles in 1862," and by many others.[17]

In fact, in 1868, which was still sixteen years before Koller published his paper "The Use of Cocaine to Anesthetise the Eye," a Peruvian surgeon-general, Thomas Moreno y Maiz, wrote a paper entitled (in translation) "Chemical and Physiological Research on Cocaine and the Erythroxylon Coca of Peru."[18] Moreno y Maiz, unlike other scientists at the time, experimented with the use of cocaine acetate on frogs and concluded:

> Could one utilize it [cocaine] as a local anesthetic? One cannot make a decision on the basis of such a limited number of experiments; it must be decided by the future. For the present, we limit ourselves to publishing what we have seen, happy if we can direct the interest of observers to coca, which may become tomorrow an evident benefaction for all the world, and a new source of riches for our country.[19]

Moreno y Maiz was not the only experimenter who foresaw the potential medical application of cocaine. Von Anrep in 1879 wrote an experimental paper in which he described the locally numbing effects of cocaine and the dilation of the pupil caused by cocaine. He also suggested that someday cocaine might have medical importance.[20]

What is remarkable is that for over twenty-five years many brilliant scientists had experimented with cocaine, many had noted its numbing effect, and several had experimented on the eye, yet none had discovered the drug's anesthetic property. A possible explanation is that the overall general effects of cocaine were so spectacular that the significance of its numbing of the mucous membrane was disregarded, even though "this characteristic had been generally observed and was uniform."[21] Even Koller, who had conducted experiments in search of a local anesthetic, was not immediately aware of the significance of cocaine's numbing effect on the mucous membranes:

And it was not until he had the drug in his own possession and had noted its effect upon himself, that the numbing of the mucous membranes of the lips had sufficient impact to distract him from the purpose for which he was directly exerimenting. This . . . was to test its general physiological effect for his friend Freud.[22]

Freud

Although often told, Freud's role in discovering the anesthetic properties of cocaine and popularizing its use remains an interesting and important chapter in the history of cocaine use. He was also the source of several still-prevalent myths concerning cocaine.

In the early 1880s, Freud was a young, poor neurologist looking for some way "to make a name for himself by discovering something important in either . . . clinical or pathological medicine."[23] During this period Freud read about Aschenbrandt, a German army doctor who issued cocaine to some Bavarian soldiers during their 1883 fall maneuvers and reported that they were more energetic and exhibited a greater ability to endure fatigue. He read with great interest the many reports in the *Detroit Therapeutic Gazette* (not the *Detroit Medical Gazette*, as reported by some writers) about the use of coca/cocaine to treat a variety of medical problems. Many of the letters from physicians that appeared in the *Gazette* dealt with the use of coca, coca infusions, or cocaine as a cure for morphine addiction. One of the articles, written by Dr. E. C. Bentley, describes his many successes in using coca in treating impotency, alcoholism, and morphine addiction. This was of special interest to Freud, since one of his closest associates and friends, Fleischl, had become addicted to morphine following the development of neuromata in his amputated thumb which caused constant pain.

In the spring of 1884, Freud decided to purchase a gram of cocaine from Merck of Darmstadt for $1.27, which at that time represented a real financial strain for him. A true experimenter, Freud immediately tried it himself, dissolving 1/20 of the gram in water:

The first time I took 0.05 gram of cocainum muriaticum in a 1% water solution was when I was feeling slightly out of sorts from fatigue. . . . A few minutes after taking cocaine, one experiences a sudden exhilaration and feeling of lightness. . . .[24]

Freud then gave cocaine to Fleischl, and according to an often-quoted passage, "Fleischl clutched at the new drug 'like a drowning man' and within a few days was taking it continually."[25] However, rather than being the hoped-for life preserver, cocaine in time was to complete the destruction of Fleischl begun by morphine.

Was Freud the first cocaine "pusher"? Certainly he advocated its use, and during the ensuing few months "grew more enthusiastic about the drug and gave cocaine to his colleagues to use upon themselves and their patients."[26] According to his biographer, Ernest Jones, Freud even sent it through the mail to his fiancée, Martha, and gave some to his sister. Less than two months after obtaining his gram of cocaine from Merck, Freud finished the first of four papers he wrote on the drug.[27] *Ueber Coca (On Coca)* was published in July 1884, and was the "most complete account of cocaine yet to appear."[28] In this scholarly essay, Freud presented a detailed history of coca, an examination of the effects of cocaine on himself, and a section that detailed potential therapeutic uses, which were:

- As a stimulant to treat those suffering from depression
- To treat digestive disorders of the stomach
- To treat cachexia—diseases which involve the degeneration of tissues
- To treat morphine and alcohol addiction
- To treat asthma
- As an aphrodisiac
- As a local anesthetic

It is worth quoting his last point in its entirety, as it demonstrates how tantalizingly close Freud was to finding the discovery he sought to establish his reputation in the scientific community:

> Cocaine and its salt have a marked anesthetizing effect when brought in contact with the skin and mucous membrane in concentrated solution; this property suggests its occasional use as a local anesthetic, especially in

connection with affections of the mucous membrane. According to Collin, Ch. Fauvel strongly recommends cocaine for treating diseases of the pharynx, describing it as "le tenseur par excellence des chardes vocales." Indeed, the anesthetizing properties of cocaine should make it suitable for a good many further applications.[29]

Was Freud close to the discovery of the local anesthetic properties of cocaine? In his 1925 autobiography, he intimated as much:

While I was in the middle of this work [studying the effects of cocaine], an opportunity arose for making a journey to visit my fiancée, from whom I had been parted for two years. I hastily wound up my investigation of cocaine and contented myself in my book on the subject with prophesying that further uses for it would soon be found. I suggested, however, to my friend Konigstein, the ophthalmologist, that he should investigate the question of how far the anesthetizing properties of cocaine were applicable in diseases of the eye. When I returned from my holiday, I found that not he but another of my friends, Carl Koller (now in New York), whom I had also spoken to about cocaine, had made the decisive experiments upon animals' eyes. . . . Koller is therefore rightly regarded as the discoverer of local anesthesia by cocaine which has become so important in minor surgery, but I bore my fiancée no grudge for her interruption of my work.[30]

"Coca" Koller

What does Carl Koller make of this? In a letter to Dr. Seelig, which Seelig later sent to the *Journal of the American Medical Association (JAMA)*, Koller made the following observation on Koenigstein's role:

. . . before leaving he [Freud] asked his friend Leopold Koenigstein to try the drug on the "diseased eye." No thought of anesthesia. Koenigstein, a rather dull person, was fascinated by the vasoconstricting powers of cocaine and tried to cure iritis and trachoma with it. When I told him that it was an excellent anesthetic, he said I was mistaken. . . .[31]

Actually, Koenigstein was quickly to change his mind about cocaine's local anesthetic properties. Less than two months later, on October 17, 1884, both Koenigstein and Koller presented papers suggesting cocaine's role as a local anesthetic. But Koenigstein made no concession in his paper that Koller's work preceded his own. This was later rectified by Freud and Von Tauregg, who insisted that Koenigstein publicly acknowledge that Koller's discovery was first. He later did so in a letter to a medical journal.[32]

On Freud's role, Koller is even less kind:

> . . . the facts are that Freud did not have anything whatever to do with cocaine anesthesia, nor did he write a single word about work on cocaine in 1885 (whereas my work dates from 1884) that had not been done better and more scientifically by Anrep in 1879. Historical untruths are very difficult to destroy.

Koller goes on to say that Freud's expression in his autobiography "that he told me also of cocaine" was ambiguously worded, and was responsible for "all this untrue representation."[33]

Koller is mistaken when he states that Freud's cocaine article did not come out until 1885. It was published in July 1884, and was a very complete work for its time. Freud's methodology "has not been significantly improved upon . . . it is a classic original in a field which didn't receive its name until 1920 . . . Psychopharmacology."[34]

Exactly what was, or was not, discussed between the two men will always remain uncertain. The facts are that Freud did ask Carl Koller to assist him in his comprehensive study of the systemic effects of cocaine. It is also fact that Koller had been actively searching for a local anesthetic—in fact, he had experimented with many drugs in his effort to find a suitable one.[35]

The actual discovery that cocaine was the drug he sought came as a "flash" of inspirational genius. Koller sets the stage of the discovery with all the care and drama of a playwright:

> . . . Dr. Engle partook of some [cocaine] with me from the point of his penknife and remarked, "How that numbs the tongue." I said, "Yes, that has been noticed

by everyone that has eaten it." And in the moment it flashed upon me that I was carrying in my pocket the local anesthetic for which I had searched some years earlier.[36]

Koller left immediately for his laboratory, where he experimented with a cocaine-treated cornea of a frog by pricking the eye with a needle. Observing no response from the amphibian, he then experimented with warm-blooded animals—rabbits and dogs—and then later on himself and his friends.

The act of creation was once defined by Arthur Koestler as the ability to take two distinct forms, objects, or acts (in this case, the point of a penknife and the numbing effect of cocaine) and give them a new entity of their own (use of cocaine as an anesthetic for surgery, which involves cutting). Certainly it makes sense that the interplay between knife and cocaine "may have been critical to this discovery . . . it seems quite possible that it was the fortuitous association of the cutting function of the knife with the numbing of the tongue" that resulted in Koller's immediate departure for the laboratory.[37] In any case the proof of these experiments, conducted in early September 1884, was irrefutable—cocaine was indeed a powerful local anesthetic. On September 15, 1884, before the Heidelberg Ophthalmological Society, Koller first demonstrated his experiment.[38] The news spread quickly, and soon the use of cocaine in minor surgical procedures "such as cataract extractions, in which the use of general anesthesia would not be appropriate" was widespread.[39]

Koller's discovery was significant for other than medical reasons. As the new wonder drug, cocaine, became much talked about and widely available, it was only a matter of time before it would be abused.

Fleischl—an early cocaine abuser

When Freud received his gram of cocaine from Merck in the spring of 1884, his good friend Fleischl was in the midst of another painful attempt at withdrawal from his morphine habit. Fleischl exhibited an initial positive reaction to the cocaine, taking it in the same small doses as had Freud.[40] However, this situation changed quickly and radically so that by January 1885 he was taking up to a gram a day. He had long stopped taking the drug orally, and instead was injecting it. This rate of cocaine consumption continued for another six months, at which time he developed the classical symptoms of severe cocaine abuse, consisting of convulsions, insomnia, fainting, and such psychotic reactions as believing "white snakes were crawling over his skin."[41] Even Koller wrote about the many nights he spent with Fleischl "watching him dig imaginary insects out of his skin" in his sensory hallucinations.[42]

Fleischl never fully recovered and continued to exhibit the symptoms of chronic cocaine abuse until his death six years later.[43]

COUNTERREACTION TO THE INITIAL ENTHUSIASM

Why was cocaine use ultimately so destructive for Fleischl and not for Freud? First, Freud used small doses of cocaine, taken orally. Fleischl injected doses of up to a gram a day. Ashley[44] maintains that daily use of this amount will quickly build up to the toxic effects exhibited by Fleischl. This is largely speculation, however, since there is little hard evidence about cumulative effects of cocaine. (For further discussion of this topic, see Part III.)

In any event, by the end of 1885, Fleischl's case was merely one example of cocaine intoxication that was "being reported from all over the world."[45] By 1887, however, at least in Europe, cocaine's use was increasingly being limited to local anesthesia. In this changing medical climate, Freud's early advocacy of cocaine use to treat morphine addiction came under virulent attack by Erlenmeyer, a leading addiction specialist. Erlenmeyer accused Freud of unleashing the "third scourge of humanity"—after alcohol and morphine.[46]

In response, Freud published his fourth and last cocaine paper, "Craving for and Fear of Cocaine." While this in no way constituted a retraction of his "broad endorsement of cocaine, he finally withdrew it as a cure for morphine addiction."[47]

Freud argued in this paper that Erlenmeyer's conclusions were based "on a serious experimental error." This is because Erlenmeyer administered cocaine doses other than those "recommended effective" by Freud, and, more significantly, administered them subcutaneously rather than orally, as suggested by Freud. Having made that point:

> Freud withdrew cocaine as a cure for the morphine habit on Freud's own grounds: Morphine addicts are "so weak in will power, so susceptible" that they will take over cocaine as a new stimulant and replace morphine with an even more destructive habit. But, italicizes Freud, *"cocaine has claimed no victim on its own."* In other words, he indicates that if the patient has not been a morphine addict, he will not become a cocaine addict.[48]

Freud's personal use of cocaine: some myths explored

There were two common beliefs about Freud, expressed both in the literature and by experienced cocaine users: that he was a heavy user of cocaine, doing it for many years; and that he "found it necessary to undergo rhinoplasty (nose operation) on three separate occasions as a result of excessive indulgence in cocaine."[49]

Neither belief is true. As Brecher points out, Freud's operations were for cancer of the palate and jaw.[50] There is no evidence that Freud ever snorted cocaine. Rather, he took it orally and later by subcutaneous injection.

As to Freud's excessive and long-term indulgence in cocaine, the evidence suggests otherwise. In an exercise of deductive reasoning, Ashley suggests that Freud primarily used cocaine as a stimulant, which (according to Freud) is most effectively given in small doses (0.05–0.10 gram), "repeated so often that the effects of the dose overlap." Based on this information and the fact that Freud mentions that effects of the orally administered cocaine lasted four or five hours, Ashley concludes that "he took at least two doses a day, probably . . . three."[51] But, as Ashley warns, this is only an estimate, and a speculative one at that.

We know a little more about the duration of Freud's use of cocaine. Again, according to Ashley:

> It is generally thought that Freud gave up the personal use of cocaine in 1887, after the criticism he had received and the flood of reports of cocaine "addiction" had made its advocacy a professional liability—but there is definite proof that he used it at least in a therapeutic way (applied locally to "swellings in his nose") as late as 1895.[52]

EARLY AMERICAN EXPERIMENTERS WITH COCAINE

Concurrent with the European advances in the medical use of cocaine, several American physicians were also exploring this new "wonder drug." There was, in fact, a heated rivalry between the two sets of researchers. A number of the Americans also "fell prey to the effects of cocaine" in the course of their experimentation:

> As the medical usefulness of cocaine became apparent, so did its abuse potential. Cocaine "addicts" began to appear in Europe and America. . . . The new dangers of cocaine included acute toxic psychosis, cocaine abuse and death.[53]

Hammond

William Alexander Hammond, "a leader in the American medical profession, an international authority on neurology, a prolific writer and a powerful personality," was an early and active supporter of coca and cocaine. Hammond was so impressed with the drug that he used it on a daily basis for its invigorating properties. In Freud's final cocaine essay, he made extensive use of Hammond's research to support his position that cocaine was not addictive, except when used by morphine addicts. Hammond's position concerning cocaine was that its habituating potential was "on a par with that of coffee or tea."[54]

Hammond demonstrated one of the fundamental and frequently made errors during this initial period of coca/cocaine use and availability. In an 1887 speech before the Medical Society of Virginia, Hammond stated that while a claret of wine/coca mixture "worked wonders," cocaine worked even better.

Unfortunately, many of cocaine's early proponents similarly (and mistakenly) equated the effect of the coca leaf and its fluid extracts with that of cocaine. The problem is that the pharmacological actions involved in the two are very different:

> The leaf and fluid extract are both taken by mouth and absorption of the active material from the gastrointestinal tract is slow. Therefore, high blood levels of cocaine were not achieved, even when large oral doses were ingested. Cocaine, on the other hand, could be absorbed rapidly into the bloodstream, whether it was given by injection, by sniffing, or by topical application to the mucous membrane of the throat and elsewhere.[55]

Halstead

A handwritten 1918 letter from William Halstead of Johns Hopkins to Osler, his personal friend and confidant, sheds some light on the historical development of cocaine as a nerve-block anesthesia. Halstead describes one of the first nerve-block operations ever conducted:

> I did not know until 1914 that Richard Hall of N.Y. (son of Rev. John D. Hall) my 1st assistant at Roosevelt Hosp. had described an operation which we performed together in my house in N.Y. A rich & influential woman permitted me in 1885 to excise her inferior dental nerve (Paravicini's method) for trigeminal neuralgia, under cocaine. I injected [cocaine into] the nerve opposite or rather above its entrance into the canal before incising the mucous membrane. On exposing the nerve I clamped it with a specially designed broad (1.5 cm.) forceps to insure the excision of a long piece. The final snip of the scissors through the nerve divided a larger artery, probably the internal maxillary. The patient's mouth filled with blood as if poured in by cupfuls. Tom McBride, whose patient she was, rushed out of the room not wishing, as he told me afterwards, to be present at the death. Gauze plugging finally arrested the hemorrhage. The patient was put in my bed & 2 trained nurses summoned.

For 2 nights I slept in the same room and then transferred her to my service at the Presbyterian Hosp. She made a good recovery.

It is odd that I happened in 1914 to be attending a meeting in Berlin of the Deutsche Ges. f. [Gesellschaft für] Chirurgie when this case was referred to by Rhen. I asked him how he knew of it. He said that Richard Hall had published it. I have since then seen this case mentioned in German articles. Apropos of this, it interests me to recall a visit I made to Vienna in the autumn of 1885, when I showed Wölfler (Billroth's 1st assistant) how to use cocaine. He had declared that it was useless in surgery. But before I left Vienna he published an enthusiastic article in one of the daily papers on the subject. It did not, however, occur to him to mention my name.

Having occasion to have a tooth attended to by Thomas, the famous American dentist of Vienna, I showed him how to inject [into] the inf. [inferior] dental nerve from within the mouth. He became so enthusiastic on the subject that he requested me to inject [cocaine into] the inferior dental nerves of 2 assistants whose teeth he filled while they were insensitive.[56]

Thus early in his surgical career Halstead discovered that cocaine, which until that time was used as a surface anesthetic in eye and vocal cord surgery, could be injected "in the vicinity of the nerves to produce localized analgesia."[57] This was the beginning of regional anesthesia as practiced today. Before it was perfected, however, it was to cost several of Halstead's associates their lives.

Since this was before the extensive use of laboratory animals, it was customary for researchers to conduct experiments on themselves. Thus, Halstead and his assistants injected themselves with cocaine in "all the accessible nerves in the body—sciatic, internal pudic, brachial plexus, inferior dental, etc." with deleterious consequences. As Halstead noted in a letter to Osler in 1918:

Poor Hall and two other assistants of mine acquired the cocaine habit in the course of our experiments on themselves—injecting our nerves. They all died without recovering from the habit.[58]

Almost a year to the day after Koller had made his famous report on the local anesthetic properties of cocaine, Halstead published a paper in the *New York Medical Journal* describing the successful use of cocaine in more than a thousand surgical operations, including amputations, excision of axillary contents, and exsections of joints.

Some historians, however, have given the credit for the pioneering work in this field to Corning, a contemporary of Halstead who "was the first to use cocaine in spinal anesthesia: he was also among the first to perfect the technique for its use in minor and major surgery."[59]

Halstead opposed this assertion and in his 1918 letter to Osler stated:

> . . . I published three or four little papers in 1884–5 in the N.Y. Med. Journ. on the subject of cocaine anesthesia. They are not creditable papers for I was not in good form at the time. . . . Corning's book on cocaine anesthesia was based almost entirely on my work. He was a student of mine and followed my work with cocaine closely.[60]

It seems clear that Halstead "was not in good form at the time" because he had become a regular and heavy user of cocaine. There were reports that he used up to 2 grams a day, which, as Perry notes, "is 200 times the size of a single hit."[61] Whether he actually did use doses of this magnitude, it is clear that Halstead had a serious drug problem:

> Cocaine hunger fastened its dreadful hold upon him. He tried to carry on. But a confused and unworthy period of medical practice ensued. Finally he vanished from the world he had known.[62]

And vanish he did! In what must be one of the strangest drug-rehabilitation schemes yet devised, his friend Welch, later a co-founder of Johns Hopkins Medical School but at that time a pathologist at Bellevue Hospital, hired a schooner and with three sailors took Halstead on a long sea voyage to the Windward Islands and back.[63] The cure did not take, and shortly upon their return, Halstead entered Butler Hospital in Providence, Rhode Island, for several months. This also was not effective, and a year later he was back in Butler.[64]

According to some of the early biographical accounts, Halstead left Butler the second time cured. His cure, ironically—in light of the then-current controversy surrounding the treatment of morphine addiction with cocaine—was morphine. Apparently, Halstead remained a morphine addict until his death in 1922, at the age of 70.[65]

What lasting effect did his cocaine experience have on Halstead? Admittedly, this is conjecture, but at least one of his biographers feels that "it was William Halstead's fierce struggle against cocaine and his periods of withdrawn contemplation that explained the unique stature of his leadership in surgery."[66]

REFERENCES

1. Bejarano, J., "Further considerations on the coca habit in Columbia," *Bull. Narc.,* 1952, *4(3),* 3–19.
2. Gagliano, J. A., "Social History of Coca in Peru," Doctoral Dissertation (History), (Georgetown University, Washington, D.C., 1960).
3. Mortimer, W. G., *Peru history of coca, the divine plant of the Incas,* (New York: J. H. Vail and Company, 1901), reprinted as *History of Coca,* (San Francisco: And/Or Press, 1974).
4. Blejer-Prieto, H., "Coca leaf and cocaine addictions, some historical notes," *Can. Med. Assoc. Journal,* 1965, *93,* 700–704.
5. Woods, J. H. and Downs, D. H., "The psychopharmacology of cocaine." In: *Drug use in America: Problem in perspective,* Appendix, Vol. 1 (Washington, D.C.: U.S. Government Printing Office, 1973), 116–139.
6. Ashley, R., *Cocaine: Its History, Uses and Effects,* (New York: St. Martin's Press, 1975).
7. Ibid.
8. Woods and Downs, 1973, Op. Cit.
9. U.N. Economic and Social Council, Committee on Narcotic Drugs, "Study on coca leaves," Third Session, May, 1948.
10. Gagliano, 1960, Op. Cit.
11. Searle, W. S. "A new form of nervous disease, together with an essay on erythroxylon coca," New York, 1881. As quoted in Gagliano, Op. Cit.
12. Christison, R., "Observations of the effect of cuca, coca, etc.," *Brit. Med. Journal,* 1870.
13. Leehody, J. R., "The action of coca," *Brit. Med. Journal,* 1876, *1,* 750–751.
14. Ashley, 1975, Op. Cit.

15. Blejer-Prieto, 1965, Op. Cit.
16. Woods and Downs, 1973, Op. Cit.
17. Becker, H. K., "Carl Koller and cocaine," *Psychoanal. Quarterly*, 1963, *32*, 309, 373.
18. Von Oettingen, W. F., "Earliest suggestion of use of cocaine for local anesthesia," *Ann. Med. History*, 1933, *5*, 275–280.
19. Blejer-Prieto, 1965, Op. Cit.
20. Becker, 1963, Op. Cit.
21. Ibid.
22. Ibid.
23. Jones, E., *The life and work of Sigmund Freud* (Vol. 1), (New York: Basic Books, 1961).
24. Ibid.
25. Ibid.
26. Woods and Downs, 1973, Op. Cit.
27. S. Freud, *The cocaine papers*, A. K. Donoghue and J. Hillman (eds.), (Vienna: Dunquin Press, 1963). Reprinted in R. Byck (ed.), *Cocaine papers by Sigmund Freud* (New York: Stonehill Publ. Co., 1974). The four papers are: (1) "On coca," *Centra. Gesammte, Ther.* (Wein), 1884, 289–314, (tr. S. Edminster); (2) "Contribution to the knowledge of the effect of cocaine," *Wein. Med. Wochenschr.* 1885 *35(5)* 129–133, (tr. R. Potasky); (3) "On the general effect of cocaine," *Med-Chirurg. Centra.* 1885, *20(32)* 374–375, (tr. S. Edminster); (4); "Craving for and fear of cocaine," *Wein. Med. Wochenschr.* 1887, *28*, 929–932 (tr. W. Hammond).
28. Ashley, 1975, Op. Cit.
29. Freud, 1884, Op. Cit.
30. Freud, S., *An Autobiographical Study*, transl. J. Strachey, (New York: W. W. Norton and Company, 1952).
31. Anonymous, "History of cocaine as a local anesthetic," *JAMA*, 1941, *117*, 1284.
32. Becker, 1963, Op. Cit.
33. Anonymous, *JAMA*, 1941, *117*, 1284, Op. Cit.
34. Ashley, 1975, Op. Cit.
35. Becker, 1963, Op. Cit.
36. Ibid.
37. Woods and Downs, 1973, Op. Cit.
38. Becker, 1963, Op. Cit.
39. Woods and Downs, 1973, Op. Cit.
40. Ashley, 1975, Op. Cit.
41. Jones, *The Life and Work of Sigmund Freud*, 1961
42. Koller, as quoted in Becker, 1963, Op. Cit.
43. Eisworth, N. A., Smith, D. E., and Wesson, D. R., "Current perspectives on cocaine use in America," *Journal of Psychedelic Drugs*, 1972, *5*, 153–157.

44. Ashley, 1975, Op. Cit.
45. Woods and Downs, 1973, Op. Cit.
46. Jones, 1961, Op. Cit.
47. Musto, D. F., "A study in cocaine: Sherlock Holmes and Sigmund Freud," *JAMA*, 1968, *204(1)*, 27–32.
48. Ibid.
49. *The Gourmet Cokebook, A complete guide to cocaine,* (New York: White Mountain Press, 1972; also published by D.C. Production Enterprises, Inc., New York).
50. Brecher, E., *Licit and illicit drugs,* (New York: Little, Brown, 1972).
51. Ashley, 1975, Op. Cit.
52. Ibid.
53. Woods and Downs, 1973, Op. Cit.
54. Musto, 1968, Op. Cit.
55. Woods and Downs, 1973, Op. Cit.
56. Penfield, W., "Halstead of John Hopkins, the man and his problems as described in the secret records of William Osler," *JAMA,* 1969, *210*, 2214, 2218.
57. Ibid.
58. Ibid.
59. Blejer-Prieto, 1965, Op. Cit.
60. Quoted in Penfield, 1969.
61. Perry, Charles, "The Star-Spangled Powder or Through History with Coke Spoon and Nasal Spray," *Rolling Stone*, Issue 115, August 17, 1972.
62. Penfield, 1969, Op. Cit.
63. Brecher, 1972, Op. Cit.
64. Penfield, 1969, Op. Cit.
65. Ashley, 1975, Op. Cit.
66. Penfield, 1969, Op. Cit.

CHAPTER 4

THE ERA OF WIDESPREAD POPULARITY

Whatever his intentions, Sir Arthur Conan Doyle most certainly increased the recognition rating of cocaine when he made Sherlock Holmes a user. . . . For no author with so sure a grasp of popular taste would provide his leading character with a habit so unfamiliar to his readers that they could have no idea of its implication.

—R. Ashley, *Cocaine: Its History, Uses and Effects*

Cocaine quickly spread beyond the scientific laboratories and into the popular culture. Novelists and playwrights lauded the drug, and a whole division of the patent-medicine industry grew up around it. In this chapter, we survey some of these artistic and industrial treatments of cocaine and examine the beginnings of the strong counter-reactions to the supposed excesses of cocaine use that eventually resulted in stringent regulation of the drug all over the world.

SHERLOCK HOLMES AND COCAINE

Within two years of Koller's discovery, Sir Arthur Conan Doyle, in *A Scandal in Bohemia*, had Sherlock Holmes "alternating week to week between cocaine and ambition." However, as Ashley indicates, Doyle's knowledge of the pharmacological action of cocaine was necessarily limited, even though he was a practicing physician. He suspects that Doyle confused the effect of morphine with that of cocaine, especially when he notes the "drowsiness of the drug" and "drug-created dreams," descriptions more appropriate of narcotic drugs.[1]

However, with the publication of *The Sign of Four* two years later in 1888, Doyle demonstrated a greater familiarity and accuracy in describing cocaine's effects. In fact, the descriptions are so accurate that it has led more than one researcher to suspect that Doyle's knowledge was based on more than a passing interest in science.

In *The Sign of Four*, Doyle has Holmes discussing the stimulative properties of cocaine:

> . . . I suppose that its influence is physically a bad one. I find it, however, so transcendingly stimulating and clarifying to the mind that its secondary action is a matter of small moment.
>
> . . . my mind rebels at stagnation. Give me problems, give me work, and I am in my own proper atmosphere, I can dispense then with artificial stimulants. But I abhor the dull routine of existence. I crave for mental exaltation.[2]

But apparently Holmes' continued heavy use of cocaine—injecting it three times a day—was beginning to have a profound negative effect. By 1891, in *The Final Problem*, he was exhibiting paranoid delusions, a classic symptom of acute cocaine abuse. Holmes, "looking paler and thinner," obviously anxious, tells Watson a fantastic story about Professor Moriarty, an archvillain who is trying to kill him. Watson says he has never heard of Moriarty, and Holmes exclaims:

> "Ay, there's the genius and wonder of the thing!" he cried. "The man pervades London and no one has heard of him. That's what puts him on the pinnacle in the records of crime. . . ."[3]

But Holmes offers no evidence. He sees danger lurking all about him, and takes on various disguises to escape Moriarty. Everyday occurrences take on a new and evil Moriarty-related significance. Holmes is convinced that Moriarty is the "tall man" at the train station trying to stop the Paris-bound train on which he and Watson are passengers. Watson muses about all the "Moriartys" he has seen trying to catch a train at Victoria. A rock fall in Switzerland, described by the guide as a usual occurrence, instead brings a knowing smile to Holmes' face, "who sees the fulfillment of that which he expected."

Holmes finally "disappears" at Reichenbach Falls. However, upon his return three years later, in 1894, he no longer uses cocaine and no longer suffers from paranoid delusions.[4]

An interesting speculation as to what happened during Holmes' three-year hiatus was presented nearly a century later in Nicholas Meyers' 1974 novel *The Seven Percent Solution* (released in film form in 1976).[5] Alarmed by Sherlock Holmes' increasingly bizarre behavior (in particular his delusions concerning Professor Moriarty) and his intravenous use of cocaine (in a "seven percent solution"), Watson arranges for Holmes to go to Vienna for treatment. There Holmes is hypnotized by Freud, the founder of psychoanalysis. In addition, his supply of cocaine is removed by Freud and Watson. Without his cocaine, Holmes experienced acute withdrawal symptoms (contradictory to known medical facts). Without revealing the entire story, it develops that the archvillain, Professor Moriarty, is none other than Holmes' math teacher. With the help of Freud, hypnosis, and because of his "forced withdrawal," Holmes leaves Vienna cured of his "cocaine habit."

ROBERT LOUIS STEVENSON AND COCAINE

In a medical-journal article, Schultz makes a case that Stevenson wrote *The Strange Case of Dr. Jekyll and Mr. Hyde* while under the influence of cocaine:

> . . . with the assistance of his "Brownies" the Hermit of Skerryvore, racked by tuberculosis, wrote and rewrote within six days a phenomenally successful book about a respectable physician who is transformed into a diabolical creature by a powerful, new drug; a book which, in style and execution, was entirely out of character with his preceding or succeeding works. What could account for this extraordinary creation? The answer I would suggest is cocaine.[6]

There is the medical evidence that Stevenson was ill with tuberculosis in the fall of 1885—a time when cocaine was much in the news as a panacea for every type of illness or ailment. There is the fact that Stevenson's doctor treated him with morphine, but he complained that it dulled his mind. Schultz speculates that cocaine, the "new wonder drug," was then prescribed.[7]

But the most convincing evidence is Stevenson's prodigious feat of writing two drafts of the book, a total of 60,000 words, in six days! This when he was, by his own admission, at his "chronic sickest." As his wife later recounted:

> The amount of work this involved was appalling; that an invalid in my husband's condition of health should have been able to perform the manual labor alone of putting 60,000 words on paper in six days seems incredible.[8]

The case is a lot less likely that the drug taken by Dr. Jekyll, which turned him into the monstrous Mr. Hyde, was cocaine. Certainly if Stevenson ever used cocaine it would have been for a short duration and not anywhere near long enough for him to "experience the degenerative effects of heavy cocaine use." In any case, in the initial draft of the book, the drug potion does not change Dr. Jekyll's personality, only his appearance. It was at his wife's insistence that "Stevenson rewrote the thriller as an allegory, with the potion revealing a dark side of Jekyll's nature."[9]

THE GOLDEN AGE OF PATENT MEDICINES

Sherlock Holmes and doctors and writers were not the only ones experimenting with cocaine. The patent-medicine industry was also exploring the stimulative and curative powers of this new drug. The golden age of patent medicines and coca-based tonics was in progress, and cocaine was to figure prominently in this development.

Though cocaine had achieved a certain degree of popular usage as a cure for opiate addiction, it was not until the early 1890s that its use became widespread. The patent-medicine industry and various tonic manufacturers started promoting cocaine as the panacea for a variety of ills and ailments including alcoholism, asthma, the common cold, whooping cough, dysentery, neuralgia, seasickness, vomiting associated with pregnancy, sore nipples, vaginismus, opium and morphine addiction, and gonorrhea and syphilis, as well as for local and regional anesthesia. It seems unlikely that the average consumer was actually taken in with the hyperbole of the ads; rather:

> What does seem likely is that these claims offered them a convenient rationale for taking the drug of their choice. Those who did not like to admit to themselves or to others that they were regular users of cocaine, opium, or alcohol—facts which would be hard to conceal if they drank openly in a public saloon or bought their cocaine and opium from the neighborhood druggist—had only to buy the appropriate patent medicine.[10]

Certainly the patent-medicine manufacturers provided enough ailments to be treated with their tonics, elixirs, etc., so that everybody would have an excuse to use their products.

In fact, cocaine, in the form of cocaine-laced tonics and elixirs, provided few or no medicinal benefits in treating any of these illnesses. It did act as a stimulant and euphoriant; sufferers would at least feel better, even though the illness itself was not being treated. Medicinally, cocaine's action of drying up the mucous membranes would in all probability have provided some feeling of comfort for sufferers of hay fever, sinus congestion, and the common cold. However, at best this would be symptomatic relief, and the actual cause or source of the illness would not be affected.[11]

Catarrh powders such as Dr. N. Tucker's Specific for Asthma, Hay Fever and Catarrh were found to contain cocaine—nearly 0.5 gram (7 grains) to the ounce.[12] Several deaths were attributed to the use of this "cure."[13] And there were other "cures" on the market that even exceeded this amount of cocaine:

- Coca-Bola contained 0.75 gram per ounce. Cost—50 cents a box.
- Nyal's Compound Extract of Damina, 1 gram of cocaine to the ounce, was advertised as an aphrodisiac, for restoring "virility in debility of the reproductive organs of both sexes."[14]

- AZ-MA-SYDE, an asthma cure, contained *4.5 grams* of cocaine per ounce.
- Ryno's Hay Fever-n-Catarrh Remedy was discovered to be an incredible 99.95 percent pure cocaine![15] (This fact was established in a court of law. E. H. Ryno of Whalen, Michigan, was arrested and charged and pleaded guilty to "selling cocaine (99.95 percent hydro-chloride) as a remedy for hay fever and catarrh." He was fined $100![16]

VIN MARIANI AND OTHER COCA TONICS

Certainly most of the cocaine consumed during the late 1800s and early 1900s was in the form of a remedy, tonic, or soft drink.

Angelo Mariani, a Corsican, developed the first widespread popular drink using coca leaves. Known as Vin Mariani, it was introduced to the public in 1863 and quickly become a sensation in both Europe and America.[17] Vin Mariani was advertised and apparently used for treating a variety of ills. In *Coca and Its Therapeutic Application*, Mariani[18] presents the history of coca use and its many therapeutic applications. As testimonials, he includes letters from scores of doctors who, during its nearly thirty year history, used Vin Mariani to successfully treat a number of illnesses.

The Mariani Company compiled and published the many endorsements received from celebrities about the beneficial aspects of the wines in several volumes, under the general title *Portraits from Album Mariani*. For each of the celebrities an outline of their lives is presented "with an etched portrait, and often accompanied by a sketch showing some known forte of the individual."[19] In the 1893 album there are several testimonials from world-famous celebrities. Frederic Auguste Bartholdi suggests that "had I known of it [Vin Mariani] twenty years ago, the Statue of Liberty would have attained the heights of several hundred meters." John Philip Sousa wrote, "When worn out after a long rehearsal or performance, I find nothing so helpful as a glass of Vin Mariani. To brain workers and those who expend a great deal of nervous force, it is invaluable." Apparently, Vin Mariani was very popular among actors and actresses, including Sarah Bernhardt, who stressed the drink's stimulative properties.

The 1893 *Album* includes one curious "notable," Ulysses S. Grant, who purportedly used a Mariani product to diminish the pain of his fatal illness. We have not been able to substantiate this allegation. We note that one of his attending physicians wrote of brandy and morphine injections, but made no mention of any coca preparation.[20]

The drink's endorsers included many of the prominent and famous doctors of the time, from both Europe and America. For example, Dr. Liberman, surgeon-in-chief of the army, wrote: "I can certify that Vin Mariani is the most powerful weapon that can be put in the hands of military physicians to combat the diseases, the infirmities and even the vicious habits engendered by camp life and the servitude of military existence." Liberman used it in treating alcoholism, chronic bronchitis, nicotinism and the common cold.

An appendix to the book lists alphabetically the names of *over 3,000 doctors* who "formally endorse Vin Mariani, their experience in prescribing in hospitals and private practice having caused them to believe the preparation valuable and reliable."

Vin Mariani was soon followed by Elixir Mariani (more alcoholic and containing three times as much of the active alkaloid of coca than Vin Mariani), Pate Mariani (lozenge of gum, sugar, and coca), Pastilles Mariani (lozenges similar to Pate Mariani, but with several "milligrams of cocaine" added to each pastille), and The Mariani (Tea Mariani, a concentrated tealike extract of coca). Through the popularity of these products, Mariani became the single largest importer of coca leaves in Europe.[21] The popularity of the drinks also resulted in a number of imitators appearing on the market.

A last report of Vin Mariani

In a London wine auction house in 1970, a half bottle of Vin Mariani of 1880 vintage sold for £4 (about $11).[22]

Competitors of Vin Mariani

One of the earliest American competitors was Metcalf's Coca Wine. In an elaborate advertisement, displaying the coca branch as a centerpiece, the distributors present a short history of coca use by South American Indians, list the ailments that can be cured by drinking the wine tonic; and quote the testimony of various doctors. Ingested three times daily, it would cure, among other illnesses, impotency:

> Elderly people have found it a reliable aphrodisiac superior to any other drug.

or fatigue brought on by strenuous sports activities:

> Athletes, pedestrians and baseball players have found by practical experience that a steady course of coca taken both before and after any trial of strength or endurance will impart energy to every movement, and prevent fatigue.[23]

But the chief and lasting competitor to Vin Mariani was a product still consumed today through the world—Coca-Cola.

Coca-Cola—"it's the real thing" (or at least it once was)

John Styth Pemberton of Atlanta, Georgia, a chemist and sole proprietor of Triplex Liver Pills and Globe of Flower Cough Syrup, introduced a potential competitor to Vin Mariani in 1885: French Wine Coca—Ideal Nerve and Tonic Stimulant. The following year, 1886, he put on the market a new syrup containing cocaine, caffeine, and extracts from kola nuts. The syrup was Coca-Cola, and it was mixed with soda water or other carbonated water.[24] The "soft" drink was born, but in its early days it, too, was advertised as a medicinal tonic. An early advertisement of Coca-Cola indicates:

> This "INTELLECTUAL BEVERAGE" and TEMPERANCE drink contains the valuable TONIC and nerve stimulant properties of the coca plant and cola (or kola) nuts, and makes not only a delicious, exhilarating, refreshing and invigorating Beverage, (dispensed from the

soda water fountain or in other carbonated beverages), but a valuable Brain Tonic, and cure for all nervous affections—SICK HEADACHE, NEURALGIA, HYSTERIA, MELANCHOLY, etc.[25]

In 1888, Asa G. Chandler took over the rights to produce Coca-Cola. One of his first moves was to remove all references to Coca-Cola's medicinal properties, henceforth advertising it solely as a "refreshing, exhilarating drink." However, it still contained cocaine, and continued to do so for another fifteen years, until 1903. Then, pressure applied "by southerners who feared blacks' getting cocaine in any form and by those seeking passage of a pure food and drug act, led the manufacturer to omit the cocaine."[26] However, Coca-Cola, even today, continues to be flavored with decocainized coca leaves. Of some interest is that since 1969 Coca-Cola no longer has to demonstrate for the federal government that the coca leaves are completely decocainized. This led one local forensic chemist to speculate that there was *probably* some cocaine, if very minute quantities, slipping into Coca-Cola.

The success of Coca-Cola prompted appearance of other cola "soft" drinks on the market. A 1912 medical article on nostrums and quackery listed a number of these freely-available "cocaine colas": Kos-Kola, Koca-Nola, Kola-Ade, Dr. Con's Kola, Coca Calisaya, Celery Cola, Vani-Kola, Rococola, Wiseola, Care Cola.[27]

Not until passage of the Food and Drug Act in 1906 were "soft" drink manufacturers required to indicate all ingredients, including cocaine. Even then, many violated the law by failing to indicate that their beverages contained cocaine. Koca-Nola's makers went so far as to advertise their product as "Dopeless."[28]

In fact, "dope" was Coca-Cola's nickname for many years, even after it no longer contained any cocaine.[29]

THE COUNTERREACTION BEGINS

The two-decade span from the late 1880s to the early 1900s during which cocaine caught the imagination and enthusiasm of the masses is unparalleled in our national history. As Musto so aptly noted:

> The cocaine episode illustrates how easily objective evaluation may be submerged by personal enthusiasm and how remarkably difficult it may be, in spite of vast amounts of evidence, to judge correctly a widely used drug. . . . [The early] papers about cocaine abound with rapturous subjectivity; they do not only strongly assert that everyone should try it, but also impatiently question the motives of those who disagree.[30]

However, the time had come for more and more people to disagree, and the first era of cocaine was soon to be over.

REFERENCES

1. Ashley, R., *Cocaine: Its History, Uses and Effects,* (New York: St. Martin's Press, 1975).
2. A. Conan Doyle (1888), quoted in Musto, D. F., "A Study in Cocaine: Sherlock Holmes and Sigmund Freud," *JAMA*, 1968, *204(1)* 27–32.
3. A. Conan Doyle, (1891), Quoted in Musto, 1968.
4. A Conan Doyle, (1894), Musto, 1968.
5. Meyer, N., *The Seven Percent Solution,* (New York: Ballantine Books, 1976).
6. Schultz, M. G., "The Strange Case of Robert Louis Stevenson," *JAMA*, 1971, *216(1)*, 90–94.
7. Ibid.
8. Ibid.
9. Perry, Charles, "The Star Spangled Powder or Through History with Coke Spoon and Nasal Spray," *Rolling Stone Magazine*, Issue 115, August 17, 1972.
10. Ashley, 1975, Op. Cit.
11. Ibid.
12. *Nostrums and Quackery, articles on the nostrum evil and quackery,* with additions and modifications from the *Journal of the American Medical Association,* (Chicago: American Medical Association, 1912), 429.
13. Perry, 1972, Op. Cit.
14. *Nostrums and Quackery*, 1912, p. 429, Op. Cit.
15. Ibid.
16. Moffett, C., "Rx Cocaine," *Hampton's Magazine*, 1911, *26*, 595–606.
17. Becker, H. K., "Carl Koller and Cocaine," *Psychoanal. Quarterly*, 1963, *32*, 309–373.
18. Mariani, A., *Coca and Its Therapeutic Application,* (New York: J. N. Jaros, 1890).

19. Mortimer, W. G., *Peru history of coca, the divine plant of the Incas*, (New York: J. H. Vail and Company, 1901), reprinted as *History of Coca*, (San Francisco: And/Or Press, 1974).
20. Shrady, G. F., *General Grant's Last Days with a Short Biographical Sketch of Dr. Shrady*, (New York, 1908).
21. Becker, 1963, Op. Cit.
22. Perry, 1972, Op. Cit.
23. Quoted in Ashley, 1975, Op. Cit.
24. Ibid.
25. A copy of this advertisement was provided to us by Dr. Michael Aldrich of the Fitzhugh Ludlow Memorial Library, San Francisco.
26. Ashley, 1975, Op. Cit.
27. *Nostrums and Quackery*, 1912, p. 429, Op. Cit.
28. Ibid.
29. Ashley, 1975, Op. Cit.
30. Musto, 1968, Op. Cit.

CHAPTER 5

PUBLIC REACTIONS TO THE USE OF COCAINE

It is a generally known fact that during the last twenty years cocaine has been diverted from its original use by the surgeons as a local anesthetic to pander to the supposed needs of large numbers of our population. It is estimated, after a wide consultation, that 15,000 or 20,000 ounces of this drug are sufficient to satisfy the demands of surgery in the United States. Today [1911] there are manufactured in the United States at least 150,000 ounces of the drug, the larger part of which is put to improper use.

—E. Marshall, "Uncle Sam Is the Worst Drug Fiend in the World"

By the early 1900s, the use of cocaine in various forms was very popular in the United States. It was the active ingredient in scores of patent medicines, tonics, and "soft" drinks. In 1906 alone, more than 21,000 pounds of cocaine was manufactured for a population of less than 90 million.[1] The prevailing notion that cocaine was a "wonder drug," a panacea for the ills of mankind, was to change dramatically to a view of the drug as the "most terrible vice ever acquired by a civilized people."[2]

Many factors—political, social, medical, and legal—combined to produce this dramatic change:

- Physicians were increasingly seeing the results of cocaine abuse in their patients. There was also a growing concern among other health professionals (especially pharmacists) as to their role in inducing drug habits.
- There was growing national concern and publicity about the contents of patent medicines.
- The popular press was beginning to print horror stories

about drug addiction, which resulted in widespread fear of all drugs viewed as addicting.

- The use of the addicting drugs became identified with particular minorities—for opium, the Chinese, and for cocaine, the blacks—which spurred regulatory legislation.
- Drug abuse was increasingly associated with the criminal element. A popular syllogism equated drug abuse with complete moral degradation inevitably followed by criminal behavior.
- This was the period of the "muckraking" social reformers (Sinclair, Wiley, and others). Among their targets were the patent-medicine manufacturers.
- This was a period in which the constitutional powers of Congress, especially federal commerce and tax powers, were being expanded and tested. With passage of the Mann Act and the Lottery Act, a precedent was set for legislating the morals of Americans.
- Lastly, cocaine had not been "long enough established in the culture to ensure its survival; and it had not, though used by them, become identified with the elite; thus, losing what little chance it had of weathering the storm of criticism."[3]

Together, these factors constituted a significant negative force, resulting in the eventual passage of legislation that regulated and greatly restricted the use of cocaine.

THE CHANGING ATTITUDES OF PHYSICIANS AND PHARMACISTS

Medicine and Pharmacy were in the active stages of professional organization when they became involved with the issue of narcotic control. The status of both pharmacists and physicians was less than desirable, and both suffered from weak licensing laws, meager training requirements, and a surplus of practitioners. Their intense battles for professional advancement and unification had an effect on the progress and final form of antinarcotic legislation.[4]

At the turn of the century the American Medical Association was a small, primarily Eastern organization with only 8,500 members. By 1913, it had grown to over 36,000 members nationwide and had become an influential force on the American medical scene, especially through its *Journal of the American Medical Association* (*JAMA*).

Physicians were becoming concerned about the number of cases of cocaine intoxication and even death. Examples of some *JAMA* headlines during this period reflect this concern:

- "Death after Spinal Tropa Cocainization" (Oct. 26, 1901).
- "Poisoning by Cocaine. A woman in London died in a drug store while under the influence of cocaine which had been administered for extraction of teeth" (Feb. 15, 1908).
- "Deaths from Cocaine Injections" (Vol. 61(14), 1913).
- "Death from Medullar Cocainization" (Aug. 17, 1901).
- "Fatal Cocaine Poisoning" (Jan. 11, 1917).

In 1923, Watson-Williams reported in the *British Medical Journal* on *fifty* fatal and many more near-fatal cases ascribed to cocaine's use in local anesthesia. Most of these cases involved minor surgery, such as tonsillectomies and even minor dental work. Watson-Williams' data show a range of 1 to 20 grains (0.065 to 1.3 grams) for fatal dosages.[5] This wide range lends weight to Freud's report on the idosyncratic pattern of toxic cocaine effects "that one does not know when and with whom a general reaction is to be expected."[6] Apparently, the fatal combination was the cocaine, the "idiosyncrasy" of each patient's metabolism, and, in some cases, professional error.

In line with this latter point, Watson-Williams also noted that in four cases the physician confused the 0.2% solution of cocaine with the 20% solutions, and the patients thus received a hundred times the intended dose and quickly succumbed to the toxic effect.[7]

The AMA's growing concern with the responsible use of cocaine by physicians was reflected in a special committee it empaneled in 1924 to study "The Toxic Effects Following the Use of Local Anesthetics."[8] Of the forty-three reported deaths due to local anesthetics of all kinds, twenty-six involved cocaine. The fatal solutions varied from 0.5% to 20%. A number of routes of administration were involved in the fatalities, but two were especially dangerous—topical application to the tonsils and urethral injections. In yet another study, Plotz reported on 151 fatal cases involving local anesthetics of which 102 were cocaine-related.[9]

Significantly—and this paradox has been reported by Woods and Downs and later by Ashley—the medical and supposedly supervised use of cocaine has resulted in more reported cases of death than has the unsupervised use of cocaine by pleasure seekers.[10] For further explanation of this curious phenomenon, see the section on the toxicity of cocaine in Chapter 9.

The search for an antidote to cocaine

By 1910, many of the claims for the beneficial medical use of cocaine had fallen into disrepute. The chief legitimate medical application of cocaine continued to be what had originally propelled it onto the medical scene—its use as a local anesthetic. However, with the increasing notoriety given cocaine's medical misuse, organized medicine began to take action. One approach was to look for preventive measures that might effectively curtail the toxic effects of cocaine in local anesthesia. Some of the measures developed were very strange indeed, as shown in the following quotes:

> As a safeguard against cocaine toxemia, I always instruct my patients to eat a full meal before the operation, since toxic substances produce a heavier degree of toxemia when the stomach is empty than when it is full.
>
> I advise the use of coffee as an aide in the prevention of cocaine toxemia.
>
> . . . I believe that smoking tends to relieve somewhat the toxemia of cocaine.
>
> . . . In severe cases of toxemia following the use of cocaine, amyl nitrite acts quite well.[11]

Later writings have also suggested alcohol and sodium barbital as antidotes to cocaine:

> . . . alcohol is an excellent drug for preventing acute cocaine intoxication, such as may occur particularly in females who exhibit an idiosyncrasy to cocaine.

> . . . [the physician] give to every patient without exception a large dose, 25 to 50 cc of whiskey and brandy by mouth ten to thirty minutes before the first injection of cocaine.[12]

Leshure reported on switching from morphine to sodium barbital and, in over a hundred cases, there were no manifestations of cocaine toxicity.[13] However, two years later, in a response to a physician's inquiry, *JAMA* stated, "There are not enough reports to state definitely that barbital is an absolute antidote for cocaine poisoning."[14]

Even while the search for effective antidotes was underway, other physicians were beginning to use substitutes for cocaine as local anesthetics. Procaine was one of them. Synthesized by Einhorn in 1905, it was less toxic and almost as effective as cocaine. Physicians were increasingly coming to depend on it and other less toxic local anesthetics.

Reactions of physicians to one patent medicine

Illustrative of the mounting concern of physicians about the proprietary medicines is the following letter, which appeared in *JAMA*, Aug. 4, 1906.

> To the Editor:—Having repeatedly found that patients coming to me for medical advice were using the secret remedy for asthma sold by Dr. N. Tucker of Mount Gilead, Ohio, I naturally became desirous of knowing its composition. It is employed locally by means of an atomizer, and those using it have claimed that they experienced undoubted relief from its employment. At my suggestion a man obtained for me some of the remedy and gave it to me in the bottle in which he bought it. It has been examined by Dr. Frank Piper and Dr. Julian W. Baird, both of Boston, and both find that it contains cocain. Dr. Baird, who is dean of the Massachusetts College of Pharmacy and has been teaching chemistry for over twenty years, also made a quantitative examination, demonstrating a little over 7 grains of the hydrochloride of cocain to each ounce of the remedy.

continued

It seems to me that others besides myself may be very glad to know this fact, in order to give their patients advice concerning the "cure." Further, I should like to inquire whether a secret remedy with so dangerous an ingredient can be legally distributed by means of the United States mails, and if not, whether it would not be well for the American Medical Association officially to call the attention of the Postmaster General to the facts.

Apparently other doctors were also noticing disturbing side effects of this cocaine-laden "cure":

> To the Editor:—Referring to the article of Dr. Vickery on "Cocain in Tucker Asthma Cure" in the Journal A.M.A., August 4, 1906, I wish to thank the author for his report and to commend his suggestion as to what ought to be done to suppress such a "cure." I had a case here, with all the symptoms of acute cocain poisoning, as the result of using the above preparation. The patient was a child 5 years of age, and I can assure you that a "remedy" that will produce as marked symptoms of poisoning in as short a time as does the Tucker Asthma Cure, needs to be removed from the market, or at least labeled as to its contents, and not retailed to an unsuspecting public as a harmless asthma cure.

Reactions from pharmacists

The pharmacists, at least those "who were eager to proclaim themselves professionals, as opposed to mere retailers of prepared medicines and sundries, became members of the American Pharmaceutical Association."[15] During this period the pharmacist competed with physicians in the dispensing of medicines, as well as with the many other pharmacists—who did a substantial amount of business with proprietary medicines containing cocaine and narcotics.

The American Pharmaceutical Association opposed the proprietary medicines, as did the AMA, on both moral and self-interest bases: ". . . they were dangerous, self medications had inherent risks, and the legitimate trade was taken from the pharmacists who prepared their own products."[16]

A special committee on the drug habit

The American Pharmaceutical Association took an active role in attempting to affect state and later federal legislation to regulate the cocaine and narcotic proprietary medicines. In order to focus national attention on the problem, the association formed an ad hoc committee at the 1901 national meeting to study "the acquirement of drug habits, and the best methods of legislative regulation of the dangers."[17] The report of the Committee on the Acquirement of the Drug Habit, the highlight presentation of the 50th Anniversary meeting in 1902, concluded that:

- Although the population had only increased by 10% during the years 1898–1902, importation of cocaine had increased 40%, opium 500%, and morphine 600%.
- Based on an estimate of five habitués per pharmacist, there were about 200,000 habitués nationally.
- Two groups were prone to cocaine abuse—women and blacks.
- Physicians were not generally the cause for the increasing use of habit-forming drugs, as they were "generally prescribing less as the danger of addictions became more widely appreciated."[18]
- Opium for smoking should be banned, uniform state laws should be enacted to protect people from the habit-forming drugs, and the American Pharmaceutical Association should ban any member who trafficked in these drugs.

The following year the committee reported further findings and survey results and suggested a model state law. Cocaine and heroin, a relatively new drug which had been in use only since 1898, figured prominently. Many states reported on the increased sale of cocaine, with several indicating increasing use of cocaine among blacks. However, the committee stressed that cocaine abuse was not restricted to blacks, criminals, or the lower classes:

> Acquiring the habit was related to many factors in American life. . . . Lawyers and preachers took cocaine

The making of a cocaine abuser—
as depicted in the popular press in the 1900s

In a 1911 *Hampton's Magazine* article, Cleveland Moffett portrayed several cocaine "habitués." The article demonstrates cocaine's rapid change of status over less than a ten-year span, from the "new wonder drug" to the "most threatening of the drug habits that has ever appeared in this country."

> "How is the habit usually acquired?" I enquired. . . .
>
> "By accident, like other drug habits. I'm sorry to say that one of these 'accidents' is the presence of cocaine in catarrh medicines."
>
> Dr. Podstata proceeded to give me details in the case of one of his patients, a man of twenty-two, who became a cocaine fiend quite innocently by taking a widely advertised "catarrh cure" that contained only a small percentage of cocaine, but unfortunately, enough to establish the habit.
>
> The young man sniffed this "catarrh cure" up his nose and after each sniffing experienced a characteristic sense of elation, a peculiar well-being. He took more and more of the snuff and soon discovered that his exhilaration came from cocaine in the powder. Now it was cocaine he wanted, not the catarrh cure; and presently he began to take the drug pure, sniffing it after the manner of adepts, and finally learning to use it in hypodermic injections.
>
> Soon he learned that the sensations were not all that pleasant. Far from it! Quick after each period of intoxication came the dread reaction that calls for more and always more cocaine. The characteristic physical and moral deterioration went on rapidly. The victim grew sallow-faced, sunken-eyed, restless, irritable. He lost ambition and perseverance. He became a liar, a wreck, helpless and useless, and within a year he was in an asylum.[21]

> in order to be "bright." Even worse, "many of the leading lights of the medical profession . . . became slaves to a vice which they are supposed to combat."[19]

The committee report concluded with a warning that "speedy action" must be taken to combat the "class of druggist who supply the 'dope fiends.' " What were needed were laws with severe penalties.[20] It would be eleven more years (in 1914) before such laws would be enacted, however.

COCAINE, BLACKS, AND CRIME

Around the turn of the century, the media increasingly pictured cocaine in association with groups that threatened the social order, in particular, criminals and blacks.

> Cocaine was especially feared in the South by 1900 because of its euphoric and stimulating properties. The South feared that Negro cocaine users might become oblivious of their prescribed bounds and attack white society.[22]

One of the more striking myths to appear in the cocaine literature is the fear by turn-of-the-century Southerners of "cocainized" blacks. The period was one of an upsurge in lynchings, and the institution of legal segregation and poll taxes that disenfranchised blacks. Newspapers and even medical journals were quick to report on the "cocaine-black" phenomenon. An 1898 *Medical News* article suggested that Southern blacks had a predilection to cocaine.[23] A *JAMA* editorial appearing less than two years later warned:

> The Negroes in some parts of the South are reported as being addicted to a new form of vice—that of "cocaine sniffing" or the "coke habit." . . . A Negro, it is said, will buy 5 cents' worth of cocaine, which is sold in a little paper box for such purposes . . . then proceed to indulge in a "coke drunk."[24]

The *JAMA* editors published another warning the following year. A 1902 article in the *British Medical Journal* depicted the white plantation owners, like the Spanish conquistadores 300 years earlier, giving their black laborers cocaine to keep them working. Given some later news reports, however, this was perhaps an accurate portrayal.[25]

But it was the popular press that most widely proclaimed the startling stories and headlined the dangers posed by cocaine-crazed blacks. Moffett's previously quoted *Hampton's Magazine* article graphically summarizes the popular view:

> In writing of the evils of the cocaine habit, it is impossible to avoid mention of one that is of grave importance; I mean the stimulation of negroes, who are as a race largely addicted to this drug, to a certain class of crimes.
>
> Most attacks upon white women of the South, declared Christopher Kock, are the direct result of a coke-crazed negro brain.
>
> Dr. Hamilton Wright confirms this opinion in the following words: "This new vice, the cocaine vice, the most serious that has to be dealt with, has proved to be a creator of criminals and unusual forms of violence, and it has been a potent incentive in driving the humbler negroes all over the country to abnormal crimes."[26]

In a long 1903 newspaper article, a Colonel J. W. Watson of Georgia asserted that "many of the horrible crimes committed in the southern states by the colored people can be traced directly to the cocaine habit." He suggested that Coca-Cola (manufactured in Atlanta and at that time containing cocaine) was partly responsible and that legislation should be enacted to stop its sale. He asserted that young whites were also the victims of this habit.[27] Later that year (1903), cocaine was dropped as an active ingredient of Coca-Cola.

Watson's article apparently set the tone for the next ten to fifteen years. Blacks were increasingly singled out as "cocaine fiends," and their use of the "coke" or "Heaven's dust" was closely associated in the popular mind with violent criminal activities.[28]

There is little, if any, evidence to support these views, although there are some indications that Southern blacks may have been more familiar with cocaine than their white counterparts. For one thing, many Southern states passed legislation banning blacks' access to liquor. The conse-

Some myths about the cocainized black

A 1914 *New York Times* article by Dr. E. H. Williams, "Negro Cocaine 'Fiends' Are a New Southern Menace," neatly "summarizes most of the myths associated with black crime and cocaine."[32] On cocaine-induced killings:

> Stories of cocaine orgies, followed by wholesale murders seem like lurid journalism of the yellowest variety. . . . [However], nine men killed in Mississippi on one occasion by crazed cocaine takers, five in North Carolina, three in Tennessee—these are facts that need no imaginative coloring.

On cocaine's effect on marksmanship:

> . . . there is another [effect], and a most important one. This is the temporary steadying of the nervous and muscular system, so as to increase . . . good marksmanship. . . .
>
> The record of the "cocaine nigger" near Asheville, who dropped five men dead in their tracks, using only one cartridge for each, offers evidence that is sufficiently convincing.

On cocaine's ability to counter the effect of bullets:

> The drug produces several other conditions that make the "fiend" a peculiarly dangerous criminal. One of these conditions is a temporary immunity to shock—a resistance to the "knock down" effects of fatal wounds. Bullets fired into vital parts, that would drop a sane man in his tracks, fail to check the "fiend"—fail to stop his rush or weaken his attack.[33]

It should be noted that Williams was not so much a racist as he was very much anti-prohibition. He believed that blacks would use more cocaine if alcohol was prohibited, and thus cause more crime. His solution, simply enough, was to allow both blacks and whites to continue to indulge in alcohol.

quence of these laws was that "lower classes . . . found they could get a jolt [from cocaine] which took the place of liquor."[29] And news reports indicated that cocaine was given to black laborers in the south:

> In the South, the use of cocaine among the lower order of working negroes is quite common. It is current knowledge throughout the south that on many public works, levee and railroad construction and in other working camps where negroes congregate, cocaine is peddled openly.
>
> . . . Inquiries have shown that contractors of labor in the South, under the impression that cocaine stimulates the negro laborers to a greater output of work, wink at the distribution of the drug to them.[30]

But when all is said and done, the majority of Southern blacks probably started using cocaine for the same reasons as did whites: its availability in patent medicine and "soft" drinks, and also because "they liked it."[31]

Obviously, no rigorous epidemiological data are available from the early 1900s to demonstrate the geographic or ethnic breakdown of drug-abuse patterns. But two studies of that era do provide some limited information as to blacks' use of cocaine.

One, conducted by the 1901–02 American Pharmaceutical Association Committee on the Acquirements of the Drug Habit, involved analysis of a mail survey of 1,100 physicians and pharmacists in the major Eastern cities with a 30% return rate.[34] The committee concluded that (1) based on their estimated average of five cocaine "abusers" per pharmacist, there were over 200,000 habitués in the United States; and (2) women and blacks were the two population groups most susceptible to cocaine's effects. Their study, clearly, was methodologically very weak.

The other was the article "Psychoses Among Negroes" by E. M. Green in the prestigious *Journal of Nervous and Mental Disorders*.[35] It reported little cocaine use among Southern blacks, at least among those committed to one particular psychiatric hospital. Green reported on the diagnoses and factors accounting for admission for 2,100 consecutive black admissions to an asylum over a five-year period. There were only two reported cocaine users in this group, and their drug use was not a factor in their admission. In a *New York Times* article later that year, the aforementioned Dr. Williams, a proponent of the "blacks-cocaine-violence" school of thought, minimized the generality of Green's findings in stating that "cocainized Negroes are to be found in jails, not insane asylums."[36]

No reputable researchers have uncovered any statistical or other type of evidence to indicate that the use of cocaine resulted in a massive (black) crime wave. Strikingly, however the popularization and eventual widespread belief in this myth had some very real consequences. In his study on the development of narcotics legislation, Musto states:

> In each instance there were ulterior motives to magnify the problems of cocaine among Negroes, and it was to almost no one's personal interest to minimize or portray it objectively. As a result by 1910 it was not difficult to get legislation almost totally prohibiting the drug.[37]

One aspect of this myth was the allegation that while high on cocaine, blacks both possessed superior marksmanship and were impervious to police bullets. In reaction, some Southern police forces changed their firearm caliber from .32 to the more powerful .38.[38]

Over the first twenty years of this century, cocaine was increasingly associated with criminal activities. Even police officials would go as far as to state that "cocaine was the drug usually taken by gunmen—to stimulate courage."[39] This further contributed to a climate conducive to legislation to restrict its use.

Police chiefs were finding cocaine and cocainized blacks a convenient scapegoat for crime waves in their cities. The police chief of Washington, D.C., considered cocaine the worst of the drug menaces, which was exacerbated by the then-current practice of selling the drug door-to-door.[40]

In 1911, Moffett wrote:

> Let it be noted that crimes are committed by "coke fiends" not only in their frenzy of desire to get the drug, but in the frenzy of exhilaration that follows taking it.[41]

Several years later, Atlanta's police chief attributed "70% of the crimes" to the use of cocaine.[42] As depicted in the popular press, cocaine use led to a life of crime, then to total physical debilitation followed by death:

> . . . once the habit is acquired, the utter undermining of the nervous system is inevitable. There is always the necessity for repeated doses, since the effects soon wear off, and is succeeded by weakness and depression, utter moral degradation, indulgence in vice and crime in their various forms, followed often, by suicide. These are the heritages of the cocaine fiend.[43]

Indeed, many writers of the period viewed death as the only release for the "coke fiend":

> There is nothing that we can do for the confirmed user of the drug. The best thing for the cocaine fiend is to let him die.[44]

Cocaine's pharmacological properties were considered the reasons that use of the drug led to criminal activities. Because the effect of cocaine is short-acting, the popular

Cocaine and the international conspiracy

Blacks and criminals were not the only dangers. Woods and Downs cite other examples of cocaine-related fears that were widespread in this country around the time of the First World War:

> During World War I, a new fear of cocaine emerged. Propaganda rumors in the popular press alleged that German agents were attempting to enslave America by selling or giving cocaine to school children, especially in Harlem where countless "dangerous child addicts dwelled." In 1918 there was a report in *The New York Times* saying that Germans had exported toothpaste and patent medicines, cocaine and narcotics so that ". . . in a few years Germany would have fallen upon a world which cried for its German toothpaste and soothing syrup—a world of 'cokeys' and 'hopfiends' which would have been absolutely helpless when a German embargo shut off the supply of its pet poison."[45]

literature presented the "cocaine fiend" as a desperate individual engaged in a constant search for money to buy more cocaine to maintain the euphoric effects of the drug. If this sounds familiar, it should, as this is the way, even today, our newspapers often portray the heroin addict. At that time, however, the daily use of narcotics (e.g., morphine) was viewed as "not incompatible with ordinary intelligence and average judgment."[46] The use of cocaine was viewed as a far worse habit.

REFERENCES

1. "Nations Uniting to Stamp Out the Use of Opium and Many Other Drugs," *The New York Times*, July 25, 1909.
2. "The Growing Menace of the Use of Cocaine, *The New York Times*, August 2, 1908.
3. Ashley, R., *Cocaine: Its History, Uses and Effects*, (New York: St. Martin's Press, 1975).
4. Musto, D. F., *The American disease: Origins of narcotic control*, (New Haven and London: Yale University Press, 1973).
5. Watson-Williams, E., *Brit. Medical Journal*, 1923, 2, 1018 (December 11, 1923).
6. Freud, S., "Craving for and fear of cocaine," *Wein. Med. Wochenschr.*, 1887, *28*, 929–932, reprinted in *The Cocaine Papers* (W. Hammond, tr.), (Vienna: Dunquin Press, 1963), reprinted in R. Byck (ed.), *Cocaine Papers by Sigmund Freud*, New York: Stonehill Publishing Company, 1974.
7. Watson-Williams, 1923, Op. Cit.
8. Mayer, E., "The toxic effects following the use of local anesthetics," *JAMA*, 1924, *82*, 876–885.
9. Plotz, A., Fatal Accidents with Local Anesthesia, Paris: Jouve et Cie, 1929. Quoted in: "Accidents with local anesthesia," *JAMA*, 1929, *92*, 1680–1681.
10. Woods, J. H., and Downs, D. A., "The psychopharmacology of cocaine." In: *Drug use in America: Problem in perspective*, Appendix, Vol. I.: (Washington, D.C.: U.S. Government Printing Office, 1973), 116–139.
11. Mackenzie, G. W., "Complications of nose operations," *JAMA*, 1913, *61*, 1200–1201.
12. Hertzfeld, A. A., "Prevention of cocaine intoxication by ethyl alcohol in surgery," *JAMA*, 1921, *77*, 1594.
13. Leshure, J., "Barbital as a preventive of cocaine toxicosis," *JAMA*, 1927, *88*, 168–169.
14. Anonymous, "Barbital as antidote to cocaine used in tonsillectomy," *JAMA*, 1929, *93*.
15. Musto, D. F., *The American disease: Origins of narcotic*

control, (New Haven and London: Yale University Press, 1973).
16. Ibid.
17. Beal, J. H., "Report on pharmacy legislation," *Proc. A. Ph. A.*, 1901, *49*, 460–461.
18. Musto, 1973, Op. Cit.
19. Ibid.
20. "Report of Committee on the Acquirement of Drug Habits," *Proc. A. Ph. A.*, 1903, *51*, 466–477.
21. Moffett, C., "Rx cocaine," *Hampton's Magazine*, 1911, *26*, 595–606.
22. Musto, 1973, Op. Cit.
23. Scheppegrill, W., "The abuse and dangers of cocaine," *Med. News*, 1898, *73*, 417–422.
24. Anonymous, "The Cocaine Habit," *JAMA*, 1900, *34*, 1967.
25. Musto, 1973, Op. Cit.
26. Moffett, 1911, Op. Cit.
27. Watson, Col. J. W., Letter *New York Tribune*, June 21, 1903.
28. "The Growing Menace," *The New York Times*, August 2, 1908, Op. Cit.
29. Musto, 1973, Op. Cit.
30. Marshall, E., "Uncle Sam is the Worst Drug Fiend in the World," *The New York Times*, March 12, 1911.
31. Ashley, 1975, Op. Cit.
32. Ibid.
33. Williams, E. H., "Negro Cocaine 'Fiends' are a New Southern Menace," *The New York Times*, February 8, 1914.
34. "Report of Committee on Acquirement of the Drug Habit," *Proc. A. Ph. A.*, 1902, *50*, 567–573.
35. Green, E. M., "Psychoses among negroes: A comparative study," *Journal of Nerv. Mental Disorders*, 1914, *41*, 697–708.
36. Williams, 1914, Op. Cit.
37. Musto, 1973, Op. Cit.
38. Ibid.
39. "Cocaine Used Most by Drug Addicts," *The New York Times*, April 15, 1926.
40. "Report of the President's Homes Commission," S. Doc. No. 644, 60th Congress, 2nd Session, January 1, 1909, 254–255.
41. Moffett, 1911, Op. Cit.
42. *Atlanta Constitution*, December 27, 1914.
43. Wiley, H. W., and Pierce, A. L., "The cocaine crime," *Good Housekeeping*, 1914 *58*, 393–398.
44. "The Growing Menace," *The New York Times*, August 2, 1908, Op. Cit.
45. Woods and Downs, 1973, Op. Cit.
46. Anonymous, "Opium and cocaine inebriety," *JAMA* 1970, *214*.

CHAPTER 6

AFTER THE FALL: COCAINE IN THE REGULATORY ERA

Prior to 1930, cocaine, rather than heroin or opium, was viewed as the primary drug menace in the United States. The development of criminal sanctions and regulatory measures concerning the drug reflects this attitude.

—G. T. McLaughlin, *Cocaine: The History and Regulation of a Dangerous Drug*

Cocaine use spread not only through America but through many other countries as well. Whenever it was used, it went through a roughly similar history: a period of increasing popular use and well-publicized misuse, after which it came under some form of regulation. As the preceding chapter showed, there were a great variety of reactions in this country, and the regulatory backlash became great. Interestingly enough, as McLaughlin shows, "State involvement in the field of drug control generally, and cocaine specifically, antedates Federal involvement."[1] In fact, the first state law regulating cocaine dispensation with a prescription came in 1887 (in Oregon), while the first pertinent federal law came only in 1906 (the Pure Food and Drug Act). In this chapter we provide a historical overview of the state and federal regulatory activity to combat cocaine, and a selective overview of the experiences that other countries had in dealing with the upsurge and increasing illegal use of cocaine.

State and federal activities are dealt with separately here, but it should be kept in mind that there are parallel efforts in both the state and federal sectors. A brief chronological overview will help to set these domestic laws in perspective:

1887	Oregon first state to prohibit cocaine dispensing without prescription.
by 1900	Eight states had passed such laws.
1900–14	Forty-six of the forty-eight states pass such laws.
1906	Pure Food and Drug Act became law.
1908	Amendment drafted to Pure Food and Drug Act, which, modified, evolved into the Harrison Narcotics Act.
1914	Harrison Narcotics Act (first specifically anti-drug law) and the Narcotics Drug Import and Export Act became law.
1919	Harrison Act amended to provide more stringent controls.
1922	Amendment to Narcotics Import and Export Act defined cocaine as a narcotic.
1930	Public Health Service regulations promulgated pertaining to the amounts of cocaine needed for legitimate medical purposes.
by 1931	All states had laws restricting the sale of cocaine; 36 states had laws prohibiting unauthorized possession of cocaine.
1932	Uniform Narcotic Drug Act adopted by forty-six states (modeled after the federal law).
1951	Both the 1914 acts amended to provide for standardized mandatory sentences for cocaine violations.
1960	Narcotics Manufacturing Act, requiring manufacturing licenses and quotas, became law.
1967	Montana and New Hampshire repealed the Uniform Narcotic Drug Act.
1970	Congress repealed all existing federal laws and passed the Comprehensive Drug Abuse Prevention and Control Act.
1971	Uniform Controlled Substances Act, to bring state and federal laws into line, drafted.
1973–	Increasing number of challenges voiced to existing legislation.

THE FIRST STATE LAWS

In 1887, Oregon became the first state specifically to prohibit the dispensing of cocaine without a doctor's prescription. Earlier, in 1877, Nevada had passed the country's first statute regulating drug distribution and sale and use of opium.[2] Montana in 1889, New York in 1893, Colorado and Illinois in 1897, Arizona and Arkansas in 1899, and Mississippi in 1900 passed laws similar to Oregon's.[3] The patent-medicine manufacturers' use of cocaine was not regulated in any of these state statutes.

By 1914, when the Harrison Act was passed, forty-six of the forty-eight states had adopted some form of legislation regulating the distribution of cocaine. In comparison, by 1914, only twenty-nine states had statutes designed to regulate and control the distribution or use of opiate drugs.[4]

A New York State law was illustrative of these early cocaine state regulations. It allowed for the legal distribution of cocaine by manufacturers, pharmacists, wholesalers, and the medical and dental professions, provided they filled out various record-keeping forms. It made unauthorized possession of cocaine a misdemeanor. But the statute made it a felony for anyone to sell, distribute, furnish, dispose of, or give away cocaine, except as authorized by the act.[5]

Most of the early state laws included a loophole for patent-medicine manufacturers, who were given exemptions permitting inclusion of limited amounts of controlled substances (narcotics and cocaine) in their elixirs and tonics.[6]

Generally, these early state laws were ineffective in combating the distribution and use of both cocaine and the opiates. States lacked the necessary manpower resources to ensure compliance with the regulatory statutes. Additionally, while one state might have a comprehensive law its neighbor might have no such regulation, or a loosely worded one:

> The "dope doctors" could simply purchase drugs by mail from another state and then dispense them to their "patients," thereby bypassing laws which relied on prescriptions and pharmacies to monitor drug abuse.[7]

Later state laws

Although the Harrison Act unquestionably represented significant federal intervention into local drug regulation, the Act was technically a revenue statute and by its terms did not directly prohibit the possession and use of cocaine. By 1931 however, every state had restricted the sale of cocaine and thirty-six had prohibited its unauthorized possession.[8]

Because of the lack of uniformity in state statutes regulating cocaine, the Commissioners on Uniform State Laws proposed, in 1932, the Uniform Narcotic Drug Act. As all but two states adopted the act (Pennsylvania and California did not, and later, in 1967, New Hampshire and Montana repealed it), it was representative of "state cocaine regulation during the period from 1932 to 1970."[9] The act was modeled on the federal law and required licensing for the manufacturers or wholesalers of cocaine, who then could distribute cocaine "only to certain categories of individuals able to present an official written form."[10] Record keeping was made mandatory for all firms or individuals involved on any level of cocaine distribution. The penalties varied from state to state, but in many cases were more severe than in the federal statute.

THE PURE FOOD AND DRUG ACT OF 1906

How widespread the custom of self-medication with "patent" nostrums became in this country is a matter of common knowledge. Newspapers and magazines were filled with fraudulent and misleading, but seductive advertisements, while from billboards "pain-killers," "cough mixtures," "soothing syrups," "women's friends," "consumption cures," and a host of others, furnished a constant suggestion that could not fail to have its effects upon a considerable portion of the population. The peak of the "patent medicines" industry was reached just prior to the passage of the Federal Pure Food and Drug Act in 1906.[11]

The Pure Food and Drug Act of 1906 was the first federal legislation to regulate the distribution of narcotics and cocaine in the United States. It was not the first *anti-drug* federal law (that would come in 1914 with the passage of the Harrison Narcotic Act) but was the first attempt, albeit indirect, to regulate cocaine distribution.[12] It evolved partly in response to the statutory exemptions of patent medicines by existing state regulations, and also because of the growing concern raised by physicians, pharmacists, and the popular press about growing use and misuse of proprietary medicines. The Pure Food and Drug Act prohibited "the introduction into any state or territory or the District of Columbia from any other state or territory or the District of Columbia, or from any foreign country or shipments to any foreign country of any article of food or drugs which is adulterated or misbranded, within the meaning of this Act."

Specifically, this meant that all foods and/or drugs had to disclose on the label if any opiates, alcohol, cocaine, or any derivatives of these substances were present. Not to do so constituted misbranding the product. Adulteration of the food took place if any added poisonous or other deleterious ingredients were added to the food making it injurious to health.[13]

The law prohibited shipment of any food, soda, or patent medicine that clearly did not indicate the presence and amount of the specified drugs. The Act did "curtail somewhat the marketing of dangerous patent medicines and sodas."[14]

According to one contemporary source, the act was ineffectual because of the "farcical leniency" in sentencing violators. Complaining that "not once has there been a prison sentence, not once has there been a maximum sentence," Moffett cites the lenient adjudication that many guilty manufacturers received:

> On January 10, 1910 the Sethness Company of Chicago pleaded guilty to shipping "Kos Kola," a soft drink containing cocaine, from Illinois to Michigan, and the court imposed a *fine of $10 for each offense.*
>
> On November 10, 1910, the American Beverage Company of St. Louis, Missouri pleaded guilty to adulterating and misbranding their "Great American Coca Cream," a product containing cocaine, *and was fined $20 and costs.*[15]

And although the law had provided for jail terms for second offenders, no one was ever given this sentence. The maximum fine for a violator was $200. The Pure Food and Drug Act was also the first federal regulation to place restrictions, though minimal, on cocaine importation. The importer had to "swear that the drug was intended for use in a manner not dangerous to health."[16]

It was estimated that the Pure Food and Drug Act reduced by about one-third the patent medicines containing narcotics and cocaine.[17] Although the contents of patent medicines were generally labeled in accordance with the law, their continued large sale was viewed with alarm by the act's enforcer, Dr. Harvey Wiley. Head of the Department of Agriculture's Bureau of Chemistry, Wiley believed that even stronger measures than those provided for by the Pure Food and Drug Act were necessary. In an article on "The Cocaine Crime," he explained why:

> One of the most despicable methods of establishing this habit is through the sale of the drug in mixtures advertised to cure or relieve catarrh, epilepsy, hay fever, asthma, colds, etc. . . . To be sure, Dr. Lepper's Microtine is labeled "cocaine 18⅔ grains per ounce," but it also bears the statement, "Guaranteed under the Food and Drug Act." . . . Not only ignorant people, but many fairly well-informed, would not be much alarmed by this brief declaration of a comparatively unknown substance, with its cure of instant antiseptic relief, all guaranteed under the law.[18]

Retail and compounding pharmacists enlisted Wiley's assistance in designing an amendment to the Pure Food and Drug Act intended to prevent interstate transportation of any patent medicine containing habit-forming drugs unless under a physician's prescription.[19] Pharmacists would also benefit from this amendment, since mail-order firms could no longer conduct interstate sales and their business would go to local pharmacists. The 1908 draft amendment was sent for review to the State Department, which, because of the extent of the international narcotics problem, was taking a greater interest in federal legislation concerning drug control. The State Department felt the amendment was not sufficient, or broad enough in scope, and that a new and separate federal law was required.[20] Over the next several years this desire evolved into the Harrison Narcotics Act.

THE HARRISON NARCOTICS ACT OF 1914

Prior to the 1900s, federal controls regulating either the use of drugs or the prescription practices of physicians were considered unconstitutional. As indicated, however, the combination of increasing Congressional assertion on moral issues, as in the Mann Act and the Lottery Act, and a broadening of tax and commerce powers laid the groundwork for development of a law to control the drug problem through regulation of the narcotics and cocaine. In fact, international attention was being paid to the drug question, culminating in the Hague International Opium Conference of 1912, at which the United States and many other countries pledged passage of regulatory legislation.[21]

The State Department and Treasury Department created a joint committee "to unite a bill acceptable to the drug trade, the medical professional, and the Internal Revenue Bureau, which would have enforcement responsibilities."[22]

The bill became the Harrison Act and was signed into law in 1914. It was to become the cornerstone of all subsequent federal regulations controlling dangerous drugs, until passage of the Comprehensive Drug Abuse Prevention and Control Act of 1970.

Specifically, the act required that "every person who produced, imported, manufactured, compounded, dealt in, dispensed, sold, distributed, or gave away opium or coca leaves or their derivatives (cocaine)" must register with the Internal Revenue Service, and pay a special tax.[23] The act required that all exchanges involving coca (cocaine) or the narcotics must be noted on special forms obtainable only from the Internal Revenue Service. In effect, the law required that all drug transfers would be between duly registered persons. Possession of cocaine by an unregistered person "although not a crime in itself, was presumptive evidence of violation of the registration and special tax provision."[24]

Violation of the act was punishable by a fine of up to $2,000, a prison term of up to five years, or both. And, although the act allowed the proprietary medicines to include minimal amounts of opium or its derivatives, no such allowance was permitted for any preparation containing cocaine, "no matter how minimal the amount."[25]

A companion bill was also passed in 1914, the Narcotic Drugs Import and Export Act, which prohibited the exportation of cocaine to any country, unless that country had regulations controlling its own drug imports. Violations of this act were punishable by a fine of not less than $50 nor more than $5,000, or by imprisonment of up to two years, or by both.[26]

Interestingly enough, the passage of neither bill generated much publicity or general public awareness. The country was much more concerned at that time with the intense debates about the prohibition movement.

> But almost no one ever used the term temperance in discussing the use of opiates or cocaine after 1900: by the teens of the century both classes of drugs were deemed in public debate to have no value except as medicine. . . . By 1914 prominent newspapers, physicians, pharmacists, and congressmen believed opiates and cocaine predisposed habitués toward insanity and crime.[27]

FEDERAL LEGISLATION FROM 1915 TO 1930

With the passage of the Harrison Act and the Export Act, both the internal distribution and the exportation of cocaine were regulated. But the Harrison Act was to undergo many close and even unfavorable court tests "until its broad police powers were upheld in 1919."[28]

In that year, the act was amended to provide even more stringent controls on the distribution of both cocaine and opium. The tax, initially $1 per year for all registered persons, was increased to $3 per year for physicians and dentists and up to $24 per year for manufacturers, producers, and compounders. The amendment also provided a commodity stamp tax of one cent per ounce on all opium, coca leaves, or coca derivatives imported into or produced in the United States. The result of this act made it a violation to purchase, sell, or distribute cocaine other than from a stamped package.[29]

A 1922 Amendment to the Narcotic Drugs Import and Export Act of 1914 absolutely banned cocaine and restricted the importation of coca leaves to the amount needed for "medical or other legitimate uses" (such as a flavoring ingredient for Coca-Cola).[30]

The 1922 Amendment had other key features. Firstly, for the first time cocaine was defined as a *narcotic* in a federal statute. This definition still holds today, despite the fact that its pharmacologic properties are decidedly not narcotic. Secondly, violators were to be treated stringently. Where the original act provided alternative sentencing (a fine or imprisonment or both), the amendment provided for both a fine of up to $5,000 and imprisonment for up to ten years.[31]

Another federal regulation concerning cocaine came in 1930. Congress asked the surgeon general of the Public Health Service to conduct studies to determine the amount of coca leaves (and opium) that would be necessary to meet the country's medical and legitimate business needs. However, his findings were to be taken under advisement by the Commissioner of Narcotics. Congress also permitted the importation of decocainized coca leaves by the beverage manufacturers, provided all the cocaine contained in the leaves was destroyed.

In his analysis of the early state and federal statutes regulating cocaine's use, manufacture and distribution, McLaughlin offers evidence to support his belief that, until 1930 at least, cocaine was the most feared drug in the country:

- As of 1914, forty-six of the forty-eight states had some type of legislation to control or regulate cocaine, while only twenty-nine states had comparable laws on the opiates.
- Harsher penalties were provided for violations of the cocaine statutes than for violations of the opiates statutes.
- Many of the federal provisions discriminated against cocaine.

The Harrison Act, for example, permitted inclusion of minimal amounts of opium or its derivatives in patent medicines, while no such exceptions were allowed for the previously cocaine-based medicines.

McLaughlin speculates:

> This special fear of cocaine may also explain its puzzling classification as a narcotic drug in the 1922 amendments to the Narcotics Drug Import and Export Act, a classification contradicting pharmacological evidence.[32]

EXPERIENCE WITH COCAINE IN OTHER COUNTRIES: 1900–1930

Cocaine use spread through many countries of Europe and Asia. The particular events that brought cocaine public notoriety varied from country to country, but each nation eventually demanded stricter regulation of the drug. The literature reviewed and summarized here discusses cocaine use in only a few of the major countries. But it can be assumed that cocaine use was considerably more widespread than this list of countries implies. We begin with England.

England

Prior to the First World War, England had a problem with the reportedly widespread use of cocaine by unlicensed dentists, of whom there were over 20,000, as compared to 5,000 registered dentists.[33] A committee was appointed by the Home Secretary to study the problem and make recommendations as to whether permission to use cocaine should be limited to registered dentists only. The committee majority recommended that unlicensed dentists continue to be permitted to use a 1% solution of cocaine with their patients for two reasons. First, no "unqualified dentist" had the required skills to use novocaine, the most widely used cocaine substitute, and thus might cause harm to patients. Second, there was no evidence "to show that there is any serious or perhaps even noticeable prevalence of the cocaine habit among the civilian or military population," so that continued use by unlicensed dentists should not contribute to harmful use of the drug. Only three years later (July 1916), however, in an effort to stop the reportedly spreading cocaine habit among British soldiers, the government prohibited sale of cocaine to *any* nonauthorized persons, which clearly included the unlicensed dentists.[34]

And a few years thereafter, it was reported:

> For some time addiction to cocaine has been a prevalent vice. The death of an actress, after an orgy in which the drug played a part, just drew public attention to the extent of the vice. The sale of cocaine, except for medicinal purposes, has been made penal, but this has not stopped traffic in the drug.[35]

In a joint 1923 letter to the London *Times*, Professor Bayliss (who gave the minority opinion in the previously mentioned Home Secretary's committee report on the use of cocaine by unlicensed dentists) and Dr. Saleeby stated:

> The abolition of the use of cocaine by international action is the only effective means of ending the evils to which the drug gives rise, and that is now feasible without detriment to surgery. . . . So long as the drug is manufactured, it will be misused. According to leading dental surgeons, cocaine is *no longer needed in dentistry*, completely effective substitutes, such as procaine, being available. A new synthetic substitute known as butyn has also been widely tested with good results.[36]

Germany

The 18th Congress of Legal Medicine for French-speaking countries met in Paris in 1923 to discuss the problem of the international sale of narcotics and the "considerable extension of the cocaine habit."[37] Of the European countries, Germany was singled out as the major producer of both narcotics and cocaine. Strict control of the drugs at their source (i.e., Germany) and increased border surveillance were recommended, because most of the other European countries (Germany itself, and also Italy, Switzerland, England, and Belgium) had cocaine laws less stringent than those of France. The congress recommended that the League of Nations be involved in suppressing the abuse of illicit sale of cocaine and narcotics. The congress passed the following resolution:

> In view of the increasing extent of the illegal traffic in cocaine and other narcotics and the dangers arising from cocaine addiction the Congress of Legal Medicine hereby recommends that (1) prosecution against traffickers be carried out indefatigably and that measures for their repression be rigidly enforced; (2) international control be established in order to prevent importation and clandestine trade in narcotics; and (3) repressive measures be supplemented by educative propaganda.[38]

The German cocaine problem was also recognized in Germany. According to the speakers at a 1923 meeting of the Berlin Medical Society, the habit of "snuffing" cocaine became widespread following World War I:

> The commonly assigned causes for this [use of cocaine] are: a desire to gain relief from the sufferings of the war . . . and secondly, an endeavor to find a substitute for alcohol.[39]

Solutions to the problem advanced by speakers at the meeting were to encourage physicians to use cocaine substitutes and to limit manufacture of the drug.[40]

Berlin was considered the only German city with a major cocaine problem, with an estimated 5,000–6,000 users.[41] Among them were some of Berlin's most prominent citizens, especially actors and artists, and the police were in a "quandary for a method to suppress the drug [cocaine] at after theatre parties in private homes."[42]

Cocaine was readily available in Berlin, and a drug culture similar in many ways to that of Haight-Ashbury of San Francisco in the late 1960s developed. The "snuff" was to be found in "bars, low dives and even on the street." Cocaine users had their own "special resorts throughout the city, where restaurant keepers, waiters and women (particularly those in charge of public comfort stations) sell the cocaine powder."[43] The existing laws controlling distribution of cocaine were apparently easily circumvented in Berlin. Doctors readily prescribed cocaine and, if the prescription failed to expressly limit the amount, refills were reportedly easily obtained. Further, pharmacists were confronted with a rash of forged prescriptions.

France

The French viewed Germany as the culprit for the growing cocaine problem in France after World War I,

> . . . as the Germans are selling it in profusion for 600 francs per kilogram and it can be resold for 10,000 or 15,000 francs in France. The soldiers of the [allied] armies of occupation [in Germany] take advantage of this to trade in it, and the aeroplanes favor the smuggling of the drug into France.[44]

According to another source, however, cocaine was also plentiful in France during the war itself. In a confessional on cocaine abuse, an American member of the A.E.F. related his experience in France during World War I, where apparently cocaine was used to obliterate the fighting and sounds of war. He says, "unfortunately, cocaine was easy to obtain in France."[45]

Belgium

Belgium also complained of "the ease with which importation can be made from Germany," where the "low value of the mark as compared with that of the franc is a favoring factor." And despite the heavy penalties, "the traffic in the drug continues to progress in a disquieting manner." At the time, the Belgian laws were hardly "stringent." A physician or dentist was allowed to purchase from a pharmacist up to 30 grams (462 grains) of morphine, 10 grams (154 grains) of cocaine, and 5 grams (77 grains) of heroin. Purchase of any amount of these limits had to be logged in a register in which "all receipts and expenditures of these drugs" would be recorded. Excessive use of these drugs could result in a medical inquiry examining the physician's practice or possible judicial action.[46]

Austria

The Viennese police noted a sudden increase in the number of victims of the cocaine habit in 1923. This was a "new" problem for Austria, "having been introduced by visitors." In a letter, *JAMA*'s "regular correspondent" in Vienna stated that since Austrian laws prohibited the dispensing of cocaine unless accompanied by a physician's prescription,

> . . . it is clear that the quantities required for addicts can be obtained only by smuggling. Although no great harm has yet been done, the public is aroused to the possible danger.[47]

As well they might be, for the following year the Viennese correspondent was writing about "The Statistical Data on Cocainism and Morphinism in Austria":

> In connection with the arrest of a band of smugglers, the police have secured a list of surreptitious dealers in

> cocaine and morphine. It was ascertained that a single dealer has disposed of 73 kg. of cocaine hydrochloride in a single year, although the normal consumption of cocaine in the republic of Austria does not exceed 60 kg. yearly (normal use for medicinal purposes only). It was established that the licensed sellers of narcotics (apothecaries, wholesale houses and drug dealers) had received 210 kg. of cocaine. It would appear that 150 kg. of the drug had either been "snuffed" in Austria or exported to foreign countries. The police of Vienna have the names of 200 notorious cocaine addicts of both sexes and 150 dealers have been fined for illegal sales. . . . Public attention has been directed, this year, especially to the cocaine menace, owing to the fact that not less than five fatal poisonings following the cocaine "snuffing" have become known, while others have doubtless been suppressed. The harvest of crime that follows in the wake of cocainism is also a heavy burden on public welfare.[48]

India

The problem of cocaine abuse was not restricted to Europe and the Western Hemisphere. In 1913 the *British Medical Journal* warned that cocaine was becoming a problem in India:

> . . . notwithstanding the stringent measures adopted by the Government against the possession and sale of this substance by unlicensed persons, there is reason to believe that the cocaine habit has much increased and is rapidly expanding.[49]

In 1930, in fact, the Calcutta customs authorities seized *7,200 ounces*, and estimated they were only intercepting between 2% and 5%! If their estimates were correct, 12,000 to 15,000 pounds of cocaine were being illicitly imported. This seems an incredible figure, given that an estimate of the worldwide legitimate consumption of narcotics (including cocaine) was calculated in 1924 as being only 40,000 kilograms or about 100,000 pounds.[50] In any case by the end of the 1920s it was estimated that there were between 250,000 and 500,000 "individuals who were taking cocaine habitually in India for its euphoric effect."[51]

Apparently, the police found it difficult to apprehend illicit cocaine users. To avoid arrest, wholesale and retail dealers devised effective methods of quickly disposing of the drug. One of these methods

> . . . was to have some water handy, and as soon as a police raid was anticipated the drug was thrown into water and the solution poured down the nearest drain, thus hiding from the police any trace of the drug.[52]

Some worldwide illicit cocaine prices

As more and more nations imposed some form of criminal sanctions on its use, cocaine became a black-market commodity. In the roundup of prices below we present data on purity, where available. Dollar equivalents are expressed in the foreign exchange rates of that era.

- *Paris:* $2–3 a gram, but usually of only 25% purity (*New York Times*, June 24, 1921)
- *Berlin:* $5 a gram (*New York Times*, September 14, 1926)
- *New York City:* $5 a gram. Pre-1910 legal cocaine cost $2.50 per ounce but druggists were illicitly selling cocaine for $1 per 1/16 ounce. This was broken down into 10-cent "hits"—enough cocaine to cover the spot on a playing card (*New York Times*, August 2, 1908). By the late 1920s, however, illicit cocaine sold for $30 a gram (*New York Times*, February 1, 1930).
- *Cairo:* $75 a kilogram in 1918 (Ashley, 1975)
- *India:* Up to $150 an ounce (New York Times, *Current History 16 (1922)*:949)

Summary: the international reaction

The increasing awareness of cocaine abuse resulted in more and more nations imposing strong measures to combat the illicit use of cocaine. Manufacturing quotas of cocaine and narcotics for use in legitimate pharmaceutical preparations were similarly affected. The result of the quotas was that in 1931 the Council of the League of Nations reported that compared to 1929, morphine production had declined 31%, heroin production 29%, and cocaine production 58%.

The end result was that, as the table below demonstrates, there was a drop-off in production. The heroin and cocaine stocks in the manufacturing countries were off 32% and 85% respectively from the 1929 figure. Somewhat surprisingly, of all the countries reporting on drug consumption to the League of Nations, Australia had the highest per capita consumption figure.[53] The table shows a decrease in licit use between 1931 and 1934.

TABLE 1

Use of Cocaine for Medicinal Purposes, 1931 and 1934

(Data is of consumption of cocaine in kilograms per million inhabitants)

	1931	*1934*
Great Britain	5.48	5.00
United States	6.88	6.37
Australia	12.97	12.76
New Zealand	5.31	4.52

Source: G. T. McLaughlin, "Cocaine: the history and regulation of a dangerous drug."

FEDERAL ACTIVITY, 1930 TO 1960

The thirty years, from 1930 to 1960, were a period of continuous escalation of penalties for drug abuse, including cocaine. Prior to 1951, the Harrison Act and the Import-Export Act had different sentencing provisions. In 1951, both acts were amended to include standardized sentences that required a mandatory minimum prison sentence.

For a first offender, the penalty was a fine of up to $2,000 and a prison term of not less than two nor more than five years. However, part or all of the sentence could be suspended and first offenders could be placed on probation. For a second offense, the fine remained the same, but the prison term became five to ten years. With a third or subsequent offense, the offender was given ten to twenty years' imprisonment. Further, after the first time, subsequent offenders were allowed neither suspended sentences nor probationary action.[54]

In 1956, Congress amended the law again. This time they increased the mandatory minimum prison terms "but at the same time returning to a penalty structure which took into account the nature of the offense committed."[55] The serious violations of cocaine trafficking resulted in mandatory five-year sentences with possible fines of up to $20,000. (At the same time, fines were also increased for violations of the Harrison Act.) There was no provision for probationary adjudication for the first offender or the drug trafficker.[56]

The last major pre-1970 federal statute regulating cocaine was the Narcotics Manufacturing Act of 1960 that required manufacturers of cocaine (and other narcotics) to be licensed by the Treasury Department and also provided for manufacturing quotas, to be set by the Secretary of the Treasury.

CURRENT FEDERAL LEGISLATION

In 1970, Congress repealed existing Federal drug laws and in their place enacted the Comprehensive Drug Abuse Prevention and Control Act. Title II is known as the Controlled Substances Act. This legislation requires registration of every person in the legitimate chain of drug distribution, detailed record keeping, and production quotas for the manufacture of certain drugs. It establishes strict import and export limitations and extends the harsh penalties for those convicted of involvement with the illicit drug traffic. In regard to cocaine, the law changes little of the substance of the previous restrictions. The Controlled Substances Act divides drugs (controlled substances) into five categories, depending on their potential for abuse and their actual medical values. Drugs in Schedule 1 have a high potential for abuse and no medical value. Appearing in the second schedule of controlled substances—drugs that have a currently accepted medical use but a high potential for abuse that can lead to severe psychological or physical dependence—cocaine is incorrectly still classified as a narcotic drug.[57]

CURRENT STATE LEGISLATION

With the passage in 1970 of the Comprehensive Drug Abuse Prevention and Control Act, Congress "destroyed" the federal-state relationship that existed between the Harrison Act and the Uniform Narcotic Drug Act.[58] To replace this latter act, the Commissioners on Uniform State Laws drafted the Uniform Controlled Substances Act. Similar to the 1970 federal act, this new act divides controlled substances into five categories, depending on their potential for abuse and medical utility. Cocaine is again listed in the second category (high abuse potential, with limited medical application) and also is again incorrectly classified as a narcotic substance. This continues to perpetuate the mistake made in the 1922 Narcotic Drug Import and Export Act.

The Uniform Controlled Substances Act requires every person involved in the manufacture, distribution, and dispensing of cocaine to obtain an annual registration form from the state. Compliance with federal law on record keeping and other formal requirements is deemed to be compliance with the act. Each state imposes its own penalties for violations.

Although there have been no recent changes in the laws prohibiting cocaine use, there have been increasing legal arguments against the drug's classification as a narcotic, at least at the state level. A discussion of these recent state court events is presented in Chapter 14.

REFERENCES

1. McLaughlin, G. T., "Cocaine: The history and regulation of a dangerous drug," *Cornell Law Review*, 1973, 58, 537–572.
2. Ibid.
3. U.S. Public Health Service, "State laws relating to the control of narcotic drugs and the treatment of drug addiction," 1931.
4. Ibid.
5. Ibid.
6. Musto, D. F., *The American disease: Origins of narcotic control*, (New Haven and London: Yale University Press, 1973).

7. Ibid.
8. McLaughlin, 1973, Op. Cit.
9. Ibid.
10. Ibid.
11. Cramp, A. J., "The Indispensable Use of Narcotics," *JAMA*, 1931, *96*, 1050–1052.
12. McLaughlin, 1973, Op. Cit.
13. Ibid.
14. Ibid.
15. Moffett, C., "Rx cocaine," *Hampton's Magazine*, 1911, *26*, 595–606.
16. McLaughlin, 1973, Op. Cit.
17. Street, J. P., "The patent medicine situation," *Am. Journal of Public Health*, 1917.
18. Wiley, H. W., and Pierce, A. L., "The cocaine crime," *Good Housekeeping*, 1914, *58*, 393–398.
19. Musto, 1973, Op. Cit.
20. Ibid.
21. Ibid.
22. Ibid.
23. McLaughlin, 1973, Op. Cit.
24. Ibid.
25. Ibid.
26. Ibid.
27. Musto, 1973, Op. Cit.
28. Ibid.
29. McLaughlin, 1973, Op. Cit.
30. Ibid.
31. Ibid.
32. Ibid.
33. Anonymous, "Deaths from cocain injections," *JAMA*, 1913, *61*, 1307.
34. Anonymous, "Cocain and unqualified dentists," *JAMA*, 1917, *68*, 1196–1197.
35. Anonymous, "The campaign against cocain," *JAMA*, 1922, *78*, 1828.
36. Anonymous, "Abolition of cocain," *JAMA*, 1923, *80*, 1254.
37. Anonymous, "International control of the sale of narcotics, more particularly cocain," *JAMA*, 1923, *81*, 761–762.
38. Ibid.
39. Mayer, E., "The toxic effects following the use of local anesthetics," *JAMA*, 1924, *82*, 864–865.
40. Ibid.
41. Ibid.
42. "Spread of drug habit alarms Berlin police," *The New York Times*, August 16, 1925.
43. Mayer, E., 1924, Op. Cit.

44. Courtois-Suffit, G. R., "Traffic in Cocaine," *Bull. Acad. Med.*, 1921, *85*, 720 (Abs.: *JAMA*, 1921, *77*, 494).
45. Snowbird, "The nightmare of cocaine," *The North American Review*, 1929, *227*, 419.
46. Anonymous, "The campaign against cocain," *JAMA*, 1922, *78*, 667.
47. Anonymous, "Cocainism in Vienna," *JAMA*, 1923, *80*, 710.
48. Anonymous, "Statistical data on cocainism and morphinism in Austria," *JAMA*, 1924, *84*, 1936.
49. Bose, C., "Cocaine poisoning," *Brit. Med. Journal*, 1913, *1*, 16–17.
50. Anonymous, "Movements to combat drug addiction," *JAMA*, 1929, *92*, 329–330.
51. Chopra, I. C., and Chopra, R. N., "The cocaine problem in India," *Bull. Narc.*, 1958, April–June, 12–24.
52. Ibid.
53. Anonymous, "Use of Cocaine for Medical Purposes," *JAMA*, 1938, *111*, 1675.
54. McLaughlin, 1973, Op. Cit.
55. Ibid.
56. Ibid.
57. Wynne Associates, *Cocaine—Summaries of Psychosocial Research*, Research Issues Series No. 15, DHEW Publ. No. (ADM) 77–391, (Rockville, Maryland: NIDA, 1976).
58. McLaughlin, 1973, Op. Cit.

CHAPTER 7

COCAINE AND THE ARTS

[There was a marked] expansion of cocaine use as it suffused from the cultural world and professional classes down to the less wealthy economic levels. In Europe, the descent of the depraved cocainist was brilliantly portrayed in Pitigrilli's 1921 novel Cocaine, *and in Aleister Crowley's* Diary of a Drug Fiend. *American tabloids boosted their circulation with lurid articles on the drug underworld, which were later collected into books like Fred V. Williams'* The Hopheads *(1920). . . .*

—M. Aldrich and R. Barker,
"Historical Aspects of Cocaine Use and Abuse"

Although the legal status of cocaine changed with its widespread regulation, its use continued, all around the world. The particular events that brought cocaine public notoriety varied from country to country, but each nation eventually demanded strict regulation of the drug. Worldwide, then, cocaine went underground from the 1920s up until its popular resurgence in the late 1960s. Though out of the public eye, cocaine caught the imagination of artists around the world, who produced a variety of works featuring the drug (or at least its more notorious aspects). Perhaps the most direct insight into the attitudes that led first to regulation and later to the falloff in manufacture of cocaine is gained from such works of popular imagination.

COCAINE AND BELLES LETTRES

From a period just after the turn of the century when a number of lawyers and even preachers ostensibly used cocaine to enhance their intelligence,[1] we move to a recognition by the end of the first decade that "many great writers [use cocaine] . . . to whip their inventiveness to action."[2] While some writers took cocaine to facilitate their craft, others wrote about the drug itself. In fact, a great variety of works were produced—fiction, autobiography, drama, semifictionalized accounts of the drug scene, and even a number of movies—principally in America, England, France, and Germany, but elsewhere in the world as well.

Overall, many of these works are melodramatic, often with strong moralistic overtones: boy (or girl) leaves home, meets bad company, is introduced to cocaine, turns to crime (or if the hero or heroine is of the upper classes, turns to sex and the like), goes rapidly downhill, and dies a noxious death. A number of autobiographical treatments seemingly begin with this stock tale but report the salvation and turning to righteousness of the former drug abuser, whose writings are meant to sound a cautionary note. Much of the so-called "drug abuse education" literature of the late 1960s drug scare was of this nature, also.

Another characteristic of much of this work is its pharmacological inaccuracy (or unlikeliness). For instance, in an enthusiastically reformist work, Chester's *Shot Full: The Autobiography of a Drug Addict* (1938), we find the hero using cocaine for the first time at age sixteen (ca. 1912) and then, the very next day, becoming a confirmed user of heroin! In many other works cocaine is thoroughly confused with morphine and/or heroin.

As examples of works about cocaine, we discuss an American play, an Italian novel (about French society), an anti–Harrison Act tract written by an Englishman about America (the latter two books have recently been reprinted), and two British murder mysteries (one recently serialized on public TV). Examples of other works about cocaine are also mentioned.

The play: Pendleton King's *Cocaine* (1917)[3]

Produced by the Provincetown Players, later to premiere many of Eugene O'Neill's plays, King's melodrama hardly reaches O'Neillian levels. It is the story of Joe and Nora, a former boxer and his lover, who share a Bowery hotel room. They are broke and in desperate need of cocaine, referred to as "de stuff." The play incorporates many of the then-current beliefs about cocaine. For instance, connecting cocaine and crime, Nora complains that her inability to pick any pockets for the past several days would change if she had some cocaine:

> If I'd had a wee bit of a sniff
> tonight
> I'd got some money out of that
> crowd!

Connecting it with moral degeneration in general, she says:

> When the dope got me I just went down because I didn't care about anything. I gave up my job and just let myself slide. I intended to kill myself when my money gave out. . . .

and later:

> Joe, you've slipped. You've slipped away further than I thought. The stuff's got you sure enough. . . . Don't you see that your life is finished. You are nothing. You are less than nothing.

As indicated earlier, a principal reason given in the press for cocaine's deleterious effect on morals was its short-acting effect. The cocaine user constantly had to be on the prowl for more money to buy more cocaine:

NORA . . . I wouldn't have believed I could go so long. I don't see how you stand it Joe. . . .

JOE . . . Don't worry about me. I can git on witout de stuff—for awhile.

NORA I can't. But then I've been using it so much longer than you have.

This image of the constant craving and demand of the cocaine habitué is reprised in the portrayal of heroin addicts in the popular press of the late 1960s and early 1970s. The literary premise that cocaine is physiologically addicting is a falsehood.

King's *Cocaine* concludes with the couple attempting suicide by gassing themselves. Unfortunately (for them), they have not paid their gas bill, and the attempt fails; fortunately (for us), the play ends in this wretched resolution.

The novel: Pitigrilli's *Cocaine* (1921)[4]

The theme of cocaine-crazed couples seeking relief through suicide was not King's alone. Four years later, in 1921, Pitigrilli published a long melodramatic novel, also entitled *Cocaine*, in which the principal characters attempt suicide by prostrating themselves on a train track. They change their minds as the train approaches, however.

Originally in Italian, an English translation was first published in 1933 and reprinted in 1974 by the And/Or Press of San Francisco. In the introduction to this latest edition, William Daily makes an interesting point:

> *Cocaine* has had to wait for rediscovery by the drug-energized consciousness of the '70s, while the novels of his alcohol-influenced contemporaries, Fitzgerald and Hemingway among them, found immediate success.

The novel tells of the adventures and misadventures of Tito, a young Italian journalist, with cocaine and with the two women he loves. Arriving in Paris just after World War I, he quickly becomes an active participant in the Parisian demimonde, where cocaine is much desired and used. His initial introduction to the drug comes in a Montparnasse café where he has gone with a friend:

> "But why pick on this joint . . ."
>
> "Because this place suits me well enough for what I am looking for."
>
> "And what is that?"
>
> "Cocaine, of course!"

As another man joins Tito and his friend and offers them cocaine, "four frenzied women swoop . . . down upon him":

> "He lied when he said he hadn't any more."
>
> "He'd sooner see us dead with craving!"
>
> One of the women brought her thumb and forefinger together and thrust them into the box [of cocaine], but the male, with a well aimed blow of his hand held out rigidly like a blade, pushed her rudely away.
>
> "Hands off that stuff!" he roared.
>
> But the women refused to quiet down.
>
> "The dope!"

"The drug!"
"Cocaine!"

Overcome with desire for cocaine, the women rush the man. Tito is amazed. He is even more startled when one of the women attacks still another man who has just finished sniffing some cocaine. The woman, "clutching his head between her palms . . . and with moistened lips, quivering and palpitating, flung herself at his mouth and licked his upper lip with gluttonous fury."

Witnessing this behavior, Tito surmises that "decency and will power are the . . . first things cocaine destroys." But it will only be a matter of time before he, too, experiments with and is eventually destroyed by the drug. Shortly thereafter, he is to be found at parties, especially those given by Kalantan, "an Armenian . . . very famous for her white [cocaine] orgies."

The Parisian elite are shown as frequent participants at cocaine parties

> . . . between the Champs Elysées and the Bois, in that mundane quarter where the cocaine aristocrats dwell in security. Within the many sumptuous villas . . . one sees many organized parties, who meet and share together the gay ebriety afforded by the drug. You can find there the youthful turf and theatrical snobs, the not yet fully pubescent or hardly pubescent gentlemen who deem themselves duty-bound to exhibit upon their shelves the latest poems launched in the book market, and in their beds the adolescent debutante. . . . They feed themselves with . . . the hallucinating white powder from Bolivia. Thus, from one day to the next they turn the home of a perfectly normal family into a den of cocaine-addicts. Men and women invite each other to "cocaine parties" just as they would to a dinner. In some families the infection extends itself from the nephew of fifteen to the grandfather of seventy. . . .

The description of these orgies, though they lead to Tito's eventual destruction, are tame by present-day standards for literary bacchanals. But the book does provide fascinating insights into the cocaine habits and rituals of the period, some of which are strikingly contemporary.

We learn that the cocaine dealer keeps the cocaine he

sells in "cardboard boxes of many makes: red, green, yellow; every color a cue to a motley that is more or less adulterated. He does not sell cocaine that is pure; the drug is mixed sparingly with all other ingredients: boric acid, carbonate of magnesia, lactosium . . ."

The cocaine abuser takes it a variety of ways, "with a pen point of pure gold . . . or an ivory nail file or a small spade stolen from a salt box . . . or maybe the nail of her little finger trimmed for the purpose."

Seemingly drawn from personal experience is Pitigrilli's description of Tito facing a deadline for his newspaper:

> But ideas refused to germinate. . . . The ideas were as closed as that box of cocaine, that enchanting, bewitching metal case lying there, right under his eyes, next to the inkstand. O you—the satanic conspiracy of cocaine and ink!—but to try it.
>
> He knew that under the invigorating spell of cocaine his ideas would sprout like flowers in the sun; they would spread and unfold like dry tea leaves under a splurge of boiling water. He sniffed. Then wrote: . . .

Much of what Pitigrilli says about cocaine's effects is accurate, though he may take poetic license in the matter of dosage levels. On several occasions, Tito is said to be sniffing "a few grams," an extremely large amount. However, there are some reports that the Parisian cocaine of that time was very much adulterated (only 25% pure, according to a 1921 *New York Times* article[5]).

Pitigrilli's description of cocaine's effects and its paradoxical action—a combination of stimulation and a tranquil "mellow" feeling—is very similar to that described by many of the contemporary users with whom we talked in the course of this study (see Chapter 10):

> But what a queer feeling cocaine gives me! Cold feet, fireworks in the brain, a whirlwind of nonsense, my heart beating away like a sewing machine and on top of everything else, that serene adaptation to the state of inertia.

In *The Past Recaptured*, the last volume of his masterpiece, *Remembrance of Things Past*, Marcel Proust also described the devastating effect of prolonged cocaine use on a member of Parisian society. He describes an encounter with the Vicomtesse de St.-Fiarcie, whom he had met five years earlier when "her statuesque features seemed to assure her eternal youth." Now:

> . . . features . . . so chipped away that the lines of her face could no longer be reconstructed. What had happened was that she had been taking cocaine and other drugs for three years past. Her eyes, circled with deep black rings, were almost a haunted look. Her mouth had a peculiar sneer. . . .[6]

Where Pitigrilli and Proust deal with cocaine use in upper-class Parisian society, in his semiautobiographical *Diary of a Drug Fiend* (1922), Crowley suggested the drug was equally popular in British society:

> We went to tea with Mabel Black. Every one was talking about drugs. Every one seemed to want them; Lord Landsend had just come back from Germany and he said you could buy it [cocaine] quite easily there.[7]

The political tract: Crowley's *Cocaine* (1917)[8]

Whereas Crowley's *Diary* deals with cocaine and its effects, he had earlier (in 1917) published a long essay entitled *Cocaine*, recently reissued by the Level Press of San Francisco.

Written in response to the Harrison Act, *Cocaine* presents what has since become a traditional argument against anti-drug legislation. Crowley argued that by criminalizing the use of cocaine, society forces the user to associate with illicit dealers. And, as these dealers charge high prices, users are inevitably forced to resort to criminal activities to sustain their habits.

Crowley also presents a graphic description of cocaine abuse:

> But to one who abuses cocaine for his pleasure nature soon speaks, and is not heard. The nerves weary of the constant stimulation; they need rest and food. There is a point at which the jaded horse no longer answers the whip and spur. He stumbles, falls a quivering heap, gasps out his life.
>
> So perishes the slave of cocaine. With every nerve clamoring, all he can do is to renew the lash of the

poison. The pharmaceutical effect is over; the toxic effects accumulate. The nerves become insane. The victim begins to have hallucinations. "See! There is a gray cat in that chair. I said nothing, but it has been there all the time."

Such, quietly enough spoken, is mania.[9]

The murder mysteries: Rhode's *The White Menace* (1926) and Sayers' *Murder Must Advertise* (1933)[10]

Under the pen name J. Rhode, the famous British murder-mystery writer Cecil John Charles Street, who published dozens of novels from 1924 to 1961, wrote *The White Menace* (which, apparently, had been published in German the previous year as *Weg en Traumland*). An amazing novel, with modern overtones, it has cocaine being smuggled in vials and concealed in the bottom of imported vases from South America. It has a special variety of coca plants being grown in English greenhouses and producing a poison used to kill people "who get in the way." Members of the House of Commons as well as British lords are involved as masters of the illicit cocaine trade. One smuggler has financed his brother's rise to a position of prominence in the government from cocaine sales. At the novel's end, the smuggler commits suicide by smoking a cigarette laced with the poisonous product of the special coca plant, to save his brother from public shame. The pharmacological accuracy of *The White Menace* is extremely limited, and addicts are shown in a very unfavorable light. For instance, "Once he used the first lot of cocaine, only one in 10,000 could free himself from the habit," and so on. Throughout, cocaine sounds worse than heroin.

Another (and equally pharmacologically loose) novel by a prominent British mystery writer is Dorothy Sayers' *Murder Must Advertise*, recently serialized on public TV's *Masterpiece Theatre*, and featuring her famous undercover detective Lord Peter Wimsey. The story concerns an advertising man who "codes" the ads about a nerve stimulant that he places in newspapers, to indicate to pushers where they are to pick up their cocaine after it is smuggled into the country. Throughout, cocaine is regarded much as if it were heroin.

A potpourri of the cocaine literature of the 1920s and 1930s

FIRSTHAND ACCOUNTS:

Fred V. Williams, *The Hopheads: Personal Experiences among the Users of Dope in the San Francisco Underground* (San Francisco: Brunt, 1920).

I. Klug, *Die Kokshansl,* "The Cokeheads" (Vienna: I. Klug, 1924). Describes cocaine and other vices among the "circle of the lower 10,000" in Vienna.

E. Trautner, *Gegenwart und Kokain* (Berlin: Die Schmiede, 1927). Describes a series of men who had fallen prey to cocaine and then come to Trautner for help.

Cecil de Lenoir. *The Hundredth Man: Confessions of a Drug Addict* (New York: Kendall, 1934; also published in London the year before).

J. S. Lee, *The Underworld of the East: 18 Years' Experience of the Underworld Drug Haunts* (London: Samson and Low, 1935).

Francis Chester, *Shot Full: The Autobiography of a Drug Addict* (London: Methuen, 1938).

NOVELS AND PLAYS:

Rene Schwaeble, *La Coco à Montmartre* (Paris: Faubourg St. Martin, 1920). An account of cocaine use in the Parisian underground (*la coco* is a slang term for the drug).

F. Koebner, *Cocaine, Mondaine und Demimondaine Skizzen,* "Sketches of Cocaine in the World and the Underworld" (Berlin: H. Michel, 1921). Series of fictionalized sketches of the '20s cocaine scene in Berlin.

J. Rhode, *The White Menace* (Chicago: White House, 1926).

L. Cross, *The Dope Dealers* (London: Jarrolds, 1928).

F. Bastian, *Kokain* (Strassbourg: Vomhoff in Comm., 1929). Three-act play about the depravity of cocaine users.

continued

D. L. Sayers, *Murder Must Advertise* (London, 1933).
K. R. Waldraff, *Kokain Und Dollars* (Berlin: Arka Verlag, 1949).

A handful of these works had remarkable staying power. A prime example is the novel *Down River*, which dealt with a variety of drugs including cocaine. Published in London by Seamark (1929), the pseudonym of Austin J. Small (London: Hodder and Stoughton, 1929), it was made into a movie in the early '30s starring Charles Laughton. In 1932 it was published in a German translation as *Kokainschiff* (Munich: Goldmann, 1932), and then reprinted in 1950.

Some works seemingly used the word "cocaine" in their titles as a catchphrase, and had little to do with the drug per se. Moreira, a Brazilian novelist, published *Cocaina* (Rio de Janeiro: P. de Mello, 1924), a poetic novel about wealthy and titled people, in which cocaine played only a very small role. A literary review appeared in Germany in 1925 entitled *Kokain—Eine Moderne Revue*, edited by Stefan Eggler (Vienna: Krug, 1925). The review had nothing in particular to do with cocaine, either.

COCAINE USE IN ECLIPSE: LATE 1920s TO 1960s

> By the 1920's cocaine use was restricted almost exclusively to the bohemian-jazz culture and to the ghetto where the rich dealers sported silver spoons as a symbol of their affluence.[11]

Although this view is widely held by contemporary chroniclers of cocaine use, few if any writers cited references in support of it. Ashley notes this same lack of evidence. His own personal interviews with persons familiar with the jazz-bohemian-Hollywood circuits of the era indicated a consensus that cocaine "was still around but not *much* around."[12] The period, in our view, covers the twilight years of cocaine use. The period clearly merits intensive historical study. But, based on our limited examination of the more readily available information, it seems accurate to state that:

- Cocaine was used by some jazz musicians. This use is reflected in the lyrics of many of the songs of the era.
- Cocaine was used by some of the popular movie actors. Cocaine use was the central theme of several movies.
- Prominent Germans, including some of Hitler's staff members, were cocaine users during the 1930s.
- The introduction of synthetic amphetamines in the '30s is seen by several drug researchers as the principal reason for cocaine's decline in popularity during the era.

Drug use and jazz musicians

In an article on the relationship between drugs and alcohol and jazz musicians, Winick said that jazz musicians are in a "unique favorable environment for drug use":

> Their irregular working hours, relatively good pay, frequency of one nighters, frequent traveling, contact with the occasional criminal element in the world of booking agents and night club owners, the effect of playing before semi-intoxicated night club audiences out for a "good time" . . . [all] help create a situation in which it could be expected that drug use might be common.[13]

And according to Mezz Mezzrow, a well-known clarinetist of the '30s, it certainly was. His autobiography, *Really the Blues*, while principally a chronicle of his lifelong enjoyment of marijuana, discusses his—and other musicians'—use of cocaine as well (see, in particular, the passage on p. 170).[14]

In 1954–55, Winick conducted a survey of drug use among jazz musicians. A total of 409 interviews were conducted, with 357 found usable for statistical analysis. The results:

- *For marijuana:* 82% of the interviewees said they had used it at least once; 54% were occasional users, and 23% were regular users.

- *For heroin:* The corresponding figures were 53%, 24%, and 16%.
- *For cocaine:* ". . . only a few musicians were said to be using cocaine probably because of its very high costs and the extremely short period during which it is effective."[15]

Cocaine on records

From the 1920s there have been many songs about cocaine and other drugs. It has also been documented that New Orleans, the birthplace of American jazz, had an extensive and thriving illicit drug market; "New Orleans musicians were able to buy all the opium, morphine and cocaine they wanted without any difficulties."[16]

Cocaine, a powerful stimulant, blended in well with the "aggressive or outgoing" jazz played in the New Orleans period. Winick maintains that as jazz moved northward, it became more "light and swinging," and marijuana became the preferred drug.

Some of the early jazz and blues songs about cocaine took a very positive approach towards its use. Victoria Spivey's "Dope Head" (recorded on Okeh records in 1928) openly praised the drug:

> Just give me one more sniffle
> Another sniffle of that dope
> I'll catch a cow like a cowboy
> Throw a bull without a rope.[17]

This song is a good example of how (for some) cocaine can create a heightened (and unreal) sense of self-worth and power.[18]

> Just give me one more sniffle
> Another sniffle of that dope
> I got more money
> Than Ford or John D. ever had
>
> The President is for me
> The Prince of Wales is on my trail
> They worry me so much
> I'll take another sniff
> And put them both in jail.

Another positive portrayal of cocaine is presented by Champion Jack Dupree—a famous blues pianist and heroin addict—who recorded two versions of "Junker Blues." In the first version, Dupree says his sister is the cocaine user, but in the second version he admits his own use as well.

Not all singers praised cocaine. In 1930, the Memphis Jug Band recorded "Cocaine Habit" which labelled cocaine "mighty bad"[19] and indicated a possible decline in cocaine use and a rise in heroin use.

Leadbelly's 1934 recording of "Take a Whiff on Me" was an obvious reference to the preferred manner of ingesting cocaine.

Later in 1934, Cole Porter's Broadway show *Anything Goes* included a cocaine reference in the famous song "I Get a Kick out of You."

Cab Calloway's 1943 song about opium smoking, "Kicking the Gong Around," also included some cocaine references.

While there has been a "steady flow of records" on drugs (including cocaine) and drug-related matters throughout the history of jazz and blues, they at no time have constituted more than a "tiny proportion of the popular or jazz record output of any year."[20] Further, said Winick, proportionately fewer songs concerned with cocaine and other drugs appeared from 1950 through the late '60s than during the thirty-year span from 1920 to 1950.[21]

Cocaine and the movies

In addition to jazz musicians, Hollywood actors generally are singled out during this thirty- or forty-year span as among the principal cocaine users. Ashley quotes a passage from an article entitled "Happy Days in Hollywood," from the arts magazine *Vanity Fair*, describing a West Coast drug party:

> With the brightening influence of spring there has been a distinct awakening of the social pace. Drugs are not as much in evidence as during the more trying days of winter, but they still spread their genial influence at some of the more exclusive functions. Last week little Lulu Lenore of the Cuckoo Comedy Co. gave a small house dance for the younger addicts. "Will you come to my Snow-Ball?" read the clever invitations. In one cor-

> ner of the living room was a miniature "Drug-Store," where Otho Everard kept the company in a roar as he dispensed little packages of cocaine, morphine, and heroin. The guests at their departure received exquisite hypodermic needles in vanity boxes which have caused many heart-burnings among those who were not invited.[22]

Much of the "evidence" about cocaine's use by Hollywood stars is highly inferential. For example, in his biography of Mabel Normand, the famous comedienne of the Mack Sennett (of Keystone Kops fame) studio, Gene Fowler denies that she was a "coke-head," as had been intimated, but admits that she occasionally took a "narcotic" to treat her sinus problem. However, the "narcotic" used during this era for sinus problems was almost always cocaine.[23]

Tallulah Bankhead has been identified both by her biographer Lee Israel and more recently by Lillian Hellman in her autobiography[24] as a heavy cocaine user (see Chapter 12).

Public reaction to the many reported "dope scandals" involving Hollywood personalities in the 1920s played a key role in the creation of the movie industry's own censorship bureau, the Hays Office.

The silent era[25]

Many silent films dealt with the use and effects of cocaine. Some of the Sherlock Holmes stories were given film treatment as early as 1903. In 1916 the Essanay company produced an eighty-minute film version of the successful stage play of 1901 *Sherlock Holmes.* A marvelous photograph captures the famous William Gillette, star of that play, injecting himself with "the seven per cent solution of cocaine." Scenes of Holmes using cocaine are also depicted in *A Scandal in Bohemia* (1921) and *The Sign of the Four* (1923), both produced by Stoll, directed by Maure Elvey, and starring Ellie Norwood.

Comic treatment of Sherlock Holmes began early, with many films premised on his use of cocaine. C. Pearl White, later to make her name in the famous serial *The Perils of Pauline*, starred in one of these misadventures—*Homlock*

Schemes (1913). Cecil Mannering played Holmes in the 1922 farce *The Affected Detective*, a pharmacologically confused tale in which Holmes takes cocaine, then dreams of being in the Orient. Clearly, the moviemakers had the same problems in distinguishing between the effects of cocaine and opium as did such famous novelists as Conan Doyle himself, Sax Rohmer (the Dr. Fu Manchu series), Dashiel Hammett in *The Dain Curse*, a version of which was recently televised, and the British mystery writers discussed earlier.

The best of these comic Holmesian treatments, and one of the few to survive, is the 1916 Douglas Fairbanks, Sr., production *The Mystery of the Leaping Fish*, which deals with the travails of the detective "Coke Ennyday," played by Fairbanks, in subduing a Chinese opium-smuggling ring operating out of "Short Beach," California. The film involved other big names; it was supervised by the famous director D. W. Griffith and written by Tod Browning, later to gain fame as the director of some of Hollywood's more bizarre horror films, including *Freaks, Dracula*, and many of the Lon Chaney, Sr., films. The other stars were Bessie Love, as "Inane—the little fish blower of Short Beach," and Alma Reubens, who, ironically, was later to become one of Hollywood's more notorious addicts, as an opium smuggler's mistress. At one point, the smuggler says to Alma: "Woman, we've got to make a quick getaway," a scene full of irony and pathos in view of the fact that she was to play this role in real life a few years later.

The story open with Coke Ennyday sitting in his bank-vault office, scooping handfuls of white powder from a can labeled "cocaine." In a parody of drug use, Coke blows the cocaine all over the room, and periodically jabs himself with a needle, selected from a battery of needles in a special belt. To help him decide on his next activity, he spins a large roulette-line pointer that indicates "dope," "sleep," "drink," and "eats." If the "drink" position comes up, Coke's assistant prepares and injects into his mouth with a huge syringe an opiated solution (laudanum) that also contains prussic acid. Throughout the film, Coke Ennyday, in what is perhaps the first screen portrayal of the "hophead," is seen literally dancing, jumping, and hopping up and down with every ingestion of cocaine or opium.[26]

The plot begins in earnest with the arrival of the police, requesting Detective Ennyday's assistance in apprehending a suspected opium dealer. This suspect, a wealthy gentleman, resides in Short Beach, so it's off to the beaches for Coke and into a series of predicaments in which cocaine figures prominently. In one instance, Coke rents a large rubber fish from Inane, the fish blower-upper, then swims out and finds the smugglers at work retrieving floating packages from the ocean. To speed up his pursuit, Coke pulls out a trusty syringe, jabs his fish, and goes zooming across the water. Later, sneaking into a bathhouse, Coke finds the opium, which he proceeds to sniff and eat. This sets him hopping again, with the caption informing us that "he's full of hop." Ennyday proceeds to hop for the duration of the film. In the next scene, Coke is following a Chinese laundry truck, from the "Sum Hop Laundry," in which the smugglers have hidden the dope, along with the kidnapped Bessie. Arriving at the laundry, Coke rushes into action, knocking out the opponents when he can with cocaine injections. After he takes care of the gang leader, the rest of the gang rush him. But they're taken by the surprise Coke has saved: he flattens them all by blowing large amounts of cocaine at them. In perhaps the most accurate statement of the film, the final caption finds the movie's editor admonishing Fairbanks: "No, Douglas, you had better give up scenario writing and stick to acting."

Besides the obvious stereotyping of drug users, the film clearly displays racial prejudice. All the drug dealers are foreigners. In one scene, Coke calls his Chinese adversary a "Jap." Coke's mission in another case is to rescue Bessie from miscegenation, as she is being forced to marry "Fishy Joe," one of the Chinese smugglers.

The Mystery of the Leaping Fish was not D. W. Griffith's first involvement with a film featuring cocaine. Several years earlier, he had directed *For His Sons* (1912), a precursor of a later outpouring of heavily moralistic anti-dope films. The movie features the development of a cocaine-laden soft drink and its effects on the developer's son. The father, needing money for his son's impending wedding, develops "DopoKoke," a soft drink to cure "that tired feeling." He tries out the drink on his son and on his secretary. Shortly, they are no longer satisfied with the "DopoKoke" alone, and resort to taking extra pinches from the cocaine bottle. Soon, following what was to become a typical pattern in message-laden drug movies, the son is injecting cocaine, which precipitates his decline. In short order, he attempts to persuade his financée to engage in this activity, is refused, then leaves with his father's secretary and cocaine stash. Total degeneration quickly ensues; after several months they are old and haggard looking, and the son is dying. With his death, the film concludes with a final caption warning of the "awful result of criminal selfishness."

Two other American films of this period feature cocaine somewhat less prominently. In *Sisters of Eve* (1928), Betty Blythe "cokes up" her husband, Charles King, in order to get money from him. This seems the last serious treatment of cocaine in this country. Although the drug involved is not specifically identified as cocaine, a scene in Charlie Chaplin's 1936 masterpiece *Modern Times* shows the results associated with cocaine's use. In jail, the hero sniffles a white substance identified only by a label on a jar as "nose powder." This gives him a surge of energy and enough power to overcome obstacles, such as those involved in breaking out of his jail cell. This powder could possibly have been meant to portray heroin, but unless Charlie said something on the matter before his death, we'll never know.

Britain also produced a serious crime drama involving this drug in *Cocaine* (1922), later retitled *While London Sleeps*, after trouble with the British Board of Film Censors. This film is not to be confused with other films of the same title, such as the 1926 American production in which Rin Tin Tin kills an apeman, nor the 1934 British film in which an insane radio magnate dynamites trains. This version centers around a drug king who murders the man responsible for giving cocaine to his teenage daughter. Another British film, *Cocktails* (1928), is a comedy in which an heiress's crooked guardian plants cocaine on her lover.

The talkies

The first sound film dealing with cocaine appears to be a 1932 German production, *Der Weisse Damon* ("The White Demon"). Focusing on a young singer "hooked" on cocaine, this film occasionally surfaces on the late-late-show circuit, primarily because it features Peter Lorre in an early version of the role he was to make famous—the sinister-looking villain. Pola Negri appeared in a 1937 German production, *Tango Notturno*, that deals with a young woman's involvement with cocaine, her growing disillusionment with life and her resultant suicide.

The "anti-dope" movies

A number of anti-drug films were produced around the time of passage of the Harrison Narcotic Act in 1914. Most of these films, with the exception of Griffith's *For His Sons*, dealt with the horrors of opiate addiction, and included such gems as *Dr. Killem's Dope, The Drug Terror,* and *The Narcotic Spectre*, all released in 1914. By the late '20s, however, Hollywood's enchantment with cocaine, at least on the screen, was over. Fearful in part of possible government regulation, Hollywood instituted its own form of censorship, which took the form of a new round of anti-drug propaganda films, including two classic anti-cocaine epics. The first was a silent movie, *The Pace That Kills* (1928). The second, a sound film, was *The Cocaine Fiends* (1939), which drew heavily on the earlier melodrama.

Norton Parker and Willis A. O'Connor (who directed *The Cocaine Fiends*) directed the Truelife Photoplays production of *The Pace That Kills*. The film begins with this most dramatic of warnings:

> Since the dawn of creation race after race has emerged from the dim shadows, then faded away into the mists of obscurity. History teaches that each nation, each race perished miserably when they ignored their problems and failed in their struggles against debauchery and sin. Today we—the highest civilization the world has ever known—are faced with the most tragic problem that has ever confronted mankind—a menace so threatening, so all embracing, that if we fail to conquer it our race, our people, our civilization must perish from the face of the earth! What is this octopus—this hideous monster that clutches at every heart, creeping slowly, silently, inexorably into every nook and corner of the world? It is the demon DOPE! In its slimy trail follow misery, degradation, death; and from its clutching

> tentacles no community, no class, no people are immune, regardless of birth, training, or environment.

The story line is familiar: country boy Eddie leaves his mother and girlfriend, and heads to the big city in search of both a job and his lost sister, Grace. With his departure, the mother ominously asks: "I wonder what will happen to my boy? So many good clean boys leave home and never return."

Arriving in the city, Eddie soons obtains a job in a department store, where he meets Fanny and her cure for headaches. "Here's something that will fix that headache, Country Boy." It's a white powder—cocaine, in case you were wondering—and both take a couple of snorts, with their backs to the camera.

Headaches gone, Fanny and Eddie head for a speakeasy, where Eddie sees "Nick, King of the Tenderloin," and his woman, whom Eddie recognizes as his lost sister, Grace. She, however, denies the relationship, and Eddie leaves, confused, and, most likely, hung over, since the next day he's asking Fanny for some of that "great stuff" for his headache. Later that day, an "archfiend of society" named Snowy shows up at the store (he's a dope peddler). The moviemakers insert a moral note at this point, stressing that the drug peddler is everywhere "next door in your community, in your offices," and if you try drugs just two or three times, it's a well-known fact that "the initiate becomes an addict."

Most anti-drug films contain a near-obligatory "drug party" scene, and *The Pace That Kills* is no exception. Fanny takes Eddie to a party that will be a real "sleigh ride." However, when they arrive, rather than a swinging party, Eddie notes instead a group of depressed-looking people. Fanny reassures him that one particularly withdrawn woman would be getting "a kick out of it soon," at which time Snowy, the dealer, enters and the pace quickens. Displaying symptoms of typical heroin addicts, the partygoers eagerly reach out for Snowy's bottle of cocaine, and with shaking hands, pour out little mounds of the drug and are soon in high gear. The room becomes hazy and smoke-filled, with couples dancing, kissing, and smoking six-inch-long cigarettes. The lights then fade, and we're left with the implicit warning that use of illicit drugs leads to the ultimate moral degenerative act—illicit sex! The caption is:

> A bunch of "Snowbirds" with their "happy dust" or "joy powder"—but its slimy peddlers call it "Kid Catcher" because it is the first drug that starts boys and girls on the downward path: on The Pace That Kills.

The next day, both Fanny and Eddie are fired for petty thievery, and the downward progress quickens. Eddie is kicked out by his landlady, ends up on the street, on the needle, and on morphine. The movie stresses again that cocaine is only an initial and temporary stage in addiction: the "addict quickly goes to morphine, then opium, then heroin." Once on heroin, Fanny becomes a prostitute to support their habit.

In the next scene, Eddie, stuporous in an opium den, is found by his sister. Grace, it seems, has fared little better than Eddie, having just murdered Nick and on the lam from the police, who quickly arrive and capture her, but let Eddie escape.

Meanwhile, back on the home front, Fanny is pregnant and wants to "get off the dope." But Eddie decides on one more shot to "quiet his tortured nerves." While Eddie sleeps off the drug's effects, Fanny drowns herself. Awake, and told the sad news by Snowy, Eddie, wildly hallucinating images of Fanny's drowning, rushes to the river and jumps in himself. The film concludes with the caption:

> How many mothers, how many sweethearts are waiting for the boys who will never come home? What can you do about it? Write to your Senator and lend your support to the Porter Bill for the segregation and hospitalization of narcotics addicts–the greatest constructive measure ever offered for the abatement of the narcotic evil.

In an earlier version of this unbelieveably melodramatic movie, Eddie was cured after spending several agonizing months in a hospital. Though it would have been more in line with the final caption, the producer decided on the more shocking ending.

The theme of the 1939 *The Cocaine Fiends*, directed by W. A. O'Connor, was the familiar story of youth led astray by drugs. Jane and Eddy Bradford (note marked tendency of boys named Eddie, or Eddy to fall into the cocaine habit), brother and sister, live with their widowed mother and run a chicken stand in the country. Their peaceful existence is interrupted by the appearance of a cocaine smuggler on the lam from the police. Attempting to entice Jane to join him in the "big city," he precipitates an emotional crisis in her that results in a tremendous headache. The smuggler conveniently has the perfect headache cure—cocaine. From that point on Jane wants more and more of "that headache powder." Propelled by her newfound love for cocaine, she follows the gangster to the city. In the city, she sinks ever lower, as later does her brother Eddy after he comes looking for her. Both end up on opium and meet in an opium den. "I'd sell my soul for one shot," confesses Eddy. But at least there's the possibility of a cure for him. Jane is "ruined" and there's no returning home!

The denouement of the film shows all but two of the principal characters dead or in jail. One exception is a young debutante, a former "snowbird," who kills her father, ostensibly a respectable stockbroker but in fact the local coke king. She ends up in the arms of the other survivor, the rookie detective on the case. *The Cocaine Fiends* is replete with popular mythologies concerning cocaine:[27] the first time you use cocaine, you're hooked; with cocaine use comes complete moral and mental degradation; cocaine results in a life of crime (for women, prostitution).

On the other and more realistic side, however, *The Cocaine Fiends* does not portray the cocaine user as an exaggerated and energy-crazed individual.

Cocaine and the Nazis

According to the U.S. Narcotics Commission, Germany surpassed both the United States and Peru as the largest user of cocaine in the 1930's.[28] There is little doubt that Field Marshal Hermann Göring was a cocaine user for years, and there are some indications that Hitler, a user of many drugs, probably resorted to cocaine. But the extent of cocaine use by the German high command (and Germany as well) during this period has not yet been adequately researched.

The development of the amphetamines

As indicated, there were fewer songs on cocaine and other drugs as the era wore on. The same relative decrease seemingly holds for other popular media. Also, there was a relatively limited amount of police involvement with either cocaine users and seizures during this period. Only 52 pounds of cocaine were seized by law-enforcement officials during 1969, well into the era of widespread drug use among American youth.[29]

The major factor accounting for the demise in cocaine's popularity, however, according to Brecher (and others) was

> . . . the result of pharmacological research. Cocaine was replaced by a new group of synthetic drugs, the amphetamines, which were available far more cheaply than cocaine after 1932, and which had certain other advantages over the natural imported product.[30]

Brecher oversimplifies the situation, as we show in Chapter 11, but there seems some support for his claim that:

> Late in the 1960s, when narcotics law-enforcement agencies began cracking down heavily on amphetamine black market, cocaine smuggling and cocaine use enjoyed a renaissance.[31]

The factors in cocaine's resurgency and the extent of its present use are the subjects of Part IV. Part III, following, deals with the preparation, composition, pharmacology, and effects of the drug.

REFERENCES

1. "Report of Committee on the Acquirement of Drug Habit," *Proc. A. Ph. A.*, 1903, *51*, 466–477.
2. "Influence of cocaine on contemporary style in literature," *Current Literature*, 1910, *48*, 633.
3. King, P., *Cocaine—A play in one act*, (New York: Frank Shay, 1917).
4. Pitigrilli, Segre D., *Cocaine*, (San Francisco, California, And/Or Press, 1975).
5. "Soldiers Smuggle Cocaine to Grench," *The New York Times*, June 24, 1921.

6. Proust, M., *The past recaptured*, (New York: Modern Library, 1932).
7. Crowley, A., *The diary of a drug fiend*, (New York: Samuel Weisner, Inc. 1973).
8. Crowley, A., *Cocaine* (1918), reprinted by Level Press, San Francisco, 1973.
9. Ibid.
10. Rhode, J., *The White Menace*, (Chicago: White House, 1926), Sayers, D. L., *Murder Must Advertise*, (London, 1933).
11. Gay, G. R., Sheppard, C. W., Inaba, D. S., and Newmeyer, J. A., "An old girl: Flyin' low, dyin' slow, blinded by snow: Cocaine in perspective," *Int. Journal Addict.*, 1973, *8(6)*, 1027–1042
12. Ashley, 1975, Op. Cit.
13. Winick, C., "The taste of music: Alcohol, drugs, and jazz," *Jazz Monthly*, 1962(a), *8*, 8–12.
14. Mezzrow, Milton Wolfe, *Really the Blues*, (New York: Random House, 1946).
15. Winick, C., "The use of drugs by jazz musicians," *Soc. Prob.*, 1959, 7, 240–253.
16. Ibid.
17. Winick, C., "The taste of music: Alcohol, drugs and jazz, Part 2," *Jazz Monthly*, 1962 (b), *8*, 10–12.
18. Ibid.
19. Ashley, 1975, Op. Cit.
20. Winick, 1962 (b), Op. Cit.
21. Winick, 1962 (a), Op. Cit.
22. Ashley, 1975, Op. Cit.
23. Ibid.
24. Hellman, L., *Pentimento*, (New York: Signet, 1974).
25. Much of the material in this section was researched especially for us by Michael Starkes.
26. Aldrich, M. R. and Barker, R. W., "Historical aspects of cocaine use and abuse." In: S. J. Mule (ed.), *Cocaine: Chemical, Biological, Clinical, Social and Treatment Aspects*, (Cleveland: CRC Press, Inc., 1976), 1–12.
27. Ashley, 1975, Op. Cit.
28. *The Gourmet Cokebook: A complete guide to cocaine*, (New York: White Mountain Press, 1972; also published by D. C. Production Enterprises, Inc., New York).
29. Woods, J. H., and Downs, D. A., "The psychopharmacology of cocaine." In: *Drug use in America: Problem in perspective*, Appendix, Vol. I, (Washington, D.C.: U.S. Government Printing Office, 1973, 116–139).
30. Brecher, E., *Licit and illicit drugs*, (New York: Little, Brown, 1972).
31. Ibid.

Part III

Scientific Aspects

CHAPTER 8

SOURCE, PRODUCTION, AND CHEMICAL COMPOSITION

. . . coca grows in valleys between the eastern or Oriental range of the Andes. Eternally filled with mist which rises from the steaming jungles to break in clouds on the icy peak 23,000 feet above, these valleys, with altitudes between 7,000 and 3,000 feet, have the proper warmth and moisture for coca culture.

—L. W. Hughes, "The Curse of Coca" (1946)

THE NATURAL SOURCE OF COCAINE: THE COCA SHRUB

The alkaloid cocaine is extracted from the leaves of several of the *Erythroxylon* species. Although over a hundred plants belonging to this species have been identified, fewer than a dozen have been chemically analyzed and only two of the species are currently utilized as a source for cocaine. The two are *Erythroxylon coca* (Lamarck) and *Erythroxylon novogranatense* (Morris) Hieronymus.

Erythroxylon coca, also known as the Bolivian or Huanuco coca, has leaves that are greenish brown and clear brown, smooth, and slightly glossy. The nearly elliptical leaf blades are from 1 to 3 inches long with a short and narrow bassal portion. The midrib is very prominent on the back side of the leaf. The taste is bitter and faintly aromatic and is followed by a numbness in the tongue and lips.[1] The leaves usually contain from 0.5% to 1.0% of ether-soluble alkaloids, and approximately 70–90% of this total alkaloid content is cocaine.[2] *Erythroxylon novogranatense*, also known as the Peruvian or Truxillo coca, has leaves that are pale green and smooth but not shiny.

The blades are from 6 to 12 inches long and about one-third to one-half as broad. The odor of the Truxillo leaves is "more tea-like than the Huanuco and their taste and numbing effect are similar."[3]

Concentration of cocaine in the different strains of coca

While Truxillo leaves contain about the same amount of ether-soluble alkaloids (0.5% to 1.0%) as the Huanuco leaves, their proportion of true cocaine is much less—only 50–70% of the total alkaloid material. The Truxillo coca was exported and cultivated in Java. The Java strain contains almost twice as much total alkaloid as its South American parent (from 1.0% to 2.5% ether-soluble alkaloids), but only 20–50% of the total is true cocaine.[4]

TABLE 2

Chemical Analysis of Coca (with Spanish Equivalents)

Chemical substance	*% of total*
Dextrine (*dextrina*)	1.12
Sugars (*azucar*)	11.46
Coloring matter & similar substances (*clorofila*)	.25
Starch (*almidon*)	36.19
Cocaines and related alkaloids*	.50 to 1.50
Protein (*fibrina*)	7.80
Crude fiber (*lenoso*)	28.57
Volatile oils (*aceite, pectico*)	1.82
Ash (*ceniza*)	6.00
Moisture (*agua*)	6.50

* Includes truxilline, benzoyl ecgonine, hygrine, cuchygrine, and tropacocaine.

Source: J. Maher, "Coca—Erythroxylon coca" (unpublished)

Harvesting of coca

Coca leaves are manually harvested thrice yearly, generally by women and children, who take considerable care to avoid injuring the buds. In March the bush is trimmed back. At the end of June, a scanty crop is gathered. The last and largest crop is picked in October and November. Harvesting always takes place during the dry weather, to facilitate drying of the leaves. The harvested leaves are placed in 2–3-inch layers and left for six to eight hours on drying pavements that resemble shallow swimming pools. Once dry, the leaves are packed in bags holding 25–150 pounds each and carried, often by llama, to processing plants where they are converted into cocaine.[5] Since large quantities of coca are required to produce small quantities of cocaine–one ton of coca leaves yields from 15 to 20 pounds of cocaine[6]—the processing plants are usually located near the coca fields.

EXTRACTING COCAINE FROM COCA

The following description of the "legitimate" (commercial) and illicit extraction processes is primarily adapted from Maher.[7]

First stage:

1. The coca leaves are pulverized to a coarse powder which is then placed in a large tank or vat. Alcohol, introduced by gravity, removes the active principals of the leaves during the course of three washings. The alcohol mixture percolates in the bottom of the tank and is then piped to a still. The alcohol is distilled off and the residues are then run through cooling coils to a wax tank.
2. Water is added to the residue in the wax tank and the mixture is heated by steam coils to a temperature of 60° C. At that point, the heat is turned off, and cold water is then run through the coils in the tank. This process continues all night.
3. By the next morning all the waxes have solidified and formed hard cakes on the coils. The liquid portion that is left contains most of the alkaloids. This portion is run through a filter to remove any remaining wax particles.
4. Sodium carbonate is added to the mixture to make it alkaline. Benzole is then added and the whole mixture containing all the alkaloids is then pumped to another tank.
5. There, the benzole solution is agitated with sulfuric acid and water. The alkaloids combine with the acid to

form a soluble sulfate and go into suspension in the aqueous layer. The benzole is removed.

6. Sodium carbonate is added to this acid solution to precipitate the cocaine and associated alkaloids into a solid form.

7. The alkaloid precipitates are collected and dissolved in kerosene (formerly, gasoline was used).

8. After the dissolution of the alkaloids in the kerosene is completed, the mixture is chilled. This results in a heavy sedimentation which collects on the bottom of the tank. The top layer contains "a mushy crystallization of natural cocaine." This top layer is scraped off, subjected to further washing with kerosene, and then crystallized out of the kerosene bath. The crystalline substance, known as "gas crystals," is approximately 60% cocaine and 40% kerosene.

The dark residue on the bottom of the tank is subjected to four additional kerosene treatments. After each treatment, the natural or base cocaine is removed. After the fourth washing, most of the crude natural cocaine has been removed. Since this crude cocaine (cocaine base) is not very soluble in water and will not pass through the mucous membranes, it has little medicinal or social value.[8] It must first be processed into the hydrochloride stage as follows:

Second stage:

1. The "gas crystals" are dissolved in sulfuric acid. Ice is added to prevent any breaking down of the cocaine.

2. Potassium permanganate is added to the mixture to destroy the associated alkaloids.

3. When the oxidation process is completed, sodium carbonate is added to check the action of the potassium permanganate and to precipitate the cocaine alkaloids. At this stage the cocaine product is a minimum of 70% pure and can be as high as 86% pure.

4. The oxidation precipitates are collected, dried, dissolved in toluol, and filtered to remove all traces of the manganese.

5. The toluol solution is treated with dry hydrochloride gas. The gas combines with the cocaine alkaloids to form

cocaine hydrochloride, which, insoluble in toluol, is then precipitated.

6. The precipitated cocaine hydrochloride is collected, centrifuged, and dried.

7. The cocaine muriate powder is then subjected to three crystallizations from methyl alcohol. The final crystallization is referred to as the Columbia Spirit Crystals. At this point, the cocaine is 99% pure.

Illicit extraction process

The illicit process, though less sophisticated than the legitimate process, is done with relative ease and results in high-grade cocaine—in the mid-90% purity level.

1. The pulverized leaves are soaked with alcohol for several hours. Benzole is added and the entire mixture is thoroughly agitated. The agitation causes the cocaine alkaloids to join the benzole. The alcohol is drained off and sulfuric acid is added to the remaining mixture. The solution is agitated again, which causes the alkaloids to join the acid. Sodium carbonate is added and a precipitate is formed.

2. At this stage the precipitate, or crude cocaine, contains all the extractable alkaloids of the coca leaf. The precipitate is subjected to repeated washings with kerosene. The kerosene solution consisting of the natural cocaine is then chilled, causing the cocaine to precipitate. The kerosene is removed from the solution, leaving behind the "gas crystals" of crude cocaine on the bottom of the tank.

3. The gas crystals are dissolved in methyl alcohol, recrystallized, and then dissolved in sulfuric acid. This produces a sulfate solution which is then oxidized with potassium permanganate. A solvent, either acetone or benzole, is added and the potassium permanganate is removed, leaving a residue of cocaine alkaloids. Dilute sulfuric acid is added to extract the cocaine alkaloids, and the resulting salts are converted to the corresponding bases by neutralization of the solution with sodium carbonate, similar to the procedure described for the second stage of the legitimate, commercial extraction process.

CHEMICAL STRUCTURE OF COCAINE

Chemically, cocaine, or benzoylmethylecgonine, is an ester of benzoic acid and an ecgonine nitrogen-containing base.[9] Ecgonine is closely related to tropine, the amino alcohol base in atropine. Both atropine and cocaine are tertiary aminoesters of aromatic acids. Many of the tertiary aminoesters of organic acids have both a local anesthetic and antimuscarinic effect (combating the alkaloids of poisonous mushrooms). However, atropine possesses a mild local anesthetic action, and cocaine has little or no antimuscarinic properties.[10]

Cocaine fact sheet[11]

Methyl benzoylecgonine
$C_{17}H_{24}NO_4$

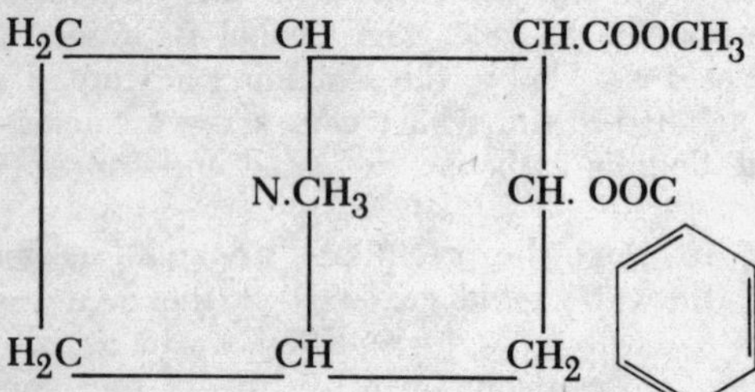

Molecular weight: 303.4

C 67.31%, H 6.98%, N 4.62%, O 21.10%, comes from the leaves of *Erythroxylon coca* Lam. and other species of *Erythroxylon* (Erythroxylaceae) and by synthesis from ecgonine.

Solubility:
Soluble 1 in 1300 of water, 1 in 7 of ethanol, 1 in 4 of ether, and 1 in 0.5 of chloroform (Clark, 1969).

Use:
Free-base cocaine is used for ointments and oily solutions because of its solubility in fats; otherwise the hydrochloride or the sulfate form is preferred (Merck Index, 8th edition).

continued

COCAINE HYDROCHLORIDE (COCAINE MURIATE)
Molecular weight: 339.81

C 60.08%, H 6.53%, O 10.43%, N 4.12%
O 18.83%, Cocaine 89.27%, HCL 10.73%

Extraction:
See Squibb, *Pharm. J.* 1885, *[3]15*, 775, 796; *16*, 67; Emde in *Ullman's Enzyklopädie der tech. chemie;* and Schwyzer, *Die Fabrikation pharmazeutischer und chemisch-technischer produkte* (Berlin, 1931).

Synthesis:
See Willstater, Wolfes, Mader *Ann.*, 1923, *434*, 111.

Configuration:
See Findlay, *J. Am. Chem. Soc.*, 1954, *76*, 2855.

Chromotography:
Paper: System P1-Rf 0.38. (location reagent, iodoplatinate spray, strong reaction).

Thin-layer: System T1-Rf 0.60 (location reagent, acidified iodoplatinate spray, positive reaction).

Gas: System G6—retention time 0.57 relative to codeine.

Ultraviolet Absorption Spectrum:
For cocaine hydrochloride in water, maxima at 223 μ, and 274 μ, minima at 211 μ and 261 μ.

Description:
A white crystalline, slightly volatile powder, with a slightly bitter taste, numbs the tongue and lips. Melting point is about 195°C. One gram of cocaine hydrochloride will dissolve in 0.4 ml water, 3.2 ml of cold alcohol, 2 ml of hot alcohol and 12.5 ml of chloroform. It is also soluble in glycerol, acetone, but is not soluble in ether or oils. Avoid heat in preparing solution as it decomposes easily (Merck Index, 8th edition).

continued

Toxicity:
Cocaine ingested is much less toxic than taken or administered by other routes. Not more than a 50 mg or 1 ml of a 5% solution should be applied to the mucous membrane. The course of acute poisoning is very rapid; the total dose is stated to be 1.2 g but death has occurred at doses of 20 mg (Ritchie et al., 1970). It has been reported that habitual users can tolerate up to 5 g on a daily basis (Clark, 1969).

Medical use:
Surface anesthetic only. *Dose:* Topically from 2% to 5% solution. *Side effects:* Vertigo, nausea, peripheral vascular collapse, coma may occur (Merck Index, 8th edition).

Veterinary use:
Locally in minor surgery of the eye, nose, throat, skin and extremities. Used for epidural anesthesia in dystocia, uteral prolapse, and surgery. Used as a central stimulant in cases of shock and collapse. Used as a nerve block in diagnosis of lameness in horses. Given orally in vomiting of dogs and cats. *Dose:* For horses, 300–600 mg; for dogs (gastric sedatives), 4–8 mg.

REFERENCES

1. Maher, J., "Coca—Erythroxylon Coca," (Unpublished BNDD Document, 1968).
2. U.N. Economic and Social Council, Commission on Narcotic Drugs, "Study on Coca Leaves," Third Session, May, 1948.
3. Maher, 1968, Op. Cit.
4. Tschirch, A., *Handbuck der Pharmakognoise*, (Leipzig: Chr. Herm. Tavchnitz, 1923; *Coca Leaves*, Vol. III, 9, 309–326).
5. Maher, 1968, Op. Cit.
6. Ashley, R., *Cocaine: Its History, Uses and Effects,* (New York: St. Martin's Press, 1975).
7. Maher, 1968, Op. Cit.

8. However, as shown later, comtemporary users here and in Bolivia mix cocaine base with tobacco to produce an extremely potent mixture.
9. Ritchie, J. M., Cohen, P. L., and Dripps, R. D., "Cocaine, Procaine and Other Synthetic Local Anesthetics." In: L. S. Goodman and A. Gilman (eds.), *The Pharmacological Basis of Therapeutics*, (New York: Macmillan, 1970), 371–401.
10. Clark, T., "Cocaine," *Tex. Med.*, 1973, *69*, 74–78.
11. Information for this fact sheet was compiled from the Merck Index, 8th Edition; Clarke, E. G., *Isolation and Identification of Drugs in Pharmaceuticals, Body Fluids and Post-Mortem Material*, (London: The Pharmaceutical Press, Vol. 1, 1969, Vol. 2, 1975).

CHAPTER 9

PHARMACOLOGY, TOXICOLOGY, AND TREATMENT

When one compares the literature on cocaine metabolism with that of drugs such as alcohol and barbiturates, it is apparent that relatively little is known about cocaine metabolism, especially in humans.

—J. H. Woods and D. A. Downs,
"The Psychopharmacology of Cocaine"

PHARMACOLOGICAL ACTIONS

Cocaine is legally classified as a Schedule II drug. By definition, all Schedule II drugs have an accepted medical use with a high potential for abuse resulting in psychological or physical dependence. Drugs in Schedule II include amphetamines, methamphetamines, and narcotics. Aspects of cocaine's current medical usages are discussed in Chapter 11.

Cocaine has two pharmacologically distinct actions:

- It blocks nerve conduction upon local application,[1] which is its most important clinical action.
- It is a powerful central nervous system stimulant. The specific stimulant effects are a function of the site or route of administration. The effects' duration is short and has a low margin of safety.[2]

Additionally, cocaine has numerous side actions, the more important of which are discussed below:

Effects on the central nervous system

The most notable systemic effect of cocaine is its CNS stimulation. The action of the cocaine is from above downward, with the first recognizable effect being on the cortex. In man, this cortical stimulation is manifested in garrulousness, restlessness, excitement, and euphoria. There is some evidence that small doses of cocaine cause an increase of mental awareness and cognitive speed. There may also be an increased capacity for muscular work, but this is probably the result of the stimulative property of the drug, which lessens the sense of fatigue.[3]

With small amounts of cocaine, the stimulating action results in increased motor activity. Initially, this motor activity is well coordinated, but with increasing doses the lower centers are also affected, which results in tremors and convulsive movements. Cord stimulation produces increased cord reflexes, eventually progressing to clonic-tonic convulsions. It is suggested that "stimulating" effects may, in fact, be caused by the depression of inhibitory neurons. There is, however, no direct evidence as yet to support this suggestion.[4]

The respiratory rate increase is due to the action of cocaine on the medulla. Initially, the depth of respiration is unaffected, but "soon it is diminished, resulting in a rapid and shallow breathing pattern."[5] With stimulation of the vasomotor and vomiting center, it is common to observe an elevation of blood pressure, sweating, and vomiting.[6]

Central stimulation is soon followed by depression. The depression is a consequence either of a cocaine-induced convulsion, or (without an antecedent convulsion) of a higher concentration of cocaine in the brain.[7] The higher centers are the first to be depressed, and this may occur when the lower portions of the cerebrospinal axis are still in the stage of excitation. With high doses of cocaine, the vital medullary centers are eventually depressed, resulting in apnea and death from respiratory failure.[8]

Effects on the sympathetic nervous system

Besides its ability to block impulse conduction, a property common to all local anesthetics, cocaine has the unique ability to affect sympathetic nervous system functioning, specifically the role played by norepinephrine.[9]

The sympathetic nervous system is involved in many of the responses to stress of the body's organs and tissues. For example, activating the sympathetic system increases the heart rate, raises cardiac output, and elevates blood sugar levels. Propagation of impulses along sympathetic nerve fibers is electrical in nature, but at the junctions—between the nerve fibers and the organ and tissue cells which they affect—the transmission is chemical. As the mediator substance released from the sympathetic nerve fibers, norepinephrine's action is similar to the effects of epinephrine, which is released by the adrenal gland in response to stress.[10]

Cocaine has the property of potentiating both the excitatory and the inhibitory responses of sympathetically innervated organs to epinephrine, norepinephrine, and sympathetic nerve stimulation (a "sympathomimetic" effect). This potentiation effect of cocaine on the sympathetic nervous system was first noted by Frolich and Loewi in 1910. Since that time there have been many explanations put forward to account for this phenomenon.

Apparently, cocaine does not stimulate these organs directly, "nor does it have a non-specific sensitizing action on them, because denervated cells show no response to cocaine alone."[11] The sensitization produced by cocaine seems to result from an inhibition of the uptake of neurohumor from the interstitial spaces into the nerve terminals. Cocaine is the only local anesthetic that has this ability to interface with neurohumoral uptake. This explains why cocaine produces sensitization to both epinephrine and norepinephrine and provides "a plausible explanation" why cocaine produces vasoconstriction and mydriasis:

> Thus, during tonic sympathetic discharge less neurohumor is inactivated by tissue uptake in the presence of cocaine so that the effective concentration of extracellular norepinephrine in the organ increases. Any tonic contraction of the smooth muscle in the walls of blood vessels or of the radial muscle of the iris is enhanced, thereby producing the vasoconstriction and mydriasis classically associated with cocaine.[12]

Effects on the cardiovascular system

Cocaine's effects on the cardiovascular system are complex. Its effects upon heart rate are dose-related. Small doses given systematically act to slow the heart as a result of stimulation of the vagus nerves. Moderate doses increase the heart rate due to stimulation of the cardiac accelerator nerve and the potentiating effects of norepinephrine. Larger doses can produce sudden cardiac arrest resulting from direct cardiotoxicity.[13]

Cocaine, according to Woods and Downs:[14]

- Has a direct effect upon the heart and blood vessels.
- Causes stimulation of both the autonomic nervous systems (both sympathetic and parasympathetic).
- Potentiates the action of norepinephrine.
- Causes a rise in blood pressure, primarily the result of its vasoconstrictor property. There appears to be both a central and peripheral component to this effect, since cocaine both stimulates the vasomotor center in the medulla and also constricts blood vessels when applied locally.

Effects on the eye

The local anesthetic action of cocaine on the eye was what initially propelled cocaine into medical prominence. The cornea can be anesthetized with solutions of from 0.25% to 0.5%, and the anesthesia may extend to the iris. Mydriasis (dilation of the pupil) occurs, due to the effects of norepinephrine tonically released from the sympathetic fibers that are responsible for innervating the radial muscle of the iris. With large doses of cocaine both exophthalmos (protrusion of the eyeball) and cycloplegia (paralysis of the eye's ciliary muscle) have been noted. The proper concentrations of cocaine used for corneal anesthesia occasionally precipitate an attack of glaucoma. In this instance it is thought that the cocaine-caused mydriasis leads to a mechanical block of drainage from the eye's anterior chamber.

Another drawback in using cocaine in the appropriate concentrations is its deleterious effect on the cornea. Cocaine's toxic action often causes the cornea to become clouded and pitted. Ulceration occasionally results. As a consequence of these drawbacks, cocaine has largely been replaced in ophthalmological operations by safer, synthetic local anesthetics.[15]

Effects on body temperature

Cocaine elevates the body temperature. This pyrogenic action occurs via three mechanisms:

- Increased muscle activity because of cocaine's stimulating property, which results in increased production of heat.
- Vasoconstriction due to central vasomotor stimulation, which results in a decrease in heat loss.
- Cocaine is likely to have a direct action upon the thermoregulatory centers.[16] The basis for this observation is that the onset of cocaine fever is often preceded by a chill, indicating that the body is adjusting its temperature to a higher level.[17]

ABSORPTION, DISTRIBUTION, AND FATE

Cocaine can enter the body by several routes, but it is absorbed from *all* sites of application.[18] Some routes and sites result in greater blood-level concentrations of cocaine than others:

- Ingested orally, cocaine is largely rendered ineffective because of poor absorption into the bloodstream from the gastrointestinal tract.[19] In fact, cocaine is largely hydrolyzed in the gastrointestinal tract.[20]
- Intramuscular and subcutaneous routes result in low but sustained blood levels of cocaine.[21]
- The most common route of administration is by nasal inhalation,[22] whereby cocaine is absorbed via the mucous membranes of the nose and throat. Absorption from these mucous membranes is "surprisingly effective."[23]
- Intravenous injections result in the highest blood levels with the most pronounced behavioral effects.[24]

The local vasoconstriction caused by cocaine limits its absorption rate. Despite this fact, however, the *rate of absorption may easily exceed the rate of detoxification,* which accounts for cocaine's highly toxic effects.[25] It has been estimated that the equivalent of nearly one minimal lethal dose (MLD) of cocaine can be detoxified per hour.[26]

Cocaine's action in the body is terminated by three means: metabolism by the liver, execretion in urine, and distribution to inactive sites. Although some of the cocaine is excreted unchanged in the urine, the detoxification occurs principally within the liver.[27] There the cocaine is hydrolyzed to benzoylecgonine and probably to ecgonine, both of considerably lesser toxicity.[28]

Woods and Downs summarize a report by McIntyre of an accidental cocaine overdose that provides additional information on human excretion rates:

> An injection of 800 mg. of cocaine was made by error in a woman into the "tonsillar area." Approximately 50% of the total quantity of the cocaine was excreted in the urine in 12 hours following the injection; 25% of the total dose was excreted in the first hour, while most of the remaining 25% was excreted over the next six hours. The patient's death coincided with the end of the twelfth one-hour urine collection period.[29]

Other studies have reported from 1% to 21% unchanged cocaine in urine samples, indicative of a very complex situation.

COCAINE TOXICITY

Soon after cocaine's introduction as a local anesthetic, it became evident that the drug produced toxic, often fatal reactions in some patients. Several reports from this early period document the toxic effect of medicinally administered cocaine.

In 1923 Watson-Williams reported on fifty fatal (and many near-fatal) cases resulting from cocaine's use as a local anesthetic.[30] A summary of Watson-Williams' study reveals:

- Four deaths were not attributable to the administration of cocaine.
- Thirteen deaths followed large oral ingestions of cocaine. The average for eight of the cases was 22 mg/kg of body weight.
- Twelve deaths were the result of definite overdose amounts. In five of these cases the cocaine was administered as subcutaneous injections of 0.5–1.5 grams.

- In twelve deaths the amount of the administered cocaine was not known.
- Nine fatal doses were less than 5 grains (0.3 grams). In eight of these cases cocaine entered the circulation very quickly and the onset of death was very rapid.

Mayer, summarizing the results of a specially appointed AMA committee that studied "The Toxic Effects Following the Use of Local Anesthetics," reported on forty-three deaths, of which twenty-six were cocaine-related.[31] The cocaine solutions used varied from 0.5% to 20%, and many different routes of administration were involved. Two methods were particularly dangerous—topical applications to the tonsils and urethral injections (or instillation). Plotz reported on 102 cocaine-related deaths in 151 fatal cases involving local anesthetics.[32] Reaching conclusions similar to Mayer's, Plotz indicated that cocaine accidents were generally the result of:

- Overdosage (in one case a total of between 1.5 to 2 grams [30 to 40 cc of 5% solution] was administered by instillation!)
- Injection
- The use of solutions of high cocaine concentration
- Excessive doses of epinephrine

In a specially commissioned study of the role of cocaine in sudden unexplained deaths, Finkle and McCloskey carefully studied reports of the five-year period 1971–76 from the medical examiners of twenty-seven major U.S. and Canadian sites.[33] The study sought sudden deaths in which cocaine and/or its metabolites were detected and identified by toxicological analysis. Over the five years, 111 deaths were reported, most of white males, under thirty. This is an extremely low incidence compared with fatalities attributed to almost any other street drug.

Of the 111, 86 were drug-related, while the other 25 were mainly from homicides. Of the 86 drug deaths, only 26 involved cocaine alone and 6 of these were suicides; 28 deaths involved cocaine in combination with morphine, and the others involved a variety of other drugs. In the morphine-related deaths, the blood cocaine concentrations were significantly lower than in the 111 deaths as a whole, and the 26 cocaine-only deaths in particular. Thus morphine was a major factor in the deaths.

Most of the cocaine-only deaths were in persons who habitually injected cocaine. Only seven deaths were in people who habitually snorted the drug (the more typical route). However, it is clear that there are real dangers from snorting, in the face of a widespread street belief to the contrary.

It is interesting to note that the incidence *rose* over the five-year period:

TABLE 3

Occurrence of Cocaine Deaths by Year*

1971	*1972*	*1973*	*1974*	*1975*	*1976*
2	3	11	25	37	29 (58†)

* Total cases for all 27 study sites, 1971–76.

† Extrapolated figures to Dec. 31, 1976.

Source: Finkle and McCloskey, 1977.

But, as Finkel and McCloskey point out, the growth may be due as much to an increased awareness of cocaine's use and improved analytic tools as to any "real" growth in the death rate.

Table 4 presents a comparison of drug-related deaths reported from medical examiners in twenty-one metropolitan areas throughout the country. Although there has been a reported upsurge in the use of cocaine, and nearly a 100% increase in reported cocaine deaths between 1974 and 1977, it is significant to note that, in comparison with other drugs of abuse, cocaine is clearly less life-threatening.

Comparative lethality of cocaine and heroin

An incidental finding of a study by Pickett indicates that cocaine may be more toxic than heroin, at least by weight.[34] This finding appears nowhere else in any of the literature we reviewed. The primary purpose of the proj-

TABLE 4
A Comparison of Drug-Related Deaths as Reported from Medical Examiners (by calendar year)

	Years/Deaths			
Drugs	*1974*	*1975*	*1976*	*1977*
Heroin/morphine	1455	1789	1597	1596
Methadone	929	646	369	229
Barbiturates	1095	967	840	795
Other Depressants	587	615	598	674
Amphetamines	48	21	34	32
Other stimulants	76	132	133	181
COCAINE	14	16	16	27
Cannabis	3	1	1	5
Hallucinogens	11	9	18	22

Source: Drug Enforcement Statistical Report, 1978. Information for this table was derived from medical examiners located in 21 major SMSA's throughout the continental United States. They are part of the DEA/NIDA DAWN System.

ect was to study the acute toxicity of heroin, alone and in combination with cocaine and quinine, rather than to conduct a comparative analysis on the lethality of cocaine and heroin. To establish his baseline figures for the two drugs, Pickett injected them intravenously at the rate of 0.1 ml/min into white mice until fatal collapse occurred. The mean lethal doses (calculated as base) were 30.7 $\pm$ 1.7 mg/kg for cocaine and 56.7 $\pm$ 2.4 mg/kg for heroin. Clearly, then, intravenous cocaine, in white mice, is considerably more toxic than heroin, amount for amount. While further research is needed before any conclusive statement on the comparative toxicity of the two drugs can be made, we would stress that Pickett's findings further underscore the fact that cocaine is a highly toxic and potentially life-threatening drug, particularly if administered intravenously. It must be noted, however, that the preferred route of cocaine administration is intranasal rather than intravenous, which minimizes the chances for acute toxic reactions.

Fatal dosage levels

There is considerable uncertainty in the literature as to what constitutes a lethal dose of cocaine for humans. What is obvious, after examining medical case studies of fatal reactions to cocaine, is that there is considerable variability in individual susceptibility to cocaine. This supports Freud's observation about the unpredictability of the drug's toxic effect:

> It is important to note that some toxicity also occurs with small doses of cocaine. So the sensitivity of certain individuals to cocaine, together with the absence of any reaction to larger doses in other cases, has aptly been labeled an idiosyncrasy. I believe this one unreliability of cocaine—that one does not know when a toxic effect will appear—is very intimately tied in with another, which must be attributed to the drug itself—that one does not know when and with whom a general reaction is to be expected.[35]

According to a major text in the field,[36] it is almost impossible to definitively describe the lethal dose of any given substance because there are so many confounding variables, including body weight, age, health, rate of detoxification, speed of elimination from the body, pattern of dry use, and so on. Animal studies are generally the bases for determining lethal dose, but there are problems with this approach because humans do not always demonstrate the same reactions as animals to specific toxic agents. The results of such studies are reported as *minimum lethal doses (MLD)* or as the *lethal dose (LD) that is fatal to 50 percent, or to 100 percent* of the animals in the study. These latter figures are typically reported as LD 50 or LD 100. Generally, when dealing with human toxicities, the MLD is considered the more practical value.

Some of the fatal dosage ranges reported in the literature follow:

- In Watson-Williams' study of cocaine-related fatalities, lethal dosages ranged from 0.065 to 1.3 grams.

- Kaye reported 0.5 gram as the MLD for a 150-pound man.
- According to Cooper, 0.5 gram is the lethal dose after oral ingestion, but after "mucosal application estimated lethal dose is 30 mg or less."
- Thienes and Haley state that 1 gram is generally considered a fatal dose, but, in "susceptible individuals as little as 30 mg has caused death."
- Gay et al. cite the fatal dosage of 1.2 grams, as stated by Ritchie et al., but add a warning that severe toxic effects have been reported with doses as low as 20 milligrams.
- Van Dyke and Byck summarize reports of lethal dosages in medical practice that range from 22 milligrams (for submucosal injection) to 2,500 milligrams (for subcutaneous injection).

However, according to Kestenbaum et al., these assertions as to fatal dosages generally "are not documented and the premorbid conditions, route and rate of administration are not specified. . . ."

Gay et al., using cocaine as a baseline, compared it with four other local anesthetics in tabular form.[37]

TABLE 5

A Comparison of Potency and Toxicity of Commonly Used Local Anesthetics (Cocaine is the baseline; it equals 1)

Drug	*Potency*	*Toxicity*
Cocaine HCl	1	1
Procaine HCl ("novocain")*	1/5	1/4
Pentocaine HCl ("Tetracaine"—commonly used for spinals)	2	3
Lidocaine HCl ("xylocaine")	1/3	1/5

* Procaine ("novocaine") is the only one of the local anesthetic drugs that does not possess a topical anesthetic effect (e. g., when directly applied to mucous membranes).

Source: G. R. Gay, C. W. Sheppard, D. S. Inaba, and J. A. Newmeyer, "An old girl: flyin' low, dyin' slow, blinded by snow: cocaine in perspective."

Further, according to Barash:

> Upper limits for the dose of cocaine vary and are somewhat arbitrary. Despite the fact that the [official drug handbook of the AMA] suggests a maximum dose of 1 gm/kg, standard reference textbooks in pharmacology and anesthesia indicate that the maximal safe dose is 200 mg (=3 gm/kg).[38]

Animal toxicity studies

Apparently, the same unpredictable and idiosyncratic pattern of varying lethal doses occurs with laboratory animals:

- Astron and Persson reported the LD 50 values in rabbits for cocaine were: intravenous, 15 mg/kg; intratracheal, 30 mg/kg; intranasal, 50 mg/kg; and intravesical, 310 mg/kg.
- Downs and Eddy reported that the lethal dose in rats appeared to be 80 mg/kg when injected intraperitoneally.
- Malone, citing work done in 1958 by Luduena et al., reports a lethal dose as 19 mg/kg in mice when administered intravenously.[39]

Malone suggests that animal toxicity studies are "reputed to be a good measure" of a drug's effect in man. Given the interspecies variability in lethal doses of cocaine in animals, however, it seems clear that more conclusive research than that done to date, must be performed to establish specific toxic levels.

Symptoms of acute poisoning

The symptoms of cocaine poisoning are mainly attributable to the stimulation of the CNS. The individual exhibits signs of anxiety, depression, restlessness, garrulousness, confusion, dizziness, dry throat, and fainting. Death from an overdose of cocaine is almost always prompt, with the accompanying signs of a mixture of CNS stimulation, respiratory depression, and cardiovascular collapse.[40] Delirium, Cheyne-Stokes respiration, convulsions, and unconsciousness are symptomatic of acute cocaine intoxication.[41] Fainting is usually the first indication of a serious problem in many patients.[42] Death results from respiratory failure,[43] with the heart continuing to beat after respiration has ceased.[44] However, there is a type of acute cocaine poisoning that results in an almost immediate death, due to cardiovascular failure. In all probability, this is the result of an abnormally rapid absorption of cocaine that has a toxic effect on the heart.[45]

In nonfatal cases of cocaine intoxications, many of the same CNS-related symptoms present in fatal cases are present. According to Woods and Downs these symptoms include:

> . . . extreme restlessness and nervousness, delirious behavior such as shouting and fighting, hallucinations, tremors and convulsions. Respiratory depression may follow, and appear to be the result of, convulsions; in other cases, respiratory depression appears first, and the subsequent convulsions seem to be the result of brain anoxia. If the respiratory depression is more marked than the circulatory collapse, the patient will appear cyanotic; if the circulatory failure is more marked, the patient will show pallor rather than cyanosis. Associated with the circulatory collapse it is common to see a weak, thready pulse, tachycardia, and profuse sweating. Acute pulmonary edema, with froth appearing at the mouth, occurs in some cases and is an ominous sign.[46]

Chronic toxicity

The consequences of chronic use of cocaine are largely secondary. Chronic nasal inhalation results in mucosal irritation, inflammation, necrosis, and sloughing of the nasal tissue.[47] This ulceration of the nasal septum is a consequence of prolonged, repeated local ischemia caused by cocaine's sympathomimetic properties. Ulceration of the nasal septum often results in nose bleeding. With intravenous use of cocaine (or other drugs) the user runs the risk of hepatitis, septicemia, and endocarditis.[48]

Cocaine-related deaths—a paradox

Several researchers have noted that considerably more cocaine-related deaths have been reported as occurring from medical uses (under supervised conditions) than from illicit uses (under relatively unsupervised conditions). These reports may not reflect reality and there are several likely explanations for this seeming paradox, the first three of which are taken from Woods and Downs.[49]

- Medically related deaths typically occur as the result of a single large dose of cocaine. Illicit users/abusers administer frequent small doses to themselves, a much safer pattern.
- There may be reporting errors in the causal attribution of death. That is, an occasional illicit cocaine user may die from the drug's effects, but death may be causally attributed elsewhere.
- Or, the death may be erroneously attributed to another drug taken in combination with cocaine, usually a barbiturate or heroin (as a "speedball"). Death, which results from the combined respiratory depressant effects of cocaine and heroin, might easily be reported as a death caused by an overdose of heroin alone.
- On the other hand, it may be that there really are fewer "street" deaths because of the relative lack of potency of "street" as compared to pharmaceutical cocaine. It is clear from DEA statistics that the purity of illicit cocaine is relatively low, thus making it unlikely that a street-user could suffer an overdose.

"WITHDRAWAL" EFFECTS

Unlike the situation with the narcotics (with which it is legally—and incorrectly—classified), the continued use of cocaine does not produce either tolerance or physical dependence, though it has other, psychic effects.[50] According to the World Health Organization:

> Cocaine is probably the best example of a substance to which neither tolerance nor physical dependence develops and with which psychic dependence can lead to a profound and dangerous type of drug abuse.[51]

In several early studies, particularly those conducted by Tatum and Seevers and a series of experiments conducted by Downs and Eddy, no discernible withdrawal effects were noted in laboratory animals who had their daily injections of cocaine terminated.[52] In the Tatum and Seevers study three dogs were given daily cocaine administrations for two years, and revealed "no abstinence symptoms on withdrawal."

Eddy et al., in a study of dependence to a number of drugs, stated that although no physical dependence on cocaine develops, "Severe depression may occur and delusions may persist for some time after withdrawal."[53] Clearly, there is some dispute as to the symptomatic concomitants of cocaine withdrawal. Brecher, who formerly supported the notion that the withdrawal of cocaine resulted in "deep depression,"[54] said more recently in a court affidavit:

> The deep depression following cocaine use described in my book—a depression which compels the user to return to cocaine—is . . . rare or nonexistent among cocaine users today.[55]

In the same court affidavit, Harvard's Norman Zinberg wrote that he did not find "the serious, profound depression upon cessation of use that is the standard description in the literature."

Obviously, more research needs to be done on the effects following the discontinued chronic use of cocaine.

AN EARLY ACCOUNT OF CHRONIC COCAINE USE

A mid-1920's medical correspondent in Berlin described the results of cocaine use as follows:

> Cocain snuffers can often go several days without feeling the need to sleep. Finally, a hallucinatory stage follows, which is attended by excitability, fear states, and delusions of persecution, which gives rise to malicious resistance. The snuffing of cocain causes a characteristic distortion of the nose, while the formation of small ulcers within brings about the perforation of the nasal septum. . . . If the habit is not broken up, bodily and mental degeneration and premature death are the results."[56]

TREATMENT

> "There are no specific antidotes for the lethal actions of cocaine."[57]

Until recently, the treatment of choice for acute cocaine poisoning in man has been the intravenous administration of a short-action barbiturate such as secobarbital (Seconal), or, as is perhaps more common today, the minor tranquilizer diazepam (Valium).[58]

A recently developed alternative that might be a specific antagonist of cocaine's sympathomimetic effects is propranolol (Inderal), a blocker of peripheral adrenergic receptors. Fifty cases have been successfully treated with 1 milligram of propranolol injected intravenously every minute for up to eight minutes.[59] A recent study, however, warns that propranolol may be effective at best only against moderate cocaine overdoses and should not be regarded as a protection against lethal doses.[60]

The intravenous route is necessary because the symptoms of cocaine intoxication progress rapidly. Although the barbiturate can limit the cocaine-induced convulsions, its use can also result in post-ictal respiratory depression. Artificial respiration and cardiac massage may be necessary, and sometimes life-saving, in *some* cases of cocaine poisoning.[61] However, the death from acute toxicity is so rapid (often occurring within two to three minutes[62]) that any resuscitative measures must be instituted *immediately* upon the appearance of the symptoms:

> Said another way, non-specific supportive measures might be of value to a patient who received cocaine in a doctor's office, but in all likelihood, the cocaine abuser would be either dead or well on the road to recovery before he reached medical facilities.[63]

Ritchie et al. stress the importance of limiting the absorption of cocaine. This is to be achieved by stopping the circulation at the site of cocaine absorption by means of a tourniquet or in any other way possible. Further:

> If the entrance of the drug into circulation can be checked and respiratory exchange maintained, the prognosis is favorable because cocaine is destroyed fairly rapidly.[64]

The mythology of home remedies

As will be shown later, there are a number of medically acceptable approaches to treating toxic and other reactions from cocaine and related drugs. But there are also a number of prevalent and very dangerous myths about the effects of cocaine and about the intervention remedies for treating toxic reactions.

Myth: Intravenous use of cocaine can freeze the heart. ("I've heard that if you shoot a strong, potent cocaine, it can freeze your heart, especially if you shoot it on the same side as your heart.") *Fact*: The intravenous (IV) administration of cocaine will not "freeze" the heart, regardless of what side it is administered on. A large dose can (and has) caused total cardiovascular failure, resulting in immediate death.

Myth: People who OD (overdose) on cocaine should be given: (a) a cold shower; (b) an injection of heroin, or heroin mixed with salt water, or salt water alone, or a sugar solution; (c) barbiturates, or a muscle relaxant (such as a tranquilizer); (d) a prayer. *Fact*: There are no *specific antidotes* for a true cocaine overdose. Of the many suggested "home remedies," the only one that is advisable is to maintain breathing of the comatose individual, and get him or her expeditiously to a hospital. On no account should the victim be administered intravenous solutions of salt water, heroin, or any other mixture or concoction. The same holds for barbiturates, or any other drug! Cold showers are not recommended either.

The specific approach needed varies with the specific condition, and no one should attempt treatment based solely on the information we're presenting here. A good brief overview of treatment considerations is presented in Barach.[65]

TREATMENT INTERVENTION FOR COCAINE REACTIONS, A SUMMARY

Gay et al. present in a tabular form the "caine" reaction and appropriate treatment intervention.[66]

THE "CAINE" REACTION

Phase	*Central nervous system*	*Circulatory system*	*Respiratory system*
Early stimulation	Excitement, apprehension; other symptoms of emotional instability Sudden headache Nausea, vomiting "Twitchings" of small muscles, particularly of face, fingers	Pulse varies; probably will slow (Usual) elevation in blood pressure Fall in blood pressure may occur Pallor of skin	Increased respiratory rate *and* depth
Advanced stimulation	Convulsions (tonic and clonic)—resembles grand mal seizure	Increase in both pulse rate *and* blood pressure	Cyanosis, dyspnea, rapid (gasping or irregular) respiration
Depression	Paralysis of muscles Loss of reflexes Unconsciousness Loss of vital functions Death	Circulatory failure No palpable pulse Death	Respiratory failure Ashen-gray cyanosis Death

TREATMENT OF THE "CAINE" REACTION

1. Administration of oxygen; by positive pressure and artificial respiration if necessary.

2. Trendelenburg position (head down). Wrap arms and legs if necessary to increase central return of blood.

3. Inject small amounts of short-acting barbiturates (e.g., 25–50 mg sodium pentothal) if convulsions are present. May be repeated, but gently. Do not force general depressant effect to point of no return. [Note: diazepam (Valium) is more commonly used today.]

4. Administer intravenous stimulants for cardiotonic effect (e.g., phenylephrine 10–20 mg).

5. Keep patient cool, and keep crowds away.
6. General muscle relaxants may be given (e.g., curare, succinylcholine) to facilitate administration of positive-pressure oxygen.
7. Continuously monitor vital signs.

Other than purely supportive respiratory measures, resuscitation efforts should be carried out only in controlled situations (ambulance, hospital) and by experts.

Cocaine abusers in treatment

Tables 6 and 7 are derived from statistics by the National Institute on Drug Abuse for clients admitted to or discharged from federally funded drug treatment programs during 1977.[67] Table 6 shows there were no cocaine abusers admitted to detoxification programs of any kind during that year. This suggests that clients reporting to these treatment centers did so after passing through the acute cocaine toxicity phase, if indeed they ever experienced such a reaction. The table also shows that 99% of all clients whose primary drug of abuse was cocaine entered a drug-free treatment program of some kind (as opposed to one that provided chemotherapy of any form).

Cocaine condom ingestion

De Vito presented a case of acute cocaine intoxication resulting from the rupture of a cocaine-filled condom in a young woman's stomach.[68] Attempting to smuggle the drug into the country, this woman swallowed three condom-type bags, each containing two grams of cocaine. After her return to the States, one bag split; she suffered respiratory arrest and was rushed to the hospital. De Vito, the attending physician, noted that she presented all the signs and symptoms of acute cocaine intoxication. The symptoms were controlled, though with some difficulty, through use of oxygen, aspiration, airway protection, and, eventually a constant drip of IV barbiturates. To protect her from further intoxication, a Levin tube was in-

continued

serted and she was given large quantities of castor oil until the two unruptured condoms were passed. For several weeks thereafter, she maintained a partial amnesia for past and present events, though her physical condition quickly returned to normal.

Suarez et al. reported on three additional cases of cocaine condom ingestion. In two cases, the ingesters died. A postmortem examination revealed that one victim ingested fifty-three condoms, each containing approximately 4 grams of the drug. Only one of these bags had broken. Autopsy of the other victim revealed seventy-five packets of 75% percent cocaine in various parts of the gastrointestinal tract. In the third case, the examiner tried, unsuccessfully, to remove one of the packets with aid of a biopsy forceps. The bag ruptured, causing acute cocaine intoxication symptoms in the patient. Based on this experience, Suarez et al. recommend that operative intervention is the method of choice in removing cocaine from the GI tract. Surgical removal is expedient and the only way to ensure that all of the drug-laden bags are removed. "Since surgical exploration ordinarily carries a low morbidity and mortality, we recommend that it be seriously considered when potential rupture of a thin casing threatens the patient's life."[69]

Of these, most (59%) entered an outpatient drug-free program, as compared to only 39% of all clients. And one-fifth entered a residential drug-free program, as compared to only one-eighth (12%) of all clients. This latter form of program consists of a regimented pattern of behavior, intensive group and individual counseling, and a commitment to reside in the facility for a given period of time. In many instances, such programs are provided as an alternative to prison.

Table 7 presents some treatment-related characteristics of clients with different primary drugs of abuse. A relatively small number of cocaine abusers are included in

TABLE 6
Treatment Modalities for Cocaine Abusers
(Column entries are percentages)

• *Modality/environment at admission*	*Cocaine*	*All clients*
Detoxification		
Outpatient	0.0	16.4
Hospital	0.0	6.1
Other	0.0	1.7
Maintenance		
Outpatient	0.0	13.3
Other	0.0	1.1
Drug-free		
Outpatient	59.0	39.0
Day Care	7.4	2.5
Residential	20.2	11.9
Hospital	2.8	2.9
Prison	9.6	3.4
Other modalities		
All environments	1.0	1.7
Total N	3,369	195,410
• *Modality/environment at discharge*		
Detoxification		
Outpatient	0.5	11.6
Hospital	0.8	3.7
Other	0.2	1.4
Maintenance		
Outpatient	0.4	12.6
Other	0.3	1.5
Drug-free		
Outpatient	54.4	42.9
Day Care	7.1	2.5
Residential	20.8	12.3
Hospital	3.5	4.7
Prison	10.4	3.5
Other Modalities		
All Environments	1.5	3.2
Total N	2,906	186,865

Source: NIDA Statistical Series. *SMSA Statistics, 1977*. Series E, No. 9, 1978.

TABLE 7

Selected Characteristics of Drug Abusers by Primary Drug of Abuse at Admission to Treatment (Column entries are percentages)

	Heroin	*Alcohol*	*Marijuana*	*Amphetamines*	*Cocaine*
Age at first Use					
Less than 14	4.3	21.6	15.0	12.0	6.7
14–15	10.9	19.5	24.3	20.7	15.0
16–17	19.7	19.4	20.8	21.8	18.5
18–19	22.0	15.6	13.6	16.5	19.2
20–21	16.5	8.9	8.2	10.5	13.8
22–23	10.2	3.7	5.2	6.6	8.8
24–25	6.3	2.7	3.6	4.0	6.1
Greater than 25	10.2	8.7	9.3	7.9	12.0
Total N	107,354	16,260	9,748	10,220	3,483
*Time between first use and admission**					
Less than 1 year	2.4	1.4	4.7	6.3	9.0
1 year	8.1	4.5	16.3	15.6	17.4
2 years	10.7	5.7	19.5	15.6	15.7
3 years	9.9	5.1	14.6	12.0	10.9
4 years	8.8	4.6	11.3	9.3	10.1
5 years	8.5	4.5	8.7	8.4	8.1
6 years	7.4	3.5	5.8	6.2	5.4
7 years	9.0	4.9	5.9	6.7	8.2
8 years	9.1	3.2	4.0	5.1	4.2
More than 8 years	26.1	62.5	9.1	14.9	10.9
Total N	31,954	9,416	16,781	6,572	2,274
Number of prior treatment experiences					
0	30.0	60.2	82.8	65.0	66.4
1	27.5	18.3	12.7	20.7	20.3
2	16.9	7.7	2.7	7.6	7.2
Greater than 2	25.6	13.8	1.8	6.7	6.1
Total N	106,871	15,888	20,538	10,184	3,458

* Included only those clients with no prior treatment experiences.

Source: NIDA Statistical Series. *Annual Data, 1977.* Series E, No. 7, 1978.

this group. Note that relatively few of the cocaine and heroin abusers began use of their drug of choice prior to age fourteen. It seems reasonable to assume that a combination of costs (high) and availability (low) account for the differences. Of note is the fact that nearly one-tenth (9%) of clients admitted for treatment of cocaine abuse during 1977 had used the drug for less than one year, and just over one-quarter (26.4%) had used the drug for less than two years. These percentages are markedly higher than for the other drugs of abuse. Whether this reflects the relative "newness" of cocaine on the street or not is unclear. Finally, it is clear that most cocaine users admitted to treatment are "first-timers," with an admission pattern very similar to that of amphetamine users in treatment.

REFERENCES

1. Ritchie, J. M., Cohen, P. J., and Dripps, R. D., "Cocaine, procaine and other synthetic local anesthetics." In: L. S. Goodman and A. Gilman (eds.), *The Pharmacological Basic of Therapeutics*, (New York: MacMillan, 1970), 371–401.
2. Gay, G. R., Sheppard, C. W., Inaba, D. S. and Newmeyer, J. A., "An old girl: Flyin' low, dyin' slow, blinded by snow: Cocaine in perspective," *Intl. Journal of Addict.*, 1973(a), *8(6)*, 1027–1042.
3. Ritchie et al., 1970, Op. Cit.
4. Woods, J. H. and Downs, D. A., "The psychopharmacology of cocaine." In: *Drug Use in America: Problem in perspective*, Appendix, Vol. I, (U.S. Government Printing Office, 1973), 116–139.
5. Ritchie et al., 1970, Op. Cit.
6. Jaffe, J. H., "Drug addiction and drug abuse." In: L. S. Goodman and A. Gilman (eds.), *The pharmacological basis of therapeutics*, (New York: MacMillan and Company, 1970), 276–313.
7. Woods and Downs, 1973, Op. Cit.
8. Ritchie et al., 1970, Op. Cit.
9. Much research has been conducted on the cellular effect of cocaine and the catecholamines for a review article on this topic; Woods and Downs, 1973, Op. Cit.
10. Ibid.
11. Ritchie et al., 1970, Op. Cit.
12. Ibid.
13. Ibid.

14. Woods and Downs, 1973, Op. Cit.
15. Ibid.
16. Ibid.
17. Ritchie et al., 1970, Op. Cit.
18. Clark, T., "Cocaine," *Tex. Med.*, 1973, *69*, 74–78.
19. Ibid.
20. Ritchie et al., 1970, Op. Cit.
21. Ibid.
22. Drug Enforcement Administration, From DAWN data, 1974.
23. Woods and Downs, 1973, Op. Cit.; citing work done by Campbell, D., and Adriani, J., "Absorption of local anesthetics," *JAMA*, 1958, *168*, 873–877.
24. Woods and Downs, 1973, Op. Cit.
25. Ritchie et al., 1970, Op. Cit.
26. Adriani, J., *The chemistry and physics of anesthesia* (2nd edition), (Springfield, Illinois: Charles C. Thomas, 1962).
27. Clark, 1973, Op. Cit.
28. Woods and Downs, 1973, Op. Cit.
29. Ibid.
30. Watson-Williams, E., "Cocain and its substitutes" *Brit. Med. Journal*, 1923, *2*, 1018.
31. Mayer, E., "The toxic effects following the use of local anesthetics," *JAMA*, 1924, *82*, 876–885.
32. Plotz, A. *Fatal Accidents with Local Anesthesia*, Paris: Jouve et Cie, 1929. Quoted in: "Accidents with local anesthesia," *JAMA*, 1929, *92*, 1680–1681.
33. Finkle, B. S. and McCloskey, K. L., "The forensic toxicology of cocaine." In: R. C. Petersen and R. C. Stillman (eds.), *Cocaine: 1977*, Research Monograph Series No. 13, DHEW Publ. No. (ADM) 77-432, (Rockville, Maryland: NIDA, 1977), 153–192.
34. Pickett, R. D., "Acute toxicity of heroin, alone and in combination with cocaine and quinine," *Brit. Journal of Pharmacol.*, 1970, *40*, 145–146.
35. Freud, S., "Craving for and fear of cocaine," *Wein. Med. Wochenschr.*, 1887, *28*, 929–932, reprinted in R. Byck (ed.), *Cocaine Papers by Sigmund Freud*, (New York: Stonehill Publishing Company, 1974).
36. Kaye, S. *Handbook of emergency toxiocology: A guide for the identification, diagnosis and treatment of poisoning* (3rd edition), (Springfield, Illinois: C. C. Thomas, 1970).
37. Gay et al., 1973(a), Op. Cit.
38. Watson-Williams, 1923, Op. Cit; Kaye, S., Op. Cit.
39. Astron, A. and Persson, N. H., "The toxicity of some local anesthetics after application on different mucous membranes and its relation to anesthetic action on the nasal mucosa of the rabbit," *J. Pharmacol. Exp. Ther.*, 1961, *132*, 87–90.

40. Woods and Downs, 1973, Op. Cit.
41. Ritchie et al., 1970, Op. Cit.
42. Woods and Downs, 1973, Op. Cit.
43. Ritchie et al., 1970, Op. Cit.
44. Woods and Downs, 1973, Op. Cit.
45. Ritchie et al., 1970, Op. Cit.
46. Woods and Downs, 1973, Op. Cit.
47. Clark, 1973, Op. Cit.
48. Woods and Downs, 1973, Op. Cit.
49. Ibid.
50. Ibid.
51. Eddy, N. B., Halbach, H., Isbell, H., and Seevers, M. H., "Drug dependence: Its significance and characteristics," *Bull. WHO*, 1965, *32*, 721–733.
52. Tatum, A. L., and Seevers, M. H., "Experimental cocaine addiction," *Journal Pharmacol. Exp. Ther.*, 1929, *36*.
53. Eddy et al., 1965, Op. Cit.
54. Brecher, E., *Licit and illicit drugs,* (New York: Little, Brown, 1972).
55. Brecher, E., and Zinberg, N., Affidavit to defendant's joint memorandum, (United States v. Foss and Coveney), 1974.
56. "Cocainism," *JAMA*, 1923, *80*, 864–865.
57. Woods and Downs, 1973, Op. Cit.
58. Barash, 1977, Op. Cit.
59. Rappolt, R. T., Gay, R. G., and Inaba, D. S. "Propranolol: A specific antagonist to cocaine," *Clin. Toxicol.*, 1977, *10*, 265–271.
60. Grinspoon, L. and Bakalar, J. B., "Cocaine." In: R. Dupont, A. Goldstein, J. O'Donnell (eds.), *Handbook on Drug Abuse*, (Washington, D.C.: NIDA and Office of Drug Abuse Policy), 1979, 241–247.
61. Woods and Downs, 1973, Op. Cit.
62. Gay et al., 1973(b), Op. Cit.
63. Woods and Downs, 1973, Op. Cit.
64. Ritchie et al., 1970, Op. Cit.
65. Barash, 1977, Op. Cit.
66. Gay et al., 1973(a), Op. Cit.
67. National Institute on Drug Abuse, *Annual Data, 1977, Data, from CODAP,* NIDA Statistical Series, Series E, No. 9, (Rockville, Maryland: NIDA, 1978) and SMSA Statistics, 1977, *Data from CODAP*, NIDA Statistical Series, Series E, No. 9, (Rockville, Maryland, NIDA, 1978).
68. De Vito, J. J., In: "From the Medical Examiner's File," *Medical Times,* 1975. *103,* 89.
69. Suarez, C. A., Arango, A., and Lester III, J. L., "Cocaine condom ingestion, Surgical treatment," *JAMA,* 1977, *238,* 1391–1392.

CHAPTER 10

PSYCHOACTIVE EFFECTS OF COCAINE

Concerning the psychological, perceptual and behavioral effects of cocaine administration, there is an abundance of anecdotal information but there is a dearth of controlled, investigational data from either experimental animals or man.

—J. H. Woods and D. A. Downs,
"The Psychopharmacology of Cocaine"

Freud was among the first to report on psychic stimulation caused by cocaine. In 1884 he wrote that the ingestion of cocaine (0.05–0.10 grams) resulted in "exhilaration" and "lasting euphoria."[1] Until very recently, with the exception of some work done by South American researchers—especially Zapata-Ortiz and Guierrez-Noriega, who wrote more on the effect of coca than on that of cocaine—the literature on human use of cocaine has largely derived from uncontrolled clinical observations.

In fact, it has only been since 1974 that any controlled research on the effects of cocaine in humans has been conducted in this country. Later, we report on the first two of these controlled studies, one concerning the drug's effects in hospitalized depressed patients, and the other concerning the effects in more normal persons. We also report on the most thorough study to date of social-recreational cocaine users. These studies, and several more recent ones, ably summarized through late 1976 by Byck and Van Dyke,[2] are beginning attempts to systematically describe the subjective effects of cocaine. They shed some light on two key cocaine-related phenomena: its positive psychoactive effect, euphoria; and the negative effect most commonly associated with its continuous use, a form of paranoid-like psychosis that manifests itself in visual, auditory, and tactible hallucinations, often accompanied by persecutory delusions.

COCAINE EUPHORIA

> Woe to you, my Princess, when I come I will kiss you quite red and feed you till you are plump. And . . . you shall see who is stronger, a gentle little girl who doesn't eat enough or a big wild man who has *cocaine in his body*. In my last severe depression I took coca again and a small dose lifted me to the heights in a wonderful fashion. . . .[3]

The World Health Organization Committee on Addiction-Producing Drugs concluded that cocaine is the prototype of the stimulant drugs capable of inducing euphoric excitement.[4] As part of this study, we talked with and received numerous letters from many (alleged) cocaine users. The one constant refrain in our conversations and letters can best be summed up by the expression: "Of all the drugs, cocaine has the best high—if it wasn't for the expense, I would do it every day!"

According to many users the cocaine euphoria is a unique sensation, combining a "charge of energy and exuberance with increased physical and mental capabilities."[5] Apparently this "charge of energy" and "exuberance" can be translated into productivity:

> Several top salesmen have attributed their number one ranking in sales directly to the drive instilled in them by cocaine.[6]

Malcolm X also believed that, for some, cocaine produced the "illusion of supreme well being . . . a seeming over-confidence in both physical and mental abilities."[7] Apparently, cocaine euphoria often leads to subjective overestimations of mental and physical abilities.[8]

Freud noted that the drug produced in him a desire to move about.[9] Animal researchers have made similar observations: "These two dogs receiving cocaine or saline solution exhibit circus movements, running around the cage, whirling as fast as is possible for about five minutes. . . .[10]

The euphoric effects seem to occur in many—perhaps all—types of people:

> Euphoria is accompanied by generalized sympathetic stimulation. As in the case with amphetamines, a disturbed personality is not a prerequisite for cocaine-induced euphoria, and the drug is quite effective in relatively normal personalities.[11]

The onset of euphoria differs with route of administration. With intravenous (IV) injection, the effect is almost instantaneous. With inhalation, the more usual route, there is a latency period of up to three minutes before the euphoric effects are felt. The individual under the euphoric influence of cocaine is likely to appear restless, talkative, excited, or giddy. It has been reported that the euphoric effects following IV administration can last anywhere from fifteen minutes to as long as four hours, contingent upon the dose and the situation; "the intrusion into the drug-taking scene of strangers or threatening persons can alter drastically the response to the drug."[12]

Of all the drugs, cocaine alone seems to have brought the poet out in its many chroniclers. It has consistently been described in rich, glowing, colorful, and often hyperbolic terms. Even Freud was guilty of this excess. In his first essay on cocaine he wrote in such a glowing, extravagant manner about the drug that it led his biographer to state that Freud wrote "as if he were in love with the content itself. He used expressions uncommon in a scientific paper such as 'the most gorgeous excitement' that animals display after an injection of cocaine, and administering an 'offering' of it rather than a 'dose.' . . ."[13]

One of the best examples of the hyperbole and poetic excess associated with descriptions of cocaine's effects is the following from Aleister Crowley's 1918 pamphlet, *Cocaine*:

> Look at this shining heap of crystals! They are hydrochloride of Cocaine. . . . there was never any elixir so instant magic as cocaine. Give it to no matter whom. Choose me the last loser on the earth; take hope, take

faith, take love away from him. Then look, see the back of that worn hand, its skin discolored and wrinkled, perhaps inflamed with agonizing eczema, perhaps putrid with some malignant sore. He places on it that shimmering snow, a few grains only, a little pile of starry dust. The wasted arm is slowly raised to the head that is little more than a skull; the feeble breath draws in that radiant powder. Now we must wait. One minute—perhaps five minutes.

Then happens the miracle of miracles, as sure as death, and yet as masterful as life; a thing more miraculous, because so sudden, so apart from the usual course of evolution. . . .

The melancholy vanishes, the eyes shine, the wan mouth smiles. Almost manly vigor returns, or seems to return. At least faith, hope and love throng very eagerly to the dance; all that was lost is found.

The man is happy. . . .

I have travelled in every quarter of the globe; I have seen such wonders of Nature that my pen yet sputters when I try to tell them; I have seen many a miracle of the genius of man; but I have never seen a marvel like to this.[14]

Subtle vs. striking effects

As a stimulant, it heightens sensations and as a local anesthetic, it numbs them. Due to the interaction of both sensations, there is a resulting "high" of flowing subtlety.[15]

. . . so subtle that naive users frequently need to have its effects pointed out to them before they can recognize them.[16]

These views of cocaine's subtle effects are hard to reconcile with the graphic descriptions (many cited in this monograph) of the immediate and exhilarating impact of cocaine inhalation. Further, the consumers of illicit cocaine have come to expect a "kick" or "rush" experience with their cocaine, similar to an amphetamine-induced rush. And when they don't get it they often charge the dealer with cheating them.[17]

However, most of the cocaine users we interviewed concurred with the notion of cocaine as a subtle drug. The "true cocaine high" was invariably described as a "mellow," even "tranquil" feeling, terms more appropriate to a depressant-type drug.

Perhaps it was this characteristic of cocaine that Freud was attempting to describe when he wrote that under the effect of cocaine:

> One senses an increase of self-control and feels vigorous and more capable of work; on the other hand, if one works, one misses that heightening of the mental powers which alcohol, tea, or coffee induces. One *is simply normal, and soon finds it difficult to believe that one is under the influence of any drug at all.*[18] [emphasis added]

This extreme contrast of feelings was described succinctly by Pitigrilli in his novel *Cocaine*:

> . . . fireworks in the brain . . . my heart beating away like a sewing machine and on top of everything else that serene adaptation to the state of inertia.[19]

This tranquil or "serene" feeling might be the subtle effect mentioned by Ashley, *The Gourmet Cokebook*, and others. This issue cannot be fully explained until more methodologically sound research involving humans is conducted. In a controlled experiment the responses and reactions of the users can be monitored, and more important, the purity of the cocaine used is a known variable. The purity level of "street" cocaine undoubtedly has significant bearing on the effect of the drug as described by current users.

CONTROLLED STUDIES OF COCAINE'S PSYCHOACTIVE EFFECTS

Here we summarize only the first two of the fast-growing list of controlled studies of the subjective effects of cocaine in man that have been published since we began work on this book. The findings here are still "state of the art," but, with the recent development of more sensitive assay techniques for detecting low concentrations of cocaine in the blood, we can expect more precise answers as to how cocaine affects the mind. The first study summarized here is by Post, Kotin, and Goodwin, who studied depressed patients rather than the general population.[20] The drug's euphoriant properties prompted the study of its potential as a fast-acting antidepressant agent. Kestenbaum, Resnick, and Schwartz studied both the physiological and subjective dose-related effects of cocaine on nonpsychopathological subjects.[21] These two studies are reported in detail below.

Post, Kotin, and Goodwin (1974)

Post et al. studied the effects of cocaine on sixteen severely depressed patients on a ward of the National Institute of Mental Health. None of the patients had a history of drug dependence. The study of cocaine took place within the context of a therapeutic milieu that included group and individual therapy. Patients were aware that the researchers were studying the effects of various drugs on mood, and that some of the drugs they received would be a placebo. But they did not know that one of the drugs was to be cocaine.

Throughout the study, a team of research nurses made twice-daily behavioral ratings of depression, mania, anger, anxiety, and psychotic symptomology. A detailed mood rating scale was completed four times each day by the nurses and by the patients themselves. Vital signs were measured a minimum of four times daily. Twelve of the patients received a total of fifty-seven IV infusions of cocaine. The starting IV doses ranged from 2.5 to 8 milligrams, while the highest dose reached for each of the twelve patients ranged from 5 to 25 milligrams.

It was found that the orally administered cocaine did not have a profound effect on mood, body temperature, blood pressure, or respiration. The drug did, however, demonstrate a marked effect on sleep. Cocaine suppressed rapid-eye-movement (REM) sleep and reduced the total amount of time that the patient spent sleeping. The reduction of REM sleep appeared to be dose-dependent, with a greater reduction occurring at higher dose levels.

In contrast to the oral route, the IV administration of cocaine resulted in "marked effects on mood and vital signs." The phenomenon of varied response to similar dose levels (or similar responses to varied dose levels), first described by Freud, was also noted.

> Sensitivity to intravenous cocaine varied widely among individuals. The dose to affect pulse and blood pressure among the 12 patients ranged from 2 mg to 16 mg. This intersubject variability in physiological responsiveness to intravenous cocaine was not significantly related to age, sex, diagnosis, degree of depression, or type of affective response. For each individual patient, however, there was a clear and positive dose-response relationship.

Within each patient's effective dose range, there was a high positive correlation between psychological and physiological reactions to cocaine. (E.g., when there were no vital-sign changes—pulse or blood pressure—there were either no or only very limited behavioral changes. Marked behavioral changes accompanied marked changes in the vital signs.)

Infusions of cocaine which produced moderate physiological changes were more likely to be accompanied by positive affective changes and a general sense of wellbeing. The higher doses of cocaine, which produced more intense physiological changes, tended to be accompanied by intense ambivalent feelings and, in several cases, fits of crying.

> . . . within one minute after the infusion, patients would report a sudden onset of the feeling of drowsiness or calmness. Tearfulness would begin abruptly several minutes later, coincident with peak evaluations in pulse and blood pressure, and would end after five to ten minutes with a return of the vital signs toward baseline. Affective change was dramatic. Bland conversation about events on the ward and their families would become affectively charged and patients would reminisce, often with tearfulness, about significant people in their lives and about their hopes and disappointments.

To observers—and these consisted of individuals who both did and did not know about the purpose of the study—these patients appeared to be "anxious and distraught." The patients' own self-rating of the experience indicated "positive and less depressed feelings as well as dysphoric and good feeling, during these periods of heightened effects."

Post et al. reported that among depressed patients, cocaine infusions producing only mild to moderate physiological changes would "be more likely to be accompanied by positive affective feelings and a sense of well being." With the higher doses came more intense physiological responses, generally accompanied by "intense mobilization of mixed affect with tearfulness." Cocaine's efficacy as an antidepressant was not demonstrated in the study, refuting Freud's earlier claim that 50–100 milligrams of cocaine successfully treated depressive states. The authors further concluded that cocaine is "not recommended for use except under the most carefully controlled clinical circumstances because of the variability of its effective dose range, its toxicity, and its potential for psychic habituation."

Kestenbaum, Resnick, and Schwartz (1975)

Kestenbaum, Resnick, and Schwartz (1975; also see Resnick et al., 1977[22]) conducted the first controlled study of dose-related physiological and subjective effects in essentially normal persons. They administered both intranasal and IV doses to volunteers aged twenty-one to forty-two, all of whom had used cocaine frequently over at least the preceding six months. In a repeated measures design, with subjects serving as their own controls, each subject received a placebo, 10 milligrams of cocaine, and 25 milligrams of cocaine.

Twelve subjects received the placebo and the two cocaine dosages intravenously. Five of the subjects participated in trials using both administration routes (N=19). Subjects were told that the purpose of the study was to evaluate effects of the drug and that they would receive an injection or some nose drops that contained cocaine. A solution of 0.5 cc cocaine in water was instilled into the nostrils or a solution of 1.5 cc was injected IV over a 90-second period. The intranasal placebo was 0.5 cc of a 1% lidocaine solution; the IV placebo was 1.5 cc of water.

Subjects' responses were measured before receiving their medication, and then at 2, 5, 10, 15, 20, 25, and 30 minutes afterward. Physiological measures were heart rate, blood pressure, respiration, oral temperature, and hand-grip strength. The subjective measures employed were rating scales to assess degree of "high," pleasantness, speeding, hunger, and strength. Acute effects were measured by the number of statements rated "true" on a thirty-six-item modification of the Addiction Research Center Inventory for acute amphetamine effects. Subjects were also encouraged to report verbally any other effects they felt.

The intranasal administration of cocaine produced significant (e.g., statistically different from the placebo) effects only at the higher (25 milligram) dose level. Systolic blood pressure was elevated slightly and subjects reported a very mild and somewhat pleasant experience. The fact that the intranasal dose (both 10 and 24 milligrams) of cocaine was in a liquid form might have had an important effect on the results. Kestenbaum et al. (1975) note that several subjects reported feeling the intranasal solution go down their throats. They speculate that directly "sniffing" the cocaine flakes, rather than taking them in solution, might have resulted in a greater response at the same dosages. The IV effects were more pronounced. Both the 10-milligram and 25-milligram dose levels of cocaine resulted in significant physiological and subjective effects. Blood-pressure and heart-rate increases were significant and dose-related (higher under 25 milligrams than under 10 milligrams). And there were significant dose-related increases in all subjective measures except strength.

The onset of intravenous effects of cocaine occurred within 2 minutes following injection. However, the effects of 10-miligram doses peaked at 2 to 5 minutes, while 25-milligram doses peaked somewhat later, 10 to 15 minutes following the injections.

The most frequent spontaneous report, regardless of dosage or route, was "I feel more relaxed." The ten items on the acute effects scale that best indicate the dose-related effects and also discriminated between the two routes of administration were:

1. I have a pleasant feeling in my stomach.
2. My thoughts come more easily than usual.
3. I feel less discouraged than usual.
4. My memory seems sharper to me than usual.

5. I fear that I will lose the contentment that I have now.
6. I have a weird feeling.
7. Right now I feel as if all my needs are satisfied.
8. I feel an increasing awareness of bodily sensations.
9. I have a floating feeling.
10. I feel more relaxed.

These ten items may be a useful scale for future studies, suggest Kestenbaum et al.

Other findings were:

- Relationship between physiologic and behavioral changes. Some individuals, especially the more experienced cocaine users, noted lesser subjective effects than did others who displayed equally large physiologic changes.
- An influence of pre-existing state on subjective effects. One subject entered the experimental session feeling depressed, and reported that his "high" was accompanied by an unpleasant feeling. This observation of a dysphoric reaction in a depressed person is consistent with the findings of Post et al. in their studies of clinically depressed patients.
- Rather than supporting "the common belief that cocaine increases muscular strength," their findings "tend to show decreased strength after cocaine."
- The most pronounced long-term effect of cocaine is anorexia—loss of appetite.

COCAINE PSYCHOSIS

The hallucinations seen in acute poisoning are still more marked in the chronic form. . . . The patient feels that the skin is filled with insects, microbes, crystals of cocain. Sometimes, he feels electric shocks, cramps or shooting pains. He sees animals, human beings, shadows, colors, change in the size of objects. He hears voices, sounds, noises. When the muscular sense is altered, the patient feels that he is lifted up in space, carried and abandoned. The hallucinations lead to the formation of delusive ideas, which are mostly of a persecutory nature. Systematization of these ideas is very rare; they are mostly of persecutory nature.[23]

Besides dysphoria (sadness, melancholia, etc.), the literature indicates that the primary negative psychoactive result of chronic cocaine use is a form of psychosis very similar to acute paranoid schizophrenia.[24] Wilson presented a user's statement about his cocaine-induced paranoid delusions:

> I imagined everyone was looking at me and watching me; even when locked in my room, I could not persuade myself there were not watchers outside, with eyes glued to imaginary peepholes. If I ventured into the street I thought I was followed and that the passer-by made remarks about me; I thought my vice was known to all, and on all sides I could hear the widespread word "Cocaine. . . ." It is curious that directly after the effects of cocaine had passed away all the suspicions and delusions vanished instantly. I could see the absurdity and impossibility of the idea that a whole town was watching and talking about one obscure individual. I realized the folly of thinking that spies were in the room above, watching me through holes pierced in the ceiling. Yet, the overpowering desire to repeat the dose would overtake me, and almost instantly after taking it all delusions would return in full force, and no reasoning would banish them.[25]

Another paranoid symptom treated in the literature is a fear of the police. Kolb reported on a cocaine user who remained awake all night looking for imaginary police officers in bureau drawers and under the bed.[26] These are not such unlikely places in which to look for police officers as they might sound. Wilson described a type of cocaine-induced visual hallucination in which persons or objects were perceived as being smaller than normal:

> Small persons, for example, may appear to climb out of shoes or out of coffee cups. Automobiles or airplanes may seem to pass under chairs and tables.[27]

Tactile hallucinations are the most common reported psychotic symptoms associated with chronic cocaine use. Variously referred to as parasitosis, formication, and paresthesias, the symptoms in all cases are the same. According to Mayer-Gross et al.:

> [The] tactile hallucinations are rather specific for cocaine psychosis, although not always present. . . . The patient feels small animals, worms, ants, lice in the skin of his hands and all over his body. . . .[28]

This first reported victim of this type of cocaine-induced psychosis was Flieschl, who complained of snakes and crawling insects on his body, much to the horror of Freud and Koller.[29]

These tactile symptoms, which can also occur with chronic amphetamine abuse, are often felt "about the face, neck, shoulders, forearms and hands."[30] In some cases, the abuser not only "sees" the tormenting insect but the "reality of the hallucinations may be so great that he pierces his skin with needles to try to pick out these foreign bodies."[31]

A side effect of chronic cocaine abuse, resulting from these tactile symptoms, is "skin abrasions, chronic sores or even local wounds where the sufferer has attempted to remove the 'bugs.' "[32] Mayer-Gross et al. suggest that the tactile hallucinations might possibly result from the effect of cocaine on the peripheral nerves.[33] Ellinwood, on the other hand, argues that these hallucinations result from some central nervous system effect.[34] He argues that chronic cocaine (and other stimulant) use triggers off a human version of the kind of stereotyped repetitive behavior found in many animals, such as the grooming response in which an animal picks bugs off himself or another.

In any event, it seems clear that an individual suffering from persecutory delusions is at best behaviorally unpredictable. And it has been reported that while in this state cocaine abusers have resorted to violent acts.[35]

A great deal of concern revolves around the alleged dangers of the psychotoxic effects of chronic cocaine use. Early ancedotal accounts often describe cocaine's complete degenerative effects:

> . . . Alongside of hallucinations and delusions, there is a gradual and progressive decrease in intellectual force and moral sense. . . . Dementia is the final outcome.[36]

A model for cocaine's psychoactive effects

Post ties together the various effects of cocaine described thus far. He postulates an interaction between dosage and length of use that manifests itself in increasingly impaired cognitive and emotional functioning. The postulated effects are essentially linear, culminating in symptoms of paranoid psychoses. Effects (and their associated symptoms) are:

INCREASED CHRONICITY OF COCAINE USE

No Effect	Euphoria	Dysphoria	Paranoid Psychosis
	Affective ability Increased intellectual function Loss of appetite Insomnia Hyperactivity Proneness to violence	Sadness Melancholia Apathy Inability to concentrate Painful delusions Insomnia Loss of appetite	Loss of a sense of pleasure Loss of orientation Hallucinations Concern with minutiae Stereotyped behavior Insomnia Proneness to violence

INCREASING COCAINE DOSE →

Post further suggests that the experimental set, certain genetic predispositions, and active psychopathology are likely to amplify the dose-use interaction effects:

Hypothesized Interaction of Dose and Psychiatric State in Cocaine-Induced Psychopathology

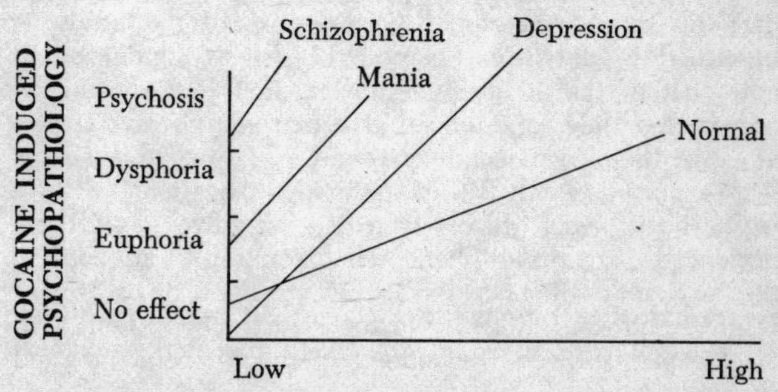

Source: R. Post, "Cocaine psychoses: a continuum model"

> For example, an acute schizophrenic patient would have a baseline psychotic symptomatology prior to drug use and would further disorganize in the psychotic spectrum after stimulant administration; therefore he would not experience typical euphoric-dysphoric effects. This schema would also predict that the psychotic decompensation would occur at lower doses than in a healthy individual. Similarly, a manic patient's dose-response prediction would begin in the euphoric-dysphoric range, reflecting pre-existing psychopathology, and stimulants would exacerbate the manic state, ultimately leading to psychotic disorganization at relatively lower doses than for normal individuals.[37]

It is not Post's claim that cocaine either induces or precipitates mania, depression, or schizophrenia per se. Rather, the conditions he studied "mirror many aspects of the endogenous psychoses closely enough to warrant comparison and the model derived from such study may be useful in conceptualizing biochemical behavioral interaction." He emphasized that alterations in the same neurotransmitter substances may be involved in these multiple psychiatric syndromes, which is in contrast to the previous "one illness, one transmitter" models.

Reactions in social-recreational users

Siegel (1977) has conducted the most thorough study to date of social-recreational cocaine users (the study is described in detail in Chapter 11). It is significant to note that of the eighty-five subjects in the study, all reported that they experienced at least some positive effects in all of their cocaine intoxications, while negative effects were reported in only 3% of the total intoxications.

Of the subjects, thirty-seven of eighty-five (44%) experienced perceptual phenomena resulting from cocaine use, principally increased sensitivity to light, halos around bright lights, and difficulty in focusing the eyes. Only 5% of Siegel's subjects developed paranoid behavior and thoughts.

Fifteen subjects (18%) reported a variety of hallucinatory experiences and indicated they first noticed them after six months or so of recreational use, and then only during episodes of intensified use. It is significant that the subjects described these events as pseudo-hallucinations and did not have concurrent delusions that such events really existed—as would be the case with true or psychotic hallucinations. Thirteen of these fifteen subjects had visual hallucinations, with eyes both open and shut.

The second most frequent form of hallucination was tactile, primarily confined to the face and hands, but also involving other body parts. The effects included itching of the skin, primarily the hands but also the legs and the back; a sensation of moving itches or foreign particles moving under the skin; and a sensation of small insects moving on or under the skin. These were again experienced as pseudo-hallucinations in that no subject believed the insects or objects actually existed, although they did scratch and rub their skin for relief.

Although these subjects manifested hallucinatory behavior, none showed any abnormal results on psychological tests (the MMPI and the Experiential World Investory were used). This seems to indicate that the effects noted were due to cocaine's effects and not to some interaction between the drug and some incipient psychotic state in the subjects. As a result, Siegel calls these perceptual changes "hallucinosis . . . events which users found to be transient and which disappeared when they went from periods of intensified use back to more moderate social-recreational use."[38]

Two other recent studies of social-recreational users are of note. Waldorf et al monitored the cocaine-using activity of thirty-two users over a six-month period and reported not even a single incident of paranoid thinking while under the influence of cocaine.[39] Spotts and Schontz intensively studied the life-style of nine cocaine users.[40] The heavy users in this group (IV administration of more than 1 gram daily) experienced intense anxieties, irrational fears, and panic reactions, as well as paranoid behavior and thought. Reactions included fleeing in panic from imaginary enemies, locking and barricading doors, a fear that police would break in at any minute, auditory hallucinations (hearing people whispering), and hallucinations that police officers were hiding in the trees or in the shadows.

Paranoia in Bolivia

Most of the data on paranoid reactions have come from observations of persons who either inhale the drug repeatedly or take large and/or frequent intravenous doses. From Bolivia came reports of a new route to paranoia: smoking a mixture of tobacco and 97% pure cocaine base, the mixture termed a *pitillo*.

> After the first inhalation of the "pitillo" . . . the subject feels an immediate paranoid-like sensation, with delusions of persecution and potential harm. We have treated patients who, after the first inhalation, closed all doors and windows . . . so that the police would not get them. Immediately afterwards, the patient experienced a compulsive need for continuous and exaggerated smoking: 60 to 80 "pitillos" in only one session, with the persistence of the paranoid sensation, as long as the "gathering" lasts.[41]

SUGGESTIONS FOR FURTHER RESEARCH

More recent and more factual information reveals a more optimistic picture. It also demonstrates areas in need of further study.

- There have been no controlled studies on the paranoid-producing, psychotoxic effect of cocaine correlated to dose or dose schedule.[42]
- There are no available statistics concerning the incidence of the drug's possible psychotoxic effects.[43]
- Once regarded as violence-inducing, cocaine—in its present popularity—has a reputation in this regard far less serious than do the amphetamines. The reasons for this warrant study.[44]
- The specific conditions under which cocaine use, especially of a heavy and chronic nature, leads to psychotic and other disturbed symptoms need more study. In line with this, Woods and Downs speculated:

> The conditions under which cocaine is abused today may be quite different from those when many early observers described the psychotic behavior presumed to be induced by cocaine. Since there is likely to be less anxiety associated with procuring and using drugs in today's society than in previous decades, it is possible that the incidences of paranoid behavior may be decreased.[45]

Also, there may be striking differences in the typical dosages and the general purity of the cocaine used in the two eras, further complicating the picture.

- Lastly, there is *no* evidence to support the notion of a causal relationship between cocaine and the moral, mental and physical debilitation of its users, so vividly portrayed by many early chroniclers. An attempt to explain these earlier observations and the conditions under which they were made seems worthwhile.

REFERENCES

1. Freud, S., "On Coca," *Centra Gesammte Ther.*, (Winc.) 1884, II, 289–314, reprinted in Byck, R. (ed.), *Cocaine Papers by Sigmund Freud*, (New York: The Stonehill Company, 1974).
2. Van Dyke, C. and Byck, R. "Cocaine: 1884–1974." In: E. H. Ellinwood and M. M. Kilbey (eds.), *Cocaine and Other Stimulants*, (New York: Plenum Press, 1977), 1–30.
3. Freud, 1884, Op. Cit., quoted in Jones, E., *The Life and Work of Sigmund Freud*, (Vol. 1), (New York: Basic Books, 1961).
4. Eddy, N. B., Halback, H., Isbell, H., and Seevers, M. H., "Drug Dependence: Its Significance and Characteristics," *Bull. WHO*, 1965, *32*, 721–733.
5. Eiswirth, N. A., Smith, D. E., and Wesson, D. R., "Current Perspectives on Cocaine Use in America," *Journal of Psychedelic Drugs*, 1972, *5*, 153–157.
6. *The Gourmet Cokebook: A Complete Guide to Cocaine*, (New York: White Mountain Press, 1972; also published by D. C. Production Enterprises, Inc., New York).
7. Malcolm X, *Autobiography*, (New York: Grove Press, 1965).
8. Jaffe, J. H., "Drug Addiction and Drug Abuse." In: L. S. Goodman and A. Gilman (eds.), *The Pharmacological Basis of Therapeutics*, (New York: MacMillan, 1970), 276–313.

9. Freud, 1884, Op. Cit.
10. Tatum, A. L. and Seevers, M. H., "Experimental Cocaine Addiction," *Journal of Pharmacologic Exp. Ther.*, 1929, *36*, 401–410.
11. Jaffe, 1970, Op. Cit.
12. Woods, J. H., and Downs, D. A., "The Psychopharmacology of Cocaine." In: *Drug Use in America: Problem in Perspective.* Appendix, Vol. I, (Washington, D.C.: U.S. Government Printing Office, 1973), 116–139.
13. *The Life and Work of Sigmund Freud*, Jones, 1961, Op. Cit.
14. Crowley, A., "Cocaine," 1918, (reprinted by Level Press, San Francisco, 1973).
15. *The Gourmet Cokebook*, 1972, Op. Cit.
16. Ashley, R., *Cocaine: Its History, Uses, and Effects,* (New York: St. Martin's Press, 1975).
17. Ibid.
18. Freud, 1884, Op. Cit.
19. Pitigrilli Segre, D., *Cocaine* (San Francisco: And/Or Press, 1975; French ed. publ. 1921).
20. Post, R., Kotin, J., and Goodwin, F., "The effects of cocaine on depressed patients," *American Journal of Psychiatry*, 1974, *131*, 511–517.
21. Kestenbaum, R. S., Resnick, R. B., and Schwartz, L. K., "Acute Systemic Effects of Cocaine in Man: A Controlled Study by Intranasal and Intravenous Routes of Administration," Department of Psychiatry, New York Medical College, New York, 1975.
22. Resnick, R. B., Kestenbaum, R. S., and Schwartz, L. K., "Acute Systemic Effects of Cocaine in Man: A Controlled Study by Intranasal and Intravenous Routes," *Science*, 1977, *195*, 696–698.
23. Gordon, A., "Insanities Caused by Acute and Chronic Intoxication with Opium and Cocaine, A Study of 171 Cases," *JAMA*, 1908, *51*, 97–101.
24. Post, R., "Cocaine Psychoses: A Continuum Model," *American Journal of Psychiatry*, 1975, *132*, 225–231.
25. Wilson, S. A. K., *Neurology*, A. N. Bruce (ed.), (Baltimore: Williams and Wilkins, 1955), 833.
26. Kolb, R., *Drug Addiction: A Medical Problem*, (Springfield: Charles C. Thomas, 1962).
27. Wilson, 1955, Op. Cit.
28. Mayer-Gross, W., Slater, E., and Roth, M., *Clinical Psychiatry*, (Baltimore: Williams and Wilkins, 1960).
29. Becker, H. K., "Carl Koller and Cocaine," *Psychoanal. Quarterly*, 1963, *32*, 309–373.

30. Ellinwood, E. H., "Amphetamine Psychosis: Individual Settings and Sequences." In: E. H. Ellinwood and S. Cohen (eds.), *Current Concepts on Amphetamine Abuse*, (Washington D.C.: U.S. Government Printing Office, 1972).
31. Mayer-Gross et al., 1960, Op. Cit.
32. Woods and Downs, 1973, Op. Cit.
33. Mayer-Gross et al., 1960, Op. Cit.
34. Ellinwood, 1972, Op. Cit.
35. Kolb, 1962, Op. Cit.
36. Gordon, 1908, Op. Cit.
37. Post, 1975, Op. Cit.
38. Siegel, R. K., "Recreational Use and Intoxication." In: Petersen, R. C., and Stillman, R. C. (eds.), *Cocaine: 1977*, Research Monograph Series, No. 13, DHEW Publication Number (ADM) 77–432, (Rockville, Maryland: NIDA, 1977), 119–136.
39. Waldorf, D., Murphy, S., Reinarman, C., and Joyce, B., *Doing Coke: Ethnography of Cocaine Users and Dealers*, (Washington D.C.: Drug Abuse Council, 1977).
40. Spotts, J. V. and Schontz, F. C., *The Lifestyle of Nine American Cocaine Users: Trip to the Land of Cockaigne*, Research Issues Series No. 16, DHEW Publication Number (ADM) 76–392, (Rockville, Maryland: NIDA, 1976).
41. Noya, N. D., "Coca and Cocaine: A Perspective from Bolivia." In: R. C. Petersen (ed.), *The International Challenge of Drug Abuse*, Research Monograph Series 19, DHEW Publication Number (ADM) 78–60498, (Rockville, Maryland: NIDA, 1978).
42. Woods and Downs, 1973, Op. Cit.
43. Ibid.
44. Smith, R., "Compulsive Methamphetamine Abuse and Violence in Haight-Ashbury." In: E. H. Ellinwood and S. Cohen (eds.), 1972, Op. Cit.
45. Woods and Downs, 1973, Op. Cit.

Part IV

Cocaine Today: Uses and Consequences

CHAPTER 11

CURRENT USE OF COCAINE IN THE U.S.

In its pharmacologic action cocaine, perhaps more than any other of the recognized psychoactive drugs, reinforces and boosts what we recognize as the highest aspirations of American initiative, energy, frenetic achievement and ebullient optimism (even in the face of great odds).

—G. Gay, C. Sheppard, D. Inaba, and J. Newmeyer, "Cocaine in Perspective: 'Gift from the Sun God' to 'The Rich Man's Drug' "

THE "NEW" POPULARITY OF COCAINE

Cocaine played a minimal role in American society for nearly thirty years, from the late 1930s through the 1960s. It was not, as we have seen, a drug uppermost either in the public's consciousness or on its consumption list. Our analysis of the twentieth-century cocaine literature shows a relative dearth of published articles between 1935 and 1960. The sudden increase of articles noted in the early 1960s was due predominantly to an upsurge of scientific interest in psychoactive drugs of all kinds.[1] Although no research has yet been done with the specific intention of explaining cocaine's sudden rise to prominence, it seems clear that the drug's current popularization is the result of no single social, legal, or cultural factor. In fact, it seems both simplistic and misleading to attempt to explain cocaine's popularity in terms of some direct causal relationship (e.g., a police crackdown on amphetamines resulting in an increase of cocaine use). Rather, the etiology of its use is rooted in a complex series of forces that came together in the late 1960s, and resulted in both a desire for and a supply of cocaine. A number of these forces have been discussed in the literature:

- "Some narcotics experts trace the current cocaine popularity to Dr. Timothy Leary, the professor turned drug cultist, who expounded the virtues of the 'consciousness expanding' drugs . . . like LSD, DMT and Methadrine or 'speed.' " Further, says Ottenberg:

  > That type of thinking helped make Methadrine extremely popular in some circles from the mid-1960s into the early 1970s. Having developed the "speed" habit, users move to cocaine for a higher high.[2]

- A corollary to this view is the suggestion that, with increasing police emphasis in the late 1960s on "cracking down on the amphetamine black market," cocaine smuggling and use enjoyed a renaissance.[3]
- Some drug enforcement experts have attributed the increase in cocaine use to the role played by post-Castro Cuban exiles who brought with them to America the habit of use, their trafficking expertise, and their South American connections.[4]
- Related to this latter view is a hypothesized law of illicit drug use that states that supply determines demand![5] And so, with the increasing amount ostensibly being brought into this country by Latin American couriers, a "market" was established.
- King suggests that the revival of cocaine use is a direct result of the channeling of heroin addicts into methadone maintenance programs in the early 1970s.[6] Methadone patients might seek out cocaine to get the euphoric feeling that they used to get (or hoped to get) with heroin. Such euphoria clearly does not result from orally administered methadone.
- During the late 1960s, there was an increased general interest in the use of illicit drugs. Reflective of these social changes were many drug-related songs, movies, books, and articles in popular magazines. For instance, a 1971 *Newsweek* article noted that cocaine was "abundant," with all the "pot-heads" on the scene trying it "at least once." A 1960s folk hero, Wavy Gravy, both on the radio and in the *Realist* magazine, talked about cocaine as "the thinking man's Dristan."[7]

The net effect of all the musical endorsements and wide-ranging media publicity was to legitimize to a degree the illegitimate—the illicit—use of cocaine.

> It had ceased to be an elitist drug, the odd habit of rich eccentricity. It had ceased be a racist drug, the nasty habit of blacks. As soon as the money of rock and roll appeared on the coke market, it became the high of Stars. And the fans followed. They were looking for a new Up anyway, now that speed was no longer "hip."[8]

Users' perspective

The cocaine users we interviewed were asked to account for cocaine's popularity. Some responses from the transcribed interviews were:

- "I think it's like an all time high, you know like you get up in the morning and you do some coke. You're wide awake, you're ready, you know, all bright-eyed, ready to face the new day. I think it's because you can do it any time of the day . . . that's why it's so popular. Also it only takes a little to get you off."
- "It's popular because it's rare. When it comes, it's like dessert."
- "Its popularity had to do with rock music. Hearing about all the groups that are having these cocaine parties after their gigs . . . I think that the popularity spread because a lot of people were trying to identify with rock groups."

The most frequently offered explanation for cocaine's popularity was its extremely pleasurable and euphoric properties. As one interviewee said: "It would be everybody's drug of choice, if they would only try it once."

Paraphrases of other frequently given explanations are:

- It enhances parties and social situations and is often taken in group settings.
- There has been almost no "bad" publicity concerning cocaine and its effects. (In fact, the most frequent request made of us by the people we interviewed was for *negative* information of any kind about the effects of prolonged cocaine use.)
- It's also popular because it's profitable, and many users also buy and sell the drug.

COCAINE AND THE POPULAR CULTURE: MOVIES, MUSIC, LITERATURE

Several writers have singled out the movie *Easy Rider* (1969), in particular the opening scene involving cocaine smugglers and dealers, as the sign of cocaine's reemergence on the American drug scene.[9] In fact, Phil Spector, who makes the buy of cocaine in the opening sequence from Peter Fonda and Dennis Hopper, later sent a still photograph from the scene as his Christmas card, with the message, "A little 'snow' at Christmas time never hurt anyone!!"[10]

In 1969, Johnny Cash released his recording of "Cocaine Blues," which earlier, in the 1930s, had been recorded in several different versions. The song warns about the dangers of the drug.

In 1970, at least one film mentioning cocaine was released—Billy Wilder's *The Private Life of Sherlock Holmes.* A number of very popular rock songs were also released that year, including the Rolling Stones' "Let It Bleed"—the Grateful Dead's "Casey Jones" and another Grateful Dead hit, "Trucking."

In 1971, Fred Neil did yet another reworking of the venerable "Cocaine Blues," and Hoyt Axton wrote "Snow Blind Fiend," recorded by Steppenwolf. The song tells the sad but true story of a friend of both Axton and John Kay who was very involved with cocaine.

Other cocaine-related songs released during 1971 were the Rolling Stones' "Sister Morphine" and the Jefferson Airplane's "Man, Man" and "Earth Mother."

In addition to the songs mentioned above, there now seem to be dozens of contemporary songs that mention cocaine explicitly, and hundreds that contain fairly obvious references to it but don't mention it by name. In fact, it now seems to have gotten to the point that one rather expects to hear about cocaine and drugs in songs and movies these days, especially when the music or film addresses itself to a young audience.

1971 was also the year that the magazines began to run stories about cocaine. These ranged from the authoritative *Journal of the American Medical Association* to the flagship of the popular hip press, *Rolling Stone*. A 1971 *Newsweek* article, "It's the real thing," said that cocaine was popular among "pot-heads" (marijuana smokers). Both *Esquire* and *New York Magazine* ran pre-publication extracts of Woodley's 1971 book *Dealer: Portrait of a Cocaine Merchant.*

This three-year period, then, 1969 to 1971, marked the establishment of cocaine in our popular culture. Ashley felt that the popular recognition also reflected a "marked" and "progressive" increase in the number of people who used cocaine.[11] Federal statistics for this period indicate an 838% increase in the annual quantities of cocaine seized (from 52 to 436 pounds). Although only presumptive evidence, the gain in amounts seized seems indicative of cocaine's growing popularity.

Since 1971 there has been increasing activity at the publishers and in the research laboratories, and the publications list is rapidly growing. The materials on cocaine and related matters have grown to include:

- Movies
- Articles in the major news media
- Reprints of classic works
- Compendia of "state of the art" scientific reviews
- Anthologies of historically important papers
- Reports on cocaine trafficking
- Reviews of legal considerations
- Comprehensive bibliographies
- Consumer handbooks
- At least one popularized survey of what's known

Is cocaine illegal in Hollywood?

1977 and 1978 have witnessed an increase in the reported use of cocaine among movie-industry professionals. A 1978 medical article reporting on the problem of a perforated nasal septum resulting from continuous or excessive snorting of cocaine underscores this observation.[12] A UCLA professor of surgery said that half a dozen of his patients with nasal-septum perforations have been "fantastically important" movie people whose names would "knock you over." Another UCLA surgeon has seen over thirty patients with the problem in the past year, half coming from the Los Angeles area. According to the first surgeon, these people are "heavy daily users, not just the occasional weekend sniffers." The second surgeon added that cocaine use can be "up to a $40,000 a year habit."

The damage noted was extensive. The perforated septums described in the article ranged in size from a dime to a quarter, considerably larger than normal. Apparently this problem is indigenous to Southern California. In a recent sampling reported upon in this same article, medical specialists from New York, Baltimore, Washington, D.C., and the Mayo Clinic in Minnesota noted that they have not seen the outbreak of cocaine-related nasal problems that has been noted in California.

In its 1977 updated overview of cocaine use in America, *Newsweek* magazine indicated that a change in usage had occurred in Southern California, with the drug being taken far more openly than in the past. "Before," said one film star's manager, "you would go to parties and the bathroom door was always locked. I could never get into a bathroom when I needed to because people were in there sniffing cocaine. . . . Now it has become socially acceptable to see people doing it. . . ."[13] But, according to another source, use has expanded from the social to a more personal and sustaining need for the drug. Harmetz, who described the Hollywood cocaine scene for *The New York Times*, indicated that "in Hollywood, where it has been a chic luxury drug for the last three years, a growing number of producers, directors and especially actors are now turning to cocaine as their main energy source—even when they are not working." Based on his discussions with a number of individuals within the industry, Harmetz feels that the creative decisions on a "substantial group of motion pictures have been made under the influence of the drug."[14]

Harmetz goes on to relate that the director of a recent expensive musical is alleged to have routinely snorted cocaine with the leading lady. Harmetz also indicates that an actor whose movie was being made on location in Europe agreed to make the trip only after receiving assurances that his weekly 7-gram supply of cocaine would still reach him.

Will heavy cocaine use among actors, producers, and crew affect the quality of movie production? That cannot at this time be determined. However, Harmetz gives several examples of stars who acted "crazed," petulant, or belligerent under the influence of heavy doses of cocaine. Hal Ashby, director of the hit movies *Shampoo* and *Coming Home* (which won several 1979 Academy Awards), said: "I started using coke in 1975, at the point when it became epidemic in Hollywood. I stopped pretty quickly. I was making *Bound for Glory* and I became short-tempered. I'd get cross at Haskel Wexler (who was later to win an Academy Award for photography on this film) for things that weren't his fault. It's not my nature to be curt and quick-tempered. I saw that this was happening and I stopped using it."[15]

Apparently, being a user of cocaine, and identified as such by law-enforcement agencies has no especially negative impact on an individual's movie career. A number of actresses have been arrested on various cocaine-related charges, and in no case has any of them had to serve any prison time. Anjelica Huston had charges dropped in return for testimony against Roman Polanski. Louise Lasser (of *Mary Hartman! Mary Hartman!* fame), MacKenzie Phillips, and Gail Fisher were allowed to enter drug diversion programs (which primarily provided anti-drug education in lieu of incarceration). Linda Blair (of *The Exorcist*) is currently fighting extradition in the Connecticut Appellate Court on charges of being part of a conspiracy to deliver and distribute cocaine. Male entertainers have seemingly fared less well in their efforts to avoid incarceration, however. The youthful lead in the TV series *Lassie* was convicted of smuggling in a liquid suspension of cocaine from Peru and is currently serving a prison term. The famous comedian George Kirby was arrested on a cocaine charge in Las Vegas and also received a lengthy prison term.

EXTENT OF CURRENT USE

In this section, we discuss the results of a number of incidence and prevalence surveys among different populations, and review of the available (primarily federal) data on the extent of use of cocaine alone and in combination with other drugs. In the next section of this chapter, on the characteristics of cocaine users, we include what data are available concerning the frequency of cocaine use (these data are very limited, however). In the next chapter, we consider some of this information in the context of routes of administration and amounts used.

A need for caution in interpreting statistics

Survey data on cocaine use (or any other illicit drug) must be interpreted with caution. Glenn warns of the strong temptation to "interpret published results as being applicable to wider populations than those which were actually surveyed." There also exists the temptation to compare one survey or study with another, "to say that drug abuse is a worse problem in one state or region than it is in another, and perhaps become alarmed or complacent on the basis of these comparisons."[16]

Attempts to generalize or compare published survey results should be avoided because of the varying degree of statistical methodologies and accuracy employed in conducting the study. Glenn suggested the following methodological requirements for designing a good survey:[17]

- Statistically designed random sample or probability sample should be drawn from the stated population.
- The problem of bias caused by nonresponse is "the most serious problem encountered in surveys for information on sensitive issues." A statistically "acceptable" method should be developed to treat the problem.
- The questionnaires should be carefully designed and pretested prior to actual use; validity checks in the questionnaire should be carefully chosen. In administering the questionnaire, anonymity of the respondents should be ensured.

Use in the General Population

Statistical information documenting the recent upsurge of cocaine use comes from a variety of sources. Glenn and Berg have both prepared compilations of studies, surveys, and polls on the illegal use of drugs.[18] Although no one study or survey was designed specifically to examine either cocaine use or its users, questions on cocaine use are typically included in the questionnaires given to the test populations.

The most popular test population has been high school students. The National Commission on Marijuana and Drug Use reviewed all available survey data from before 1972 based on student populations.[19] The commission reported that cocaine had been used by 1.2% of junior high students, 2.6% of senior high students, and 10.4% of college students.

The Marijuana Commission commissioned its own national probability sample survey of drug use.[20] The survey showed that 1.5% of the youth (ages twelve to seventeen) and 3.2% of the adults (eighteen and older) reported using cocaine. Further, 1.6% of the adults and 1.1% of the youth had used cocaine in the previous six months. However, as the commission's final report indicated:

> . . . the national survey was a household survey and therefore the sample did not include the transient "street" population among whom use of heroin and cocaine is presumably high.[21]

A significant number of high school studies, as compiled by Glenn demonstrate an increased awareness and use of cocaine at a young age.[22] Illustrative of one large survey involving both high school and junior high students was a two-year project undertaken by the Duval County School Board (Jacksonville, Florida). Over 33,000 students were polled as to their drug-use habits. The questionnaire response of the 17,538 students in 1971 and 16,046 students in 1972 indicated that:

- Cocaine use started at a young age. Of the 1971 seventh graders, 2.5% reported using cocaine (some even had used it in the past, but did no longer). In 1972 nearly 4% of the seventh graders reported cocaine use.
- During both years, the largest percentage of users were in the senior class (8% in 1971 and 9% in 1972 of the seniors were either current or former cocaine users).

- Males were considerably more likely to experiment or use cocaine than were their female classmates. In 1972 over 12% of the males in the senior class had experimented or were currently experimenting with cocaine.
- Of all ninth to twelfth graders 35.1% reported having used marijuana at least once, making this a relatively drug-oriented group.

Besides geographic factors, it has been demonstrated that socioeconomic, racial, and population-size variables are also important determinants of illicit drug use patterns.[23] Thirty-five thousand students in nineteen senior and six junior high schools in the East, Midwest, South, and Far West representing various social and ethnic backgrounds were polled as to their drug-taking behavior.

The study indicated that in the twenty-five schools surveyed the percentage of students who had tried cocaine ranged from 13.8% (in 1,324 students polled in a high school located in a large West Coast city, ethnically mixed) to a low of 1.5% (486 junior high school students located in an East Coast city). In another study involving seventh to twelfth graders in Dallas, Texas, 2,108 (4%) of the 55,745 students polled reported using cocaine.[24] In fact, 1,250 of them reported that they had used cocaine at least once during the week they were given the questionnaire.

In a more localized, but still broad-based survey, Chambers and Inciardi estimated that 6,000 individuals used cocaine six or more times per month in the State of New York.[25] Although this represented only 0.1% of the total population, Chambers and Inciardi estimated that an additional 95,000 individuals were current users of cocaine, using it less than six times a month.

The most recent estimates of cocaine use in the U.S. were presented in the 1978 *Annual Report* from the Office of Drug Abuse Policy (ODAP), a White House component with responsibility for monitoring drug abuse trends and establishing policy directives.[26] ODAP estimates, based on a national survey, that there are about 4.1 million cocaine users, mostly between eighteen and twenty-five. As shown in Table 8, there are striking increases in the use of cocaine since the Marijuana Commission's 1972 study.

TABLE 8
Estimated Number of Cocaine Users, 1972 and 1977

Age	*Percent who ever used, 1972*	*Percent who used during 1977*	*No. of users, 1977*
12-17	1.5	2.3	575,000
18-25	3.2	7.0	2,500,000*
26 and over		0.9	1,000,000†
			4,075,000

* Survey estimate was 2,100,000. ODAP added 400,000 to allow for likely underreporting.

† Surveys suggested that use among those over 35 is minimal, so estimates are principally for those 26-35.

Source: H. Abelson, R. Cohen, R. Schrayer, and M. Rappaport, "Drug experience, attitudes and related behavior among adolescents and adults;" Office of Drug Abuse Policy, *Annual Report, 1978.*[27]

Use of cocaine and other drugs

A series of surveys have demonstrated a relationship between the use of cocaine and other drugs, most notably heroin. Edmundson et al. estimated that up to 84% of regular heroin users also used cocaine (based on self-reported studies with a prison population).[28] Kestenbaum et al. reviewed the literature on studies of cocaine use among heroin users and came up with similar figures. They cite a study by the New York State Narcotic Commission which found that nearly 82% of 180 randomly selected (and certified) narcotics addicts reported using cocaine during 1969–70. They also cite a study conducted at the Clinical Research Center, Lexington, Kentucky, in which it was found that "of 1,096 opiate addicts, 72.9% reported cocaine abuse during 1968–69."[29]

But not all of the figures have been this high. Gay et al. analyzed the clinical records at one San Francisco treatment center and found that, during any one data collection period, only 20% of their addicts, at most, reported using cocaine (while treatment was underway).[30] Similarly, Chambers et al. reported that less than 20% of the addicts in a methadone maintenance program they studied concurrently used cocaine.[31]

Other sources of data on cocaine use

Other statistical sources concerning the incidence of cocaine usage are drug enforcement figures, including:

- U.S. Customs data on seizure at ports of entry
- Domestic seizure card "bugs" as reported by the Drug Enforcement Administration and its precursor, the Bureau of Narcotic and Dangerous Drugs and before them, the Federal Bureau of Narcotics (these statistics appear in Chapter 13)
- Statistical data assembled from local police arrest records, and court adjudications
- Medical and/or treatment records related to cocaine use. The two current major data gathering systems, CODAP and DAWN (described below), provide data on persons who have had sufficient difficulties with their use of drugs that they have come to the attention of the drug-abuse-treatment community and/or law-enforcement officials, and thus are unlikely to be representative of the drug-using population per se. But they are the best available source of data on user characteristics.

A caveat

As the Cocaine Policy Task Force warns, "the survey data we have examined here are instructive only in providing baseline estimates of certain parameters of the cocaine-using population . . . and should be interpreted with caution."[32]

CHARACTERISTICS OF COCAINE USERS

Cocaine is the drug of choice, not only among whites, but ever-increasingly, among affluent black drug users as well. Cocaine has traditionally been the status drug among black athletes, show-business personalities, and underworld figures (whose drug-usage is very limited and distinctly snobbish: black mob leaders condescendingly regard heroin addicts–black or white—as trash). It now seems to be attracting an even broader black clientele. Among Latin Americans in New York, cocaine is often the preferred drug of entertainers, expensive prostitutes, very successful businessmen, and certain religious sects for whom cocaine use is literally an act of faith. And among white drug users, cocaine is especially popular with rock stars, writers, younger actors and actresses, and stockbrokers and other Wall Street types. The main thing these otherwise varied people have in common is an income that can support the luxury of cocaine.[33]

Cocaine—buy low, sell high

Thirty federal agents raided the Chicago Board of Options Exchange just after the close of trading on February 7, 1979. Ten people were arrested either on the floor of the exchange or in adjoining areas.[34] At last, this confirms one of the more prevalent "facts" about cocaine users. As in the quote just above, descriptions of the current cocaine scene make reference to a cocaine-using population including stockbrokers. There have been ample reports of the cocaine use of entertainers, athletes and jet-setters, but this is the first report we've read on the money men.

According to a DEA spokesman, this federal investigation lasted over a period of a year, and drug activity on the exchange floor was described as "very blatant." Cocaine was sold for profit on the floor of the exchange as well as in nearby bars and restaurants of the city's financial district.

Sources told Laurie Cohen, the *Wall Street Journal* reporter covering the story, that drug traffic on the exchange floor was a longstanding problem. Because the exchange was founded only six years ago, many of the traders are young and newly wealthy. According to one options trader, "It [cocaine-use] happens anywhere you get a lot of money, a lot of pressure, and a lot of young people." He went on to stress that the same cocaine problems exist on other options exchanges and on both the stock and commodity trading floors.

While the initial quotation in this section neatly sums up the popular beliefs, there is little empirical knowledge about the characteristics of cocaine users ethnically, socially, or professionally. To date, only one study has addressed itself specifically to this point.[35] Unfortunately, since this study involved only nine individuals, albeit from somewhat different walks of life, there are problems in generalizing the results.

The bulk of the limited information that is currently available comes from the DAWN and CODAP systems, and concerned cocaine users who have come to the attention of the authorities—but not necessarily for their use of cocaine per se—and does not include the kinds of people mentioned above, by and large. Data from these systems will be discussed shortly.

In addition, however, there is some limited data available on the characteristics of social-recreational users—those who do not come to the attention of the authorities. These data are from several naturalistic studies and from at least one more systematic one. All support our own interview results that people use cocaine because they like it (for the psychic effects, in DAWN terms). The reports are from Ashley, who interviewed eighty-one users; Grinspoon and Bakalar, who interviewed seventeen; Waldorf et al., who interviewed thirty-two; and, in the most thorough of the studies, Siegel, who interviewed eighty-five.[36]

Siegel recruited recreational users through ads in a Los Angeles newspaper, screened them by phone, and selected eighty-five through a drug history form. All subjects selected were males, aged twenty-one to thirty-eight, and had used a minimum of 1 gram per month for at least a year. They were interviewed at length and given a variety of psychological and perceptual tests. All reported that cocaine was their drug of choice (though all were also multiple drug users), regularly snorted the drug, and reported subjective effects that corresponded generally with those reported in the literature. Siegel estimated that the average user snorted 8.7 milligrams per administration (the total for both nostrils). Most bought the drug themselves, though some shared other drugs in social settings. They viewed cocaine as an "ideal" drug, in terms of pleasant effects and lack of aftereffects, convenience, use, etc. They also viewed it as an "exotic drug which had appeal because of its rarity, high price, and historical-contemporary associations with popular and often high-status folk heroes." None showed a tendency toward overuse (or even increased use) of the drug, and, in general, had their habits well under control.

THE CODAP AND DAWN DRUG ABUSE REPORTING SYSTEMS

The Drug Abuse Warning Network (DAWN) is a data-collection system funded jointly by the National Institute on Drug Abuse and the Drug Enforcement Administration. DAWN receives information on "drug abuse incidents," adverse drug effects that have led abusers to appear in a crisis information center or a hospital emergency room, or to become the subject of a medical examiner's report (most often from an autopsy). Before mid-1975, incident data were also collected from hospital in-patient facilities. Pre-selected reporting sources are now located in the twenty-four Standard Metropolitan Statistical Areas (SMSAs).

The Client Oriented Data Acquisition Process (CODAP) is a data-collection and reporting system operated by the National Institute on Drug Abuse. The CODAP files date back to April 1, 1973, when data on patients admitted to federally financed drug-treatment agencies were first collected on the specially designed forms. Data are collected at admission to a program concerning a client's demographic characteristics, drug-use history, and treatment background. These data are reported to NIDA, via each of the state drug abuse agencies, for all clients who are considered as having been "admitted" to programs in that state. Quarterly updates are also provided to NIDA concerning all clients still in treatment at the end of each quarter of the year.

CODAP and DAWN findings

Table 9 presents information on the characteristics of cocaine abusers as reported during 1977 via the CODAP system. The data come from the 3,541 clients admitted to treatment facilities at CODAP-monitored facilities for

TABLE 9
Characteristics of Cocaine Abusers Admitted to Treatment Programs During 1977 (N = 3,541)

Sex	%
Male	78
Female	22
Race	
White	57
Black	32
Hispanic	10
Other	1
Age	
Under 18	10
18–20	21
21–25	36
26–30	20
Over 30	13
Education	
Less than H.S.	47
H.S. or more	53
Employment status	
Working	35
Unemployed	65

Arrests in 24 mos. prior to admission	%
None	37
1	34
2–3	20
4 or more	9
No. of prior treatment experiences	
None	68
1	21
2 or more	14
Source of treatment referral	
Self-referred	32
Criminal Justice System	34
Family, friends	14
Other	20

Sex by race

	Male %	*Female* %
White	54	65
Black	33	28
Hispanic	11	6
Other	1	1

Sex by race by age

	Males			*Females*		
	White	*Black*	*Hisp.*	*White*	*Black*	*Hisp.*
Under 18	8	4	15	19	14	16
18–20	22	17	20	24	24	28
21–25	40	31	33	34	30	40
26–30	20	25	16	16	20	5
Over 30	9	23	15	6	13	12

Source: NIDA Statistical Series, *Annual Data, 1977*, Series E, No. 7, 1978

whom cocaine was the primary drug of abuse. Over time, the bulk of cocaine abusers in treatment have been white, male, and under thirty. The proportion of males has been increasing, from 64% in 1974 to 78% in 1977. Compared to males, a larger proportion of both white and black female users are in their teens. Because of major changes in reporting requirements, comparison of CODAP data from year to year is often difficult. However, newer CODAP data indicate that increasing numbers of Hispanic persons are being admitted to treatment for cocaine-related problems (earlier forms did not differentiate Hispanics).

Nearly two-thirds of the clients were unemployed at time of admission to treatment, and just over half were high school graduates. Cocaine users in treatment tend to have been arrested somewhat more often during the twenty-four months preceding admission than is the case for abusers of many other drugs. For instance, only 52% of all heroin and marijuana abusers admitted during 1977 had one or more arrests prior to admission, compared to 63% of all cocaine abusers. Comparable figures for other primary drugs of abuse are: tranquilizers, 34%; other opiates, 43%; barbiturates, 56%.

Over two-thirds of the clients had no prior treatment experience, while approximately one in seven (14%) had been admitted to treatment two or more times. Marijuana abusers have had even less treatment experience than cocaine abusers (83% are in treatment for the first time). And heroin abusers, on average, have had more treatment experiences: 30% are reported to be in treatment for the first time while 42% have had two or more prior admissions.

Of the cocaine abusers, one-third were self-referred to treatment, one-third were referred from various components of the criminal justice system (probation, parole, prison, diversion programs, etc.), one-eighth were referred by family or friends, and the remainder came through a variety of sources such as physicians, mental health centers, other drug programs, and the like.

The referral pattern for cocaine abusers differs from that for abusers of other drugs. For instance, 52% of heroin abusers are self-referred, while only 14% came via the criminal justice system (CJS). For marijuana abusers, 21% are self-referred while 35% come via the CJS. For barbiturate abusers, 29% are self-referrals and 25% come via the CJS.

Current CODAP forms do not provide data on the motivations for use of cocaine. Table 10 presents motivational information from a separate 1974–75 DAWN analysis, displayed separately for drug incidents that involve the use of cocaine alone and in combination with other drugs. The data reinforce, not surprisingly, the belief that most users (59%) use cocaine for its psychic effects. What is surprising is the proportion of cases (30%) reporting the motivating factor as a dependency on cocaine. In the DAWN system, dependency is defined as:

> A state, psychic or physical, characterized by behavioral and other responses that always include a compulsion to take the drug on a continuous or periodic basis in order to experience its psychic effects; or to avoid the discomfort of its absence.[37]

The data indicate that those who use the drug alone are much more likely to seek psychic effects and much less likely to report dependency on the drug. Though we can only speculate, it seems reasonable to assume that multiple or "polydrug" users are more likely to be drug-dependent in general than are those who use only a single drug. This aspect of drug-use motivation clearly bears further study, however,

TABLE 10

Motivations for Use of Cocaine in 998 Cases (1974–75)

	Total No.	*Psychic effects %*	*Dependency %*
Total	998	58.7	30.5
Alone	560	67.0	22.2
In Combination	438	48.2	41.1

CODAP data from 1977 concerning frequency of use are shown in Table 11. Over half (54%) of the clients indicated that they use cocaine once a week or less. In marked contrast, 27% (half as many) of all clients use their drug of choice this infrequently. Somewhat surprisingly, one in seven clients indicated that they use cocaine more than once a day, compared to two in five of all clients who report such frequent use. This type of frequent cocaine usage, more typically associated with narcotic abuse, has been little commented upon in the literature.

As shown in Table 12, slightly less than 2% of all clients entering treatment programs indicate cocaine as their primary drug of choice.

CURRENT MEDICAL USE OF COCAINE

In a 1974 *JAMA* article, a Dr. Schneck supported the drug's continued use:

> The monumental effects of cocaine in otolaryngology [treatment of the ear and throat], allowing unimpeded intralaryngeal and intranasal surgery are obvious to anyone practicing the specialty. . . . otolaryngologists probably use more topical anesthetics than any other specialists and they have many uses for cocaine. Most obvious is the dependence of the nasal surgeon on topical anesthesia and vasoconstriction provided by this compound.[38]

	Suicide—estimated attempts %	*Other and unwilling* %	*Unknown/ no response* %
Total	2.1	.5	8.2
Alone	1.6	.53	8.8
In Combination	2.7	.45	7.6

Source: Drug Abuse Warning Network (Project DAWN) Files, IMS, America, Inc., Ambler, Penn.

TABLE 11

Frequency of Cocaine Use Based on 3,464 Clients Admitted to Treatment During 1977

*Frequency of use**	*Cocaine cases (%)*	*All drugs cases (%)*
Less than once/week	42.2	21.0
Once/week	11.7	6.0
Several times/week	21.9	15.5
Once/day	10.1	15.4
2 or 3 times/day	7.2	25.4
More than 3 times/day	6.9	16.7
Total (N)	3,464	193,943

* Frequency of use categories are new and reflect data from only the 1977 CODAP forms. Entries are for clients admitted during 1977.

Source: NIDA Statistical Series, *SMSA Statistics 1977*, Series E, No. 9

TABLE 12

Primary Drug of Abuse for Clients Admitted to Treatment During 1977 (N = 210,158)

Primary drug	%
Heroin	54.4
Illegal methadone	1.3
Other opiates	3.5
Alcohol	8.3
Marijuana	10.5
Barbiturates	5.0
Tranquilizers	2.0
Other sedatives	2.0
Amphetamines	5.2
COCAINE	1.8
Hallucinogens	3.7
Inhalants	1.4
"Over-the-counter" drugs	0.2
Other	0.6

Source: NIDA Statistical Series, *SMSA Statistics 1977*, Series E, No. 9

Other rhinological applications include shrinking of mucous membranes, vasoconstriction, and anesthesia in both the treatment and cautery of nosebleed and sinusitis. To a lesser degree, cocaine is used in treating diseases of the sense of smell (parosmia), treating migrane headaches, and as an aid in diagnosing certain upper-back pains (sphenopalatine neuralgia).[39]

In response to the recommendation by the National Commission of Marijuana and Drug Abuse that medical use of cocaine be banned, Dr. Schneck suggested that:

> . . . it may not be a misunderstanding of cocaine's medical value, but rather a misguided belief that eliminating its medical use may make it possible to eliminate all misuse of the drug in this country.[40]

According to a physician we consulted during this study:

> . . . the use of cocaine today [in the U.S.] is primarily a function of older physicians. It's oriented mainly to nasal solutions, particularly in the case of sinusitis. It has a good numbing effect, but other than that, it's used very little.

This is a misleading (though perhaps common) view, but some recent data quoted by Barash correct this impression:

> In documentation of the safety of cocaine, a recent survey of 741 plastic surgeons demonstrated the excellent record of cocaine as a local anesthetic in clinical practice. . . . Some 80 percent (592) of the respondents currently used cocaine for nasal surgery. This group reported that cocaine was used in approximately 93,000 operations. Mild reactions were observed in only 224 patients (0.015 percent). There were no fatal reactions in 93,004 patients.[41]

Other than this data, however, the extent of cocaine's use by other elements of the medical profession is not accurately known. There are some new thoughts on the horizon, though.

The amount of cocaine actually produced in this country has generally decreased from 1967 onward, as had the amount sold at the retail level for mainly medical applications (see Table 13). Production is largely a factor of market demand, and demand has generally not exceeded supply. Recently, however, there have been reports of shortages of legal cocaine for medical purposes, and a variety of possible causes have been advanced. Nelson, for instance, suggests that diversion somewhere along the line between producer and patient is likely, given the great cost differential between pharmaceutically pure and relatively lower-grade street cocaine (on the order of 1 to 100) and that pharmacists may be reluctant to stock cocaine because of the security problems involved in storing a highly desirable drug of abuse.[42]

A more likely explanation, however, seems to be new medical uses of the drug, going beyond the typical applications by eye, ear, nose, and throat specialists. With the recent interest in and development of hospices in America has come the unique use of cocaine as part of a painkilling elixir containing cocaine, morphine or heroin and some form of alcohol.[43] It is patterned after the Brompton's Cocktail developed in England and used with terminally ill patients. American physicians and hospice administrators are increasingly providing this form of treatment for individuals suffering extreme pain (cancer patients and the like). Due to current federal regulations, however, heroin is not one of the active ingredients in the American adaptation of the Brompton's Cocktail, generally being replaced with a morphine-type mixture.

The *Washington Star-News* in a 1974 report on the use of heroin as a powerful analgesic in England also notes the use of a cocaine elixir for patients suffering severe pain. As Arnold Trebach reports:

> A key to the differences between England and America, at least for me, was revealed in Welwyn Garden City, an hour's ride from London. Over a midday beer, a young physician said matter-of-factly, "In the first hospital I worked in, we gave cancer patients a bottle of syrup containing heroin, gin and cocaine, and we told them to take some when they felt pain. Of course, many of them were in constant pain, and this was a reasonably humane treatment."[44]

These mixtures consume relatively large amounts of cocaine. An ounce of pure pharmaceutical cocaine, on the average, is sufficient to provide a month's supply of Brompton's Cocktail to sixteen patients. And pain patients tend to require the mixture for a long time. On the other hand, an ounce is sufficient for twenty-eight nose operations, typically on a one-shot basis.[45]

Recently, the British seem to have given up the use of cocaine in their Brompton's solution. Apparently the cocaine had been included because British doctors felt it was necessary to counteract the drowsiness caused by morphine. Now the feeling seems to be that the drowsiness is only temporary and no counteraction is needed.

LEGAL PRODUCTION OF COCAINE

The "maximum aggregate production quota" (see Table 13) is the amount set by the federal government, and production cannot exceed it in any year. However, this does not mean that the entire amount produced will be either used or sold. The explanation provided us for the discrepancy between the "quota" figure and the "total production" figure is that the later includes an "inventory stock" in addition to cocaine that is actually produced in that year. The quota figure is calculated by the DEA according to a mathematical formula based on market figures, Food and Drug Administration (FDA) estimates, and other factors, including research needs.

An FDA spokesperson indicated that the agency's input to the DEA for purposes of calculating quota figures is a recent development:

> Up to 1975, we've never given them [the DEA] anything other than estimates for a few drugs like methaqualone. Last fall, when Justice [the Department of Justice, the DEA's parent agency] decided it didn't want to make cocaine quotas without FDA input, we were at a loss because we had no resources.

FDA officials then examined data in the National Disease and Therapeutic Index (maintained by IMS, America, Inc.). They found that prescription trends for cocaine were a flat-line function (no increase was indicated) and, based on this information, recommended to the Department of Justice (DEA) that there be no changes in the quota. The FDS provided no figures to the DEA, only recommendations:

> We hope by next year we'll have more sophisticated ways of meeting our responsibilities.

Our efforts to find out information from pharmaceutical manufacturers on the production of cocaine in America (amount produced, distribution process, and cost, etc.) often had the trappings of a covert intelligence operation. A spokesperson from Stepan Co.:

> I think you should contact the DEA; we're quite reticent to give any information. The less people know about us producing cocaine, the happier we are. If you get authorization from DEA, we'd be happy to cooperate.

A company spokesperson from Merck Chemical Co., in response to our queries about Merck's role in cocaine production, cost, etc., indicated that it was "proprietary information." When we attempted to clarify whether Merck imported coca leaves to produce cocaine, the response was an evasive:

> It's conceivable that we do, yes, but I'm not going to give you any more specific information than that.

According to a spokesperson of S. B. Penich, they used to buy cocaine from the Stepan Co. and resell it. They stopped this practice in December 1974, apparently for marketing reasons. However, the spokesperson indicated "there's more to it than meets the eye."

The facts, as we were finally able to get them, are the following:

- Stepan Chemical Co. is currently the only U.S. importer of coca leaves.
- Merck Chemical Co. refines a crude cocaine purchased from Stepan Co. and markets it.
- Mallinckrodt of St. Louis formerly (twenty-five years ago) produced cocaine. Presently, however, the company buys "prepared cocaine from Stepan in large quantities," repacks it, and sells it wholesale.

Recent federally compiled data provide some clarification.[46] In 1976, the Stepan Co. produced 410 kilograms of pharmaceutical cocaine, at the same time producing the "decocainized" resin extract used to produce Coca-Cola.

Clearly, as shown by our conversations with both FDA and DEA officials, and by our examination of the literature, the issues both of the medical use of cocaine and of the legitimate production and distribution of the drug should be examined on a national level.

TABLE 13
Legal Production and Distribution of Cocaine in the U.S. (1966–79) (kilograms)

Year	*Maximum aggregates production quota*	*Total production*	*Total dispositions*	*Exported to other countries*	*Sold to retail level*
1966	575	609	609	155	454
1967	615	1346	1303	867	436
1968	555	796	869	409	460
1969	977	1184	932	844	188
1970	1390	1105	1226	766	460
1971	1221	1020	901	496	405
1972	1375	955	958	508	450
1973	1162	955	912	596	316
1974	1125	834	924	489	435
1975	749	702	1050	616	434
1976	1213	654	662	332	330
1977	1249	683	637	351	286
1978	1478	1117	695	353	342
1979	1482	*	*	*	*

* Figures not yet available from DEA.

Source: Figures supplied by Compliance Division, Drug Enforcement Administration; taken from DEA reports to the United Nations. Discrepancies and fluctuations in maximum aggregate production quotas and total production quotas are due to the allowance of a surplus inventory by manufacturers as well as fluctuations in need and supply at the manufacturers', wholesalers', and retailers' levels.

REFERENCES

1. Phillips, J. and Wynne, R. D., *A Cocaine Bibliography—Nonannotated*, Research Issues Series No. 8, DHEW Publ. No. (ADM) 75–203, (Rockville, Maryland: NIDA, 1975).
2. Ottenberg, M., "Cocaine: The New No. 1 Drug," *Washington Star-News*, August 5, 1974, Al, A6.
3. Brecher, E., *Licit and illicit drugs*, (New York: Little, Brown, 1972).
4. Ottenberg, M., 1974, Op. Cit.
5. Plate, T., "Coke: The Big New Easy-Entry Business," *New York Magazine*, October, 1973, 63–75.
6. King, R., *Drug hang-up: America's fifty year folly*, (New York: Norton, 1972).
7. "Life and Leisure: It's the Real Thing," *Newsweek*, September 27, 1971, 124.
8. Hopkins, J., "Cocaine: A Flash in the Pan, a Pain in the Nose," *Rolling Stone*, Issue 81, April 9, 1971, 16.
9. Hopkins, 1971, Ibid; Malone, M. H., "It's the Real Zing," *Pacific Information Service on Street Drugs*, 1973, *2(4)*, 24–27; Perry, Charles, "The Star-Spangled Powder or Through History with Coke Spoon and Nasal Spray," *Rolling Stone*, Issue 115, August 17, 1972.
10. Hopkins, Ibid.
11. Ashley, R., *Cocaine: It's History, Uses and Effects*, (New York: St. Martin's Press, 1975).
12. "Patching Hollywood's 'Coke Noses,'" *Medical World News*, 1978, *19*, 81–82.
13. "The cocaine scene," *Newsweek*, May 30, 1977, 20–22, 25.
14. Harmetz, A., "Cocaine in Hollywood," *The New York Times*, July 11, 1978.
15. Ibid.
16. Glenn, W. A., "A compendium on recent studies of illegal drug use," Prepared for the National Institute of Mental Health, March, 1973.
17. Ibid.
18. Ibid; and Berg, D. F., "Dangerous drugs in the United States," *Int. Journal of Addict.*, 1970, *5(4)*, 795–806.
19. National Commission on Marijuana and Drug Abuse, *Drug Use in America: Problem in Perspective*, (Washington, D.C.: U.S. Government Printing Office, 1973).
20. Abelson, H., Cohen, R., Schrayer, D., and Rappaport, M., "Drug experience, attitudes and related behavior among adolescents and adults." In: *Drug Use in America: Problem in Perspective*, Appendix I, (Washington, D.C.: U.S. Government Printing Office, 1973).
21. Ibid.

22. Glenn, 1973, Op. Cit.
23. Elinson, J., *A Study of Teen-age Drug Behavior*, Summary progress report prepared by the College of Physicians and Surgeons, Columbia University, June, 1972.
24. Gossett, J. T., Lewis, J. M., and Phillips, V. A., "Extent and prevalence of illicit drug use as reported by 56,745 students," *JAMA*, 1971, *216*, 1464–1470.
25. Chambers, C., and Inciardi, J., "An assessment of drug use in the general population," Special report No. 2, New York State Narcotic Addiction Control Commission, (Albany, New York: NACC, 1971).
26. Office of Drug Abuse Policy, *Annual Report*, (Washington, D.C.: ODAP, 1978).
27. 1972 data from Abelson et al., Op. Cit.; 1978 data from ODAP, Ibid.
28. Edmundson, W. F., Davies, J. E., Acker, J. D. and Myer, B., "Patterns of drug abuse epidemiology in prisoners," *Industrial Med. Surg.*, 1972, *41*, 15–19.
29. Kestenbaum, R. S., Resmick, R. B. and Schwartz, L. K., "Acute systemic effects of cocaine in man: A controlled study by intranasal and intravenous routes of administration," Division of Drug Abuse Research and Treatment, Department of Psychiatry, New York Medical College, New York, 1975.
30. Gay, G. R., Sheppard, C. W., Inaba, D. S. and Newmeyer, J. A., "An old girl: Flyin' low, dyin' slow, blinded by snow: Cocaine in perspective," *Int. Journal of Addict.*, 1973, *8(6)*, 1027–1042.
31. Chambers, C. D., Taylor, W. J. R. and Moffett, A. D., "The incidence of cocaine abuse among methadone maintenance patients," *Int. Journal of Addict.*, 1972, *7(3)*, 427–441.
32. Drug Enforcement Administration, Report of the Cocaine Policy Task Force, (Washington, D.C.: DEA, July, 1974).
33. Plate, 1973, Op. Cit.
34. Cohen, L., "C.B.O.E. Lashes Out at U.S. Drug Unit on Cocaine Arrests," *Wall Street Journal*, February 9, 1979.
35. Spotts, J. V. and Schontz, F. C., *The Life Style of Nine American Cocaine Users: Trip to the Land of Cockaigne*, Research Issues Series No. 16, DHEW Publ. No. (ADM) 76–392, (Rockville, Maryland: NIDA, 1976).
36. Ashley, 1975, Op. Cit.
37. Drug Abuse Warning Network (Project DAWN) Files, IMA America, Inc., Ambler, Pennsylvania, 1974–1975 reports.
38. Anonymous, "Otolaryngologists hear defense of medical use of cocaine," *JAMA*, 1974, *230(5)*, 652–653.
39. Ibid.
40. Ibid.

41. Barash, P., "Cocaine in clinical medicine." In: R. C. Petersen and R. C. Stillman (eds.), *Cocaine: 1977*, Research Monograph Series No. 13, DHEW Publ. No. (ADM) 77–432 (Rockville, Maryland: NIDA, 1977), 193–200.
42. Nelson, H., "Cocaine for medical use hard to find," *Los Angles Times*, July 30, 1978.
43. Melzack, R., Ofiesh, J. G. and Mount, B. M., "The 'Brompton mixture' effects on pain in cancer patients," *Can. Med. Assoc. Journal*, 1976, *115*, 125–129.
44. Trebach, A., "Heroin, the Helper," *Washington Star-News*, July 21, 1974.
45. Nelson, 1977, Op. Cit.
46. Figures supplied directly to us by the Compliance Division, Drug Enforcement Administration, taken from DEA reports to the United Nations.

CHAPTER 12

THE USE OF COCAINE: ROUTES, RITUALS, AMOUNTS, AND MYTHS

He pulls a small vial of white powder from the pocket of his faded, embroidered jeans, carefully sprinkles two thin rows of the powder on a magazine, tightly rolls a new $20 bill, places one end next to one row, the other end in his right nostril. He presses his left nostril closed and inhales through his right, vacuuming the powder in a swift movement along the row. SNIFFFFF. He breathes deeply, then repeats the process with the other row and other nostril. SNIFFFFFFF.

—J. Hopkins, "Cocaine: A Flash in the Pan, a Pain in the Nose"

In this chapter we examine the details surrounding the use of cocaine, including:

- The various routes of administration
- How the drug is taken, including various rituals of use
- Frequency of use and amounts used
- Use of various drugs in combination with cocaine
- Activities associated with cocaine use, such as sporting events and sex
- Some of the popular misconceptions about cocaine

Since there are very few "hard" data about most of these topics, the discussion relies heavily on anecdotal information, a good bit of it derived from our personal interviews with and letters from self-reported users.

Early Illicit Use of Cocaine

During the early 1900s when the use of cocaine was coming under increasing state regulation, the illicit market was beginning to develop. This gave rise to many customs and beliefs still carried on today. Many of cocaine's current street names—"coke," "flakes," "rock candy"—were already in use by 1908. Nasal inhalation of cocaine was referred to as "sniffing" and a group of coke users often had "sniffing parties."

Cocaine was generally sold in small boxes, resembling aspirin containers. Another favorite method of dispensing coke was "by means of a playing card, asking 10 cents for every spot covered by the powder."[1] A gram of illicit cocaine would have sold for approximately 60 cents—a far cry from its price on today's illicit market.

ROUTES OF ADMINISTRATION

Inhalation

Inhalation (referred to as "snorting," "tooting," or taking a "snort" or "toot") is the most common route of administration. *The Gourmet Cokebook* estimates that approximately 90% of the users snort cocaine,[2] while data from the federal government's DAWN system (see Table 14) indicates that over 60% of the cocaine cases reported through this system snorted. Elaborate rituals involving a variety of paraphernalia have been developed for snorting. The most common procedure is to line up a small pile of cocaine powder (a "line" or "rail") on a hard, smooth surface, and then to snort the whole pile in one long and continuous inhalation. One nostril is pinched while the other is used for snorting. The effects (if any) are usually apparent to the inhaler within a few minutes.

Other ways to take cocaine

Besides snorting cocaine, it can be and is often taken orally, "either mixing it with a liquid or semiliquid, custard, or by direct application on the gums, palate and underneath the tongue."[3] A more popular area for direct application of cocaine is on the genital region, in order to prolong the sex act (discussed in later portion of this chapter).

Another area to which cocaine is locally applied is the inside of the eyelids.

According to the French correspondent in a 1923 *JAMA* article it was apparently quite the vogue among movie actors to use cocaine to enhance the "photogenic capacity of the eyes":

> The resulting increase of occular tension and the dilation of the pupil give to the eye and to the face of the artist an expression of astonishment, depth and brilliance or sometimes of wildness.[4]

The source, Dr. Salles, goes on to conclude that the continued use of cocaine is debilitating and the actors quickly lose their abilities.

Apparently, cocaine's effect on the eyes was not the answer for all movie stars. In her autobiographical *Pentimento*, Lillian Hellman recounts the following misadventure involving Tallulah Bankhead:

> Tallulah took two small bottles from her pocketbook, put them on the table. . . . As we were about to go back to rehearsal, she picked up one bottle and tipped it to put drops in her eyes. She rose from the table, repacked the bottles, led the way to the door and let out a shriek that brought the restaurant to its feet. . . . "I have put the wrong drops in my eyes. . . . I put the cocaine in my eyes and I don't tell that to doctors or to anybody else. Tell him [Herman, the director of the play she was in] to shut up about it or I won't go back to the theatre."[5]

Lastly, the direct application of cocaine has also been reported in enemas "used by rectal enthusiasts as well as hemorrhoid sufferers."[6] Aside from insuffulation (snorting) and direct application, the other route of administration commonly employed by cocaine users is by intravenous (IV) injection. Effects are apparently very intense, as in these passages from the novel *Naked Lunch*, by William Burroughs.

> Ever pop coke in the mainline? It hits you right in the brain, activating connections of pure pleasure. The pleasure of morphine is in the viscera. You listen down into yourself after a shot. But C is electricity through the brain. . . . The C-charged brain is a berserk pinball machine, flashing blue and pink lights in electric orgasm.

And:

> The full exhilaration of cocaine can only be realized by an intravenous injection. The pleasurable effects do not last more than five or ten minutes.[7]

Data on the different routes of administration

The only reasonably "hard" statistical data we have been able to find on the frequency of use by various routes of administration was compiled as part of the federal government's DAWN system, as shown in Table 14. As this table shows, nearly three fifths of the reported users snort, while a quarter of them inject. Unfortunately, there has been no further data on this type from the DAWN system, since this item was dropped from the data-collection forms in April 1974. The item that best approximates it on the

TABLE 14

Route of Administration in 2,319 Cases Involving the Use of Cocaine (July 1973–April 1974)

Method	*No.*	%
Oral	92	4.0
Injection I.V.	291	12.5
Injection other	48	2.1
Injection unspecified	252	10.9
Snorted	1,421	61.3
Other	46	2.0
Unknown	169	7.2
TOTAL	2,319	100.0

Source: Drug Abuse Warning Network (Project DAWN), files of IMS America, Inc., Ambler, Penna.

subsequent forms asks for "dosage forms," and the results from this item are considerably less helpful in indicating the route of administration used.

Reasons for preference of inhalation over injection

What anecdotal evidence there is indicates that IV use of cocaine is far less popular than is inhalation.

The main reason cited by users for the preference for inhalation over injection was the relatively short duration ("often less than 15 minutes") of cocaine effects when used intravenously. Further, many of the users expressed a fear of using syringes. A number also mentioned the relative costs. Given the shorter duration of the IV effects (in comparison with the admittedly less intense inhalation effects), more cocaine and thus more money is likely to be involved in using the drug in this manner. Other typical preferential responses included in letters to us from self-reported users were:

> I have been doing cocaine consistently for about a year and a half. Consistently means about a gram every three weeks or whenever needed. I must point out that I snort coke, I don't shoot it.
>
> This beautiful high was a thing to look forward to. He [her boyfriend] loved to snort cocaine with me. Then along comes Bobby—just like the serpent in the Garden of Eden. Bobby loved needles and thought snorting was for fairies. Chuck [her boyfriend] tried it a few times before, but when Bobby came around every day—well, you know what happened. His arms began to get greener and I just kept trying to play it cool as long as I could. That didn't last long. I soon found myself getting quite upset and sometimes even carried away a bit when they'd get out the spoons and plasti-pack syringes.

Smoking cocaine

In a recent letter to the editors of the *New England Journal of Medicine*, a researcher reported on the new twist to cocaine use in California—what seems a growing trend toward cocaine smoking. By way of a caveat, the researcher, Dr. Ron Siegel, notes that nonmedical intranasal use of cocaine has resulted in "remarkably few problems demanding clinical attention."

Siegel notes a nineteenth-century practice of prescribing coca-leaf cigars and cigarettes in the treatment of respiratory ailments. The relatively low cocaine levels in the leaves, however, prevented development of serious medical consequences. Until quite recently, cocaine smoking in the United States took the form, generally, of mixing cocaine powder with tobacco or marijuana. The principal effects seemed to be economic rather than chemical: little or no clinical effects, but high expense to mix the drugs. According to Siegel, such minimal effects are consistent with the poor volatility of the cocaine salts present in the street drug.

What has Siegel particularly concerned now, however, is that users are experimenting with the smoking of cocaine alkaloid or base, known in street jargon as "free-base." Says Siegel:

> . . . free-base is an intermediate compound in the preparation of the hydrochloride salt from coca leaf extracts and is less susceptible to decomposition upon heating. It can be reobtained from street cocaine via simple extraction kits available in commercial paraphernalia shops. Users distribute approximately 300 mg throughout a cigarette or place the free-base in special cocaine water pipes. Intoxication is marked by euphoria, rapid mood elevation and general stimulation.

He adds that free-base parties have become increasingly popular, and, because cocaine smokers do not appear to titrate, judge, or adjust doses, both frequency and quantity of dosages apparently escalate rapidly at these parties. The clinical signs associated with smoking abuse are mydriasis, anorexia, hyperactivity, insomnia, weight loss, and rapid pulse. Depending on dose and personality, the syndrome may progress to a "manic-like euphoria, depressive-like dysphoria, or schizophrenic-like paranoid psychosis." In conclusion, "the rarity of such findings with intranasal cocaine users and the increasing appeal of smoking among this population thus presents a potential medical hazard."[8]

An even more recent report from Bolivia indicates that cocaine-base smoking is popular among that country's cocaine aficionados as well. However, Bolivian cocaine base is approximately 97% pure, relative dynamite compared to the American street product. Noya notes that intense paranoid reactions are generated among cocaine smokers, after the first inhalation. Not only that, the smokers seem compelled to smoke up all the mixture they have on hand, exuding paranoia all the while![9]

RITUALS OF USE

Spoons and other machinery

Local "head shops" (stores specializing in drug-related paraphernalia) typically stock some of the many devices currently used in connection with the ritual of snorting cocaine. These include spoons, ranging from cheap metal ones (resembling salt spoons) to exquisitely designed, very expensive gold and silver ones that hold enough cocaine powder for a single snort. Interestingly enough, very few of the users we interviewed use spoons in actually snorting cocaine. One reason for this, cited by several, was the difficulty in getting the cocaine-laden spoon to the nostrils without spilling any. The difficulty is compounded, of course, if the user is nervous or anxious.

Head shops also carry curved glass tubes. Often referred to as "tooters" or "snorters," these are used in lieu of straws or rolled-up bills to snort the cocaine.

The smaller end fits in the nose, and the larger end is placed over a "line" of cocaine. The powder is typically scraped into thin lines on a tabletop, mirror, or any other smooth surface. Such fancy glass tubes or straws are in common use. Most of the users we interviewed continue to use rolled-up bills, however:

> Recently, with the influx of cocaine into the Hollywood elite and other upper economic classes, the practice of snorting or sniffing (in which a "line" of cocaine is inhaled into a nostril, often through a rolled, high denomination bill) has been revived. . . . One of the authors has witnessed a $500 bill being used for such purpose.[10]

A razor blade and a mirror are the other two typical items of cocaine paraphernalia. The razor blade is used to chop the cocaine (whether in flake, rock, or even powder form) into a fine consistency. The crushed and cut-up powder is then placed on the mirror (or any uniformly flat and smooth surface) and is usually divided into either one large or two small piles of "lines." Then the process of cutting and shaping the lines begins.

Some drug specialty stores sell complete cocaine kits, including glass snorters, razor blades, a mirror, and different-size vials in which to carry the cocaine. The entire contents fit into small leather cases resembling miniaturized versions of shaving kits.

With the rapid growth of the cocaine market has come a great outpouring of paraphernalia intended for cocaine use or that trade on the drug's popularity. In a recent issue of a major journal catering to the "head shop" industry, the following paraphernalia were discussed or advertised:

- chemicals for converting street cocaine to free-base, and a variety of pipes for smoking free-base
- a purification system advertised as able to "remove unwanted cuts from the product and make it almost 100% pure." This system is similar to the extraction system for free-base. *As yet, however, there is no scientific evidence for this argument!*
- a portable programmable melting point tester (see Chapter 15)
- hand-tooled metal "straws" and gold-plated razor blades
- a nasal irrigator, billed by its maker as simultaneously reducing the chance of nasal membrane damage and enhancing the sensation from subsequent "hits"
- a full line from a single specialist, including solid gold bottles, razors, spoons and straws; and non-gold mirrors, mirror boxes, cutting plates, strainers, mortars and pestles, scales, straws, various adulterants, testing kits, and informative literature
- incense advertised as "like coca and cocaine," and sold in 2 gm. bottles
- a dry ice system for drying out moist crystals
- a "spiffy" line of cocaine jewelry
- a combination spoon/snorter/masher
- T-shirts with imprints such as "It snows in Columbia," "Cocaine," and the like.

Exotic cocaine equipment

A unique piece of cocaine paraphernalia seen during the course of this study was a pair of glass-ball earrings with removable cork tops. The user, a young woman, felt completely safe walking around public places with her earrings filled with cocaine. Anytime she wanted some, she would simply take an earring, remove the cork top, pour a little on the palm, and quickly sniff it up. Often she would do this at her desk (she worked as a secretary), not bothering to go to the privacy of the bathroom.

Another aid to the public consumption of cocaine that we uncovered involved placing a mixture of water and cocaine in an empty nasal-spray container and then sniffing it up whenever and wherever the user desired. To all public intents and purposes, the user seemed to be medicating himself with an approved medicinal product, rather than with one of the most powerful of drugs.

Cutting and shaping the lines of cocaine

The amount of cocaine in each pile varies from user to user. A number of the users interviewed for this study said that each pile is about the amount that fits in a coke spoon (such as a small plastic coffee spoon from a fast-food franchise, or a small salt spoon). Amounts are rarely measured precisely. Rather, the size of the piles is determined by habit or individual preference. Several interviewees familiar with the subject said that this approach differed from the use of heroin, in which the amounts used are much more closely measured.

On a number of occasions during the course of this project, we witnessed cocaine users going through the cutting and shaping process. A variety of techniques were employed. Some users wielded their razor blades with the finesse of a Japanese chef using his cleaver. Others were more deliberate in their actions, first cutting the pile with many strokes of the razor, then forming the lines of cocaine, cutting and regrouping them into piles, and then repeating the entire process. There was always a considerable amount of group activity and boisterousness surrounding this step, particularly among the people who were next to get their snort or hit of cocaine. The final result was always a line of cocaine about the thinness of a felt-tip pen mark and several inches long.

Inhaling the drug

As indicated earlier, the line or rail is generally snorted in one long continuous inhalation. One nostril is pinched while the other is used for snorting. Then the other is used. A few heavy swallows usually concludes the process.

The effects of the drug are generally noted within a few minutes after inhalation and are often accompanied by cries of excitement or disappointment, depending on the quality of the drug.

One of the more curious snorting rituals we observed was something we dubbed the Cocaine Line Race. Two participants sit opposite one another across a glass-topped table. A long thin line of cocaine, stretching the width of the table, is made. The participants, armed with their favorite snorters or tooters, starting from their respective sides, race up the cocaine line. Whoever crosses over the center of the table first is declared the winner. The loser, inevitably as high as the winner, pays the cost of cocaine used in the race.

Getting high while you fly

The *Kryptonite Gazette* (1975) published by the Haight-Ashbury Free Medical Clinic (San Francisco, Calif.) had an article on various methods and drugs to use in getting high at airports and in airplanes. The article cautions the "hip" traveler from smoking marijuana in the airplane bathroom, but found that that was a good place to "snort" cocaine:

> "the airplane 'johns' come equipped with excellent stainless steel counters, so all you need is your own razor blade if you want to do a little 'toot' (snort of cocaine). The stewardess will gladly supply you with a straw."

This represented the only "game" we heard about involving the use of cocaine. But it is another indication that the use of cocaine, at least among the many users we interviewed, is very much associated with partying and group social use.

Side effects of inhalation: nose problems

A major concern associated with inhalation of cocaine is the belief that prolonged use will eventually result in an ulceration of the nasal septum. The assumption is that particles of cocaine lodge in the nose hairs and initiate the ulceration process. Because of this concern, there are several practices currently in vogue among cocaine users to prevent the build-up of particles in the nasal passages:

- Cutting or grinding the cocaine into a fine powder. The principal reason for using a razor is to get the cocaine to as fine a state as possible. The finer the grain, the less the possibility of getting some cocaine particles caught in the cilia of the nasal passages or lodged in the sinuses.
- Using nose drops and nasal sprays. A doctor in the Los Angeles area, commenting on the number of patients coming to his office with complaints that nasal sprays were not helping their congestion, said that "sales of these sprays and drops have rocketed . . . and I directly attribute that increase to the widely extended use of cocaine."[11]
- Rinsing the nasal cavities with warm water after snorting also helps soothe the irritated nasal linings.[12] Some of our interview subjects used wine.
- Two other methods of taking care of the nose were reported in the *Ann Arbor Sun Community News Service*. One consisted of cleaning out the nostrils with a moistened Q-tip after "snorting" some cocaine. The other is to take Vitamin B capsules, but it is cautioned that this advice is folk wisdom and "carried no septum back guarantee."[13]

However, the street belief about the cause of the nasal ulceration is erroneous. Ulceration results not from cocaine particles lodging in the nasal passage, although that would exacerbate the situation, but from the drug's vasoconstrictive properties. The drug causes a deficiency in blood flow (ischemia) which results in the eventual ulceration of the nasal septum.[14]

If the nose continues to be irritated and troublesome, it is indicative that too much cocaine is being snorted. A modern-day Kafkesque nightmare has a cocaine user waking up and discovering:

> Went to bed last night
> singing a song,
> Woke up this morning
> and my nose was gone—
> Imagine my embarrassment!
> Now my mucous membrane
> is just a memory.
> Sometimes I think cocaine
> is bad for me—
> Then I stop thinking. . . .[15]

Or, as a California man explained it:

> I knew this stuff [cocaine] wasn't as harmless as they say when I saw a friend of mine in the business, a $500-a-week snorter, use up a box of kleenex a day. And the guy doesn't know it. He really thinks he's had the same cold for two years.[16]

AMOUNTS OF COCAINE USED

It is very difficult to determine amounts used. One component of the equation would be frequency of use, but the available data are extremely limited both in scope and utility. Further, there are definitional confusions. The term "heavy user" will have a different meaning for many people. In defining it we took into account frequency of use as well as amount. We found that many cocaine users had difficulty estimating the amount of cocaine they did, because there is no such thing as a measured line or rail of cocaine. Secondly, it was often a shared experience. Thus a user and his friends would go through a gram of cocaine in an evening, yet the amount actually injected by any one person would be unknown. For our purposes, anyone using cocaine at least five times a week, regardless of the amount done, was considered a heavy user. Likewise anyone doing an estimated 3 grams a week was considered a heavy user. Although an arbitrary, imprecise measurement, at a minimum it gave us a frame of reference to evaluate the information provided by our interviewees. We were at all times vulnerable to their mendacity, however.

Another important factor and one we had no means of determining was the purity of the cocaine done. The use of one gram of relatively pure (70%) cocaine in the course of a week is likely to be a considerably different experience than doing a gram of only 20% pure cocaine over the same period.

Woods and Downs felt that the heaviest users of cocaine "typically are involved in [the] illicit drug trade."[17] Our interviews bear out this observation. The habitual or heavy users among the interviewees were generally heavily enmeshed in the entire drug-dealing network.

Cocaine and housework

For some, cocaine is associated not with the glamor and excitement of parties, but the dull and commonplace activity of housecleaning. Several of our interviewees said that a snort of cocaine greatly facilitated and enlivened the chore of cleaning the house. S. Murphy, who has been conducting research on cocaine users on the West Coast, has findings that parallel ours:

> If I say, what do you like to do most when you're using cocaine, they'll [the cocaine-using women the researcher interviewed] say that they like to talk and to clean their house. Clean their house is a big one. . . . [Apparently] it's a lot more fun to clean your house when you're high. . . . Seriously, every woman I've talked to says: "Well, my house is really clean whenever I try coke. . . ."[18]

There is still another distinction between the occasional and heavy user. If it is true that heavy users have access to the illicit drug network, then they are highly likely to be exposed to a purer grade of cocaine than are the frequent small-time buyers. Thus "the quantities of cocaine actually administered by the various types of users may be expected to vary as do the frequencies."[19]

Only estimates are available as to amounts typically used. Siegel estimated that the subjects in his study of social-recreational users ingested an average of 8.7 milligrams per administration.[20] Grinspoon and Bakalar, on the other hand, state the "average street dose of cocaine . . . is 20 mg to 50 mg intranasally."[21] Obviously, the final word has not been said on this point.

Factors restricting frequency/amount of use

Woods and Downs speculated that for "occasional" users, at least, the getting was the key determinant in regulating the frequency with which they used cocaine:

> That is, the availability of the drug plus the social sanctions implicit in situations such as parties where cocaine is distributed or the presence of friends who are using cocaine may serve as the antecedent conditions for indulging in the drug.[22]

Our interviewees provided support for this speculation. One said, "You go to a party where there's a lot of coke, it's a status trip . . . so you do it." Another wrote, "Cocaine is above all a social drug, and if you have some, you share it with your friends."

Another Woods and Downs speculation is that many users avoid frequent cocaine use because of the belief that extensive use has psychotoxic results (e.g., they would "freak out" or overdose).[23] There is some support for this speculation from our interviewees; the majority were keenly interested in anything we could tell them about the known "bad" side effects or negative reactions to cocaine, especially in the "speedball" combination with heroin.

And a final barrier is likely to be the price. Current U.S. street prices (mid-1979) range from $75 to over $150 per gram.

USE OF VARIOUS DRUGS IN COMBINATION WITH COCAINE

As has been stated elsewhere, many cocaine users mix their drugs—adding both to the dangers of cocaine and to the difficulty of measuring those dangers.

"Speedballs"—heroin and cocaine together

> It is a standard practice for cocaine users to sit up all night shooting cocaine at one minute intervals, alternating with shots of heroin, or cocaine and heroin mixed in the same injection to form a "speedball."[24]

There are some indications that a heroin/cocaine combination is used more frequently by heroin addicts than by "run-of-the-mill" drug users. As discussed in the preceding chapter, one survey of drug use among a prison population indicated that 84% of the regular heroin users also used cocaine.[25] Only two of our interviewees had ever used this combination, and one of them had done the mixture by snorting rather than IV. The fear of toxic, even fatal, reactions was a deterrent. And there may be grounds for this fear.

The typical speedball mixture is equal parts of cocaine and heroin, and this particular combination of the two drugs is potentially very dangerous. The best available evidence on this point comes from Pickett's study on the effects of various proportional mixtures of the drugs in rats discussed in some detail in the section on acute toxicity, in Chapter 9.[26] Pickett found that:

- Small amounts of cocaine mixed with heroin reduced the depressant effects of heroin (e.g., a small amount of stimulant–cocaine—antagonized the effects of a relatively large amount of a depressant and thus a lethal effect from the mixture of a similar amount of heroine alone).
- Equal proportions of cocaine and heroin (the typical mixture used by addicts) potentiated the depressant effects of heroin (e.g., there was a greater depressant and thus lethal effect from the mixture than from a like amount of heroin alone).

Clearly, there are some problems in translating these findings directly to humans, and we have no evidence (if such exists) as to the toxicity or lethality of the speedball combination among drug users. But Pickett's findings clearly suggest that the speedball mixture can produce a range of reactions, from an effect less than that produced by heroin alone to an effect much greater than that produced by heroin alone. And that fact makes the combination particularly dangerous and unpredictable.

The following anecdote was included in a DAWN report on the experiences of cocaine users. The interviewed subject was a twenty-one-year-old white male, claiming a history of eight years of cocaine use. He describes the procedure of making a speedball.

> He stated that he preferred to cook up heroin and cocaine in the same spoon and inject the mixture simultaneously although he knew many addicts who preferred to do the drugs separately. He preferred to cook up the heroin first and then add the cocaine just prior to administration. . . . Cocaine seemed to necrotize tissues and veins more rapidly than did heroin. . . . The total experience would usually last 15 to 25 minutes. . . . Along with many other addicts he knew, [they] preferred cocaine in combination with methadone to the combination of heroin and cocaine.[27]

Drugs other than heroin

Cocaine users, for a number of reasons, tend to be multiple (or "polydrug") users.[28] Eckerman et al. surveyed drug users arrested for crimes other than drug violation in six major cities. They found that although 19% of their sample of 1,889 had used cocaine at least once, none of them used cocaine exclusively.[29]

Many users like to use cocaine in combination with other drugs. One of our interviewees said:

> I like coke and smoking pot, coke and downs, coke . . . and anything and everything. It's hard to say. . . .The combination is whatever's available and that's that."

On the other hand, for some of the users, cocaine's relative expense and unique euphoric effect precludes their mixing drugs:

It's a treat, you just don't want to take away from a cocaine high. It's definitely a treat to most people.

It's not that plentiful. If you had a lot, you could experiment [with it and other drugs] but coke is so rare.

Many of our subjects (both letter writers and interviewees) indicated a preference for the concomitant use of cocaine with drugs possessing a depressant reaction.

I love [cocaine with] downers, barbiturates. They seem to have a nice mixture. Whereas cocaine after a while will act like an amphetamine, the downer will mellow you out. Quaaludes, as the downer, seems to mix well. Drinking and coke goes well too. [Interview]

The most popular cocaine combinations with our subjects were with marijuana or alcohol:

Cognac and cocaine was a favorite combo down there [in Culiacan, Mexico]. [Letter]

When I'm loaded on coke, I always have a thirst . . . your consumption is greater and you drink more. [Interview]

At least one subject noted that the taste of cold beer was especially good when he was high on cocaine, and that it "felt good, going down the road," apparently effectively eliminating any unpleasant aftertaste of the cocaine.

What seems to us a reasonable explanation for the use of alcohol in combination with cocaine is that because of its depressant effects, alcohol may reduce the "jittery" or anxious state that reportedly, for many users, follows upon dissipation of cocaine's euphoric effects.

To our knowledge, the use of alcohol in combination with cocaine has not previously been reported upon in the literature. This particular aspect of "polydrug" use deserves further investigation, however.

SPORTS AND COCAINE

The use of cocaine by athletes is not a new phenomenon.

Some years ago the members of the Toronto Lacrosse Club experimented with coca, and during that season

> when that club held the championship of the world coca was used in all its important matches. The Toronto club was composed of men accustomed to sedentary work, while some of the opposing players were sturdy men accustomed to out of door exercises. The games were all severely contested, and some were played in the hottest weather of one summer . . . The more stalwart appearing men, however, were so far used up before the match was completed that they could hardly be encouraged to finish the game, while the coca chewers were as elastic and as free from fatigue as at the commencement of the play."[30]

The extent to which cocaine is now used by athletes as a performance aid is unknown. It has clearly relevant physiological effects:

> Cocaine is effective in removing the sensation of fatigue and can in this manner undoubtedly raise the level of performance in the course of prolonged effort.[31]

However, because of its acute toxic effects when used in large doses, the conventional medical view is that cocaine should never be used in connection with athletics.

Few of our subjects reported using cocaine for any athletic events. (Cocaine was used as an aid in cleaning house and for sex. Admittedly, these are not athletic events, but in their way are often physically demanding.) One of the interviewed cocaine users told the following story of the use of cocaine and a sporting activity, in this case softball:

> I'm really into softball. I play the leagues down here and we've traveled and everything and have even won the championhip. I went to ——— last summer and usually I'm into fast-pitch softball. Up in ——— they didn't have any fast-pitch teams so I played a slow-pitch team. Most of the guys on my team were carpenters, made a lot of money. The whole team was into coke. So we got invited to this elimination tournament in ———. There was about twenty-five teams in it and they kept eliminating teams until it was down to two, for the finals. About four of the guys on our team brought grams of coke, and between every game we just

got really fixed up on cocaine. Got really high. And it was hot and everything was so dragged out we would just come out and have line field practice and turn the ball out really hard, really getting into it. The other teams couldn't believe it, because everybody in the bleachers were just sweating their asses off. I found that I'm too stimulated on a drug, playing sports. I don't function as well because I'm high-geared, especially when I pitch, because in fast-pitch I do pitch fast and I can't control myself. I don't wait, I don't concentrate, I just don't listen to anybody and just . . . To me, a stimulant like that isn't good for sports. But . . .

Another day I was playing softball I took coke during a game. They had me in the outfield and I'm not an outfielder because I have very bad legs. I was playing center field and as soon as the ball was hit, I knew exactly where I was going. I didn't misjudge any ball that whole day. My arm felt like it didn't have anything that could stop it. I was throwing the ball further than I ever threw in my life. I was scoring strikes to third base and I felt like Willie Mays. It was really an ego baseball trip that day.

Generally the folklore (and there's a lot of it) surrounding the use of cocaine in connection with sports involves the widespread belief that "professional athletes," as a group, use cocaine extensively. Similar beliefs are held about rock stars, other kinds of entertainers, and, to a lesser extent, the class of people known as "jet setters." The process through which cocaine became linked to athletes and professional athletes has not yet been examined in the literature, however.

We were told a number of anecdotal stories involving use of cocaine by well-known professional football or basketball players by several reliable (law-enforcement) sources. A report of a series of interviews with cocaine users conducted by a team of DAWN scientific investigators included the following account of cocaine's use by sports figures:

This contact, a 27-year-old black male, is very much involved with the drug scene in ———. . . . He supplied the following information: . . . The preferred customers

> keep the cocaine for themselves and party with it. These preferred customers are usually business, sports, professional and entertainment people. . . .
>
> The contact admitted that the night before this interview, he was at a party given by a prominent businessman in the ——— area who had as his guests several professional basketball players, several other business people, some entertainers, and the contact. An ounce was available for the guests and many of the aforementioned people took part in sniffing cocaine.[32]

In an article on the impact professional basketball has had in the black community, Rosen notes the use of cocaine by "pro ball players":

> Because their personal trip has to be shared, blacks are usually much more up front about drug usage than are white ball players. The blacks on a professional team located in the South recently took to wearing their coke spoons on flashy chains around their necks, thereby delighting the soul community and puzzling the rubes. But when the local gendarmes found out that none of the players belonged to an Egyptian fertility cult and were, in fact, using their "medallions" for other nefarious purposes, the spoons went back under their T-shirts.
>
> Only once a year, perhaps, will a ballplayer be too stoned to play. A rarely used substitute found himself in exactly that position . . . during his team's last game of the season a few years back. When his coach told him to go into the game with less than two minutes remaining the player laughed and said, "Fuck you, man. It's too cozy right here for me to be running around out there." The player stayed and the coach was fired.
>
> Cocaine is the aspirin that soothes a rich man's soul, and it is part and parcel of the ghetto fantasy made fact. Pimps and dealers drive both the fancy shorts and the fancy mamas—and black basketball players also enjoy the delights of this heavy traffic. The difference is that ballplayers are legal, and the money they spend is white money and isn't squeezed out from the slums of the nation. The black ballplayer's status is something that even preachers and teachers can respect—and the responsibility that is thrust upon them is rarely refused.[33]

EFFECTS OF COCAINE ON SEXUAL RESPONSE

> The natives of South America, who represented their goddess of love with coca leaves in her hand, did not doubt the stimulative effect of coca on the genitalia. Mantegazza confirms that the *coqueros* sustain a high degree of potency right into old age; he even reports cases of restoration of potency and the disappearance of functional weakness following the use of coca. . . . Among the persons to whom I have given coca, three reported violent sexual excitement which they unhesitatingly attributed to the coca.[34]

Explanations advanced for cocaine's sexual effects

Of all the drugs, cocaine has been most strongly identified with aphrodisiac qualities. This has historical precedence with coca's use as an aphrodisiac by some South American Indians. Cocaine can have paradoxical sexual effects. On the one hand, as a sensory stimulant, it increases the intensity of orgasm.[35] On the other hand, it can both inhibit and retard the climax, in both males and females.[36] Applied directly to the genital areas, it causes a "tingling" sensation (it is a local anesthetic) and a prolongation of the period of intercourse.[37]

> It should be added that because coke numbs all membranes, all sensation disappears when this is done and therefore the prolonged sex act is little more than an ego trip for the male.[38]

A historically interesting, incorrect, and very simplified explanation of cocaine's mechanism of action as an aphrodisiac was proferred in 1932 by Mutch. In this account, cocaine's action was described as "differential in effect. I mean that the highest centers may be depressed, whilst the lower ones are stimulated. For this reason it acts as an aphrodisiac."[39]

Animals, sex, and cocaine

Several early studies in part examined the effect of cocaine on sexual behavior in animals.

Tatum and Seevers observed that a female dog during the

> . . . latter part of the period of intoxication, one and one-half hours after injection . . . would encourage the approach of a male, standing peaceably during the copulative act. However, allow three hours to elapse after injection, recovery having occurred, or attempt to mate her during any other part of the day, she shows no ardor and will snarl and snap at the approach of the male.

The male dogs, without exception, exhibited priapism both prior to the injection and during the period of excitement following it.

> This does not occur, however, after the drug effects begin. [The males made] no attempt at copulation if placed with the female during the period of drug action.[40]

Downs and Eddy found no evidence of sexual excitement in five dogs used (two males, three females) in their experiments on the effects of repeated administration of cocaine.[41]

Cocaine vs. the amphetamines

According to several researchers, cocaine and the amphetamines (which have been studied far more extensively) have reputations as "sex drugs" based on their stimulative properties which increase the libidinal drive.[42] Based on a series of intensive interviews with fifty patients seen at the Haight-Ashbury Free Medical Clinic, Gay and Sheppard noted that similar effects were attributed to cocaine and the amphetamines.[43] Both augmented the sex drive, particularly when administered IV. Cocaine injections resulted in immediate erections for ten of the twenty males interviewed. Two of the males reported long painful episodes of priapism lasting over twenty-four hours! The primary difference reported between the two drugs was that cocaine, because of its great expense, was usually reserved specifically for sexual situations, while the amphetamines were used more generally.

Homosexuality

There has been some inference in the literature that the use of cocaine promotes homosexual activities.[44] Researchers found that "cocaine addiction" usually removed the inhibition in a bisexual man. With normally heterosexual men, they postulated that the "inversion" of homosexual acts was the result of loss of potency without a diminishing of the libido; and the craving for new sensations. Bell and Trethowan indicated that while cocaine increased the sexual drive, it could not be held responsible for any transference from heterosexual to homosexual activities[45] The type of sexual behavior displayed is strictly a function of pre-existing sexual adjustment of the individual prior to drug usage.

User expectations

It may be that some part of the aphrodisiac role attributed to cocaine results from the expectations of users who have heard that cocaine has strong sexual properties. As noted by Goode, this has likely been the case for marijuana.[46] While no physiological support has been found for the notion that marijuana is an aphrodisiac—in fact, there is some scientific evidence that the drug's action has just the opposite sexual effect—the majority of 200 respondents polled by Goode reported the use of marijuana to be sexually stimulating. Thus, if a user expects to be "turned on sexually" by cocaine, that may often be the case. One of the cocaine users we interviewed for this study said:

> Everybody says that it's an aphrodisiac. Again I think some people say it because it's supposed to be. . . . I think that it's just peer-group identification. I remember when I first started doing coke, I remember everybody would be sitting around saying "Oh, I just got to get laid." I said it a couple of times, but I never felt that way. I was more content to sit there and enjoy it.

In spite of some scientists' views that cocaine has no true aphrodisiac qualities,[47] cocaine's reputation as a sexual stimulant is still strong among users and nonusers alike.

REFERENCES

1. "The Growing Menace and Use of Cocaine," *The New York Times*, August 2, 1908.
2. *The Gourmet Cokebook: A complete guide to cocaine*, (New York: White Mountain Press, 1972; also published by D. C. Production Enterprises, New York).
3. Ibid.
4. Anonymous, "Photogenic properties of cocaine," *JAMA*, 1923, *80*, 640.
5. Hellman, L., *Pentimento*, (New York: Signet, 1974).
6. *The Gourmet Cokebook*, 1972, Op. Cit.
7. Burroughs, W. S., *Naked Lunch*, (New York: Grove Press, Inc., 1966).
8. Siegel, R. K., "Cocaine Smoking," *New Eng. Journal of Medicine*, 1979, *300(7)*, 373.
9. Noya, N. D., "Coca and cocaine: A perspective from Bolivia." In: R. C. Petersen (ed.), *The International Challenge of Drug Abuse*, Research Monograph Series 19, DHEW Publ. No. (ADM) 78-60498, (Rockville, Maryland: NIDA, 1978).
10. Gay, G. R. and Sheppard, C. W., "Sex-crazed dope fiends! Myth or reality?" In: E. Harms (ed.), *Drugs and youth: The challenge of today*, (New York: Pergamon Press, 1973).
11. Hopkins, J., "Cocaine: A Flash in the Pan, a Pain in the Nose," *Rolling Stone*, April 9, 1971, *81*, 1,6.
12. Lee, D., *Cocaine Consumer's Handbook*, (San Francisco: And/Or Press, 1976).
13. Castleman, M., "Snows Up the Nose: A History of Cocaine," *Ann Arbor Sun Community News Service*, 1975, *3(1)*, 13–15, 18.
14. Woods, J. H. and Downs, D. A., "The psychopharmacology of cocaine." In: *Drug use in America: Problem in perspective*, Appendix, Vol. I, (Washington D.C.: U.S. Government Printing Office, 1973), 116–139.
15. Dave Van Ronk's, "Cocaine," as quoted in Castleman, 1975, Op. Cit.
16. Von Hoffman, N., "High is How You Live It," *Washington Post*, April 21, 1975.
17. Woods and Downs, 1973, Op. Cit.
18. From a transcribed taped interview of Shielga Murphy in San Francisco (1975).
19. Ibid.
20. Siegel, R. K., "Recreational use and intoxication." In: R. C. Petersen and R. C. Stillman (eds.), *Cocaine: 1977*, Research Monograph Series No. 13, DHEW Publ. No. (ADM) 77–432, (Rockville, Maryland: NIDA, 1977), 119–136.

21. Grinspoon, L. and Bakalar, J. B., "Cocaine." In: R. Dupont, A. Goldstein and J. O'Donnell (eds.), *Handbook on Drug Abuse*, (Washington, D.C.: NIDA and Office of Drug Abuse Policy, 1979), 241–247.
22. Woods and Downs, 1973, Op. Cit.
23. Ibid.
24. Burroughs, 1966, Op. Cit.
25. Edmundson, W. F., Davies, J. E., Acher, J. D. and Meyer, B., "Patterns of drug abuse epidemiology in prisoners," *Industrial Med. Surg.*, 1972, *41*, 15–19.
26. Pickett, R. D., "Acute toxicity of heroin, alone and in combination with cocaine and quinine," *Brit. Journal of Pharmacol.*, 1970, *40*, 145–146.
27. Drug Enforcement Administration, Special Report, (# BH-003), (Washington, D.C.: DEA, 1974).
28. Data from the federal government's DAWN and CODAP information systems.
29. Eckerman, W. C., Bates, J. D., Rachel, J. V. and Poole, W. K., *Drug usage and arrest charges in six metropolitan areas of the United States*, prepared for the Bureau of Narcotics and Dangerous Drugs, contract No. J-30-35 (December, 1971).
30. Mortimer, W. G., *Peru history of coca, the divine plant of the Incas*, (New York: J. H. Vail and Company, 1901), reprinted as *History of Coca*, (San Francisco: And/Or Press, 1974).
31. Anonymous, "Methods used for improving athletic performance," *JAMA*, 1940, *115*, 1281.
32. Drug Enforcement Administration, 1974, Op. Cit.
33. Rosen, C., "The Great God Basketball Jones," *Crawdaddy*, 1974, 34–38.
34. Freud, S., "On coca," *Centra. Gesammte Ther.* (Wien), 1884, II, S, 289–314, reprinted in *The Cocaine Papers* (S. Edminster, tra.), (Vienna: DunQuin Press, 1963), also by R. Byck (ed.), *Cocaine Papers by Sigmund Freud* (New York. The Stonehill Publ. Co., 1974).
35. Gay, G. R., Sheppard, C. W., Inaba, D. and Newmeyer, J. A., "An old girl: Flyin' low, dyin' slow, blinded by snow: Cocaine in perspective," *Int. Journal of Addict.*, 1973(b), *8(6)*, 1027–1042.
36. Lee, 1976, Op. Cit.
37. Gay et al., 1973, Op. Cit.
38. Hopkins, 1971, Op. Cit.
39. This article was quoted in Woods and Downs, 1973, Op. Cit.
40. Tatum, A. L. and Seevers, M. H., "Experimental cocaine

addiction," *Journal Pharmacol. Exp. Ther.*, 1929, *36*, 401–410.

41. Downs, A. W. and Eddy, N. B., "The effect of repeated doses of cocaine on the dog," *Journal Pharmacol. Exp. Ther.*, 1932, *46*, 195–198.
42. Bell, D. S. and Trethowan, W., "Amphetamine addiction and disturbed sexuality," *Arch. Gen. Psychiatry*, 1961, *4*, 74–78.
43. Gay et al., 1973(a), Op. Cit.
44. Joel, E. and Frankel, F., "Cocainism and homosexuality," *Dtsch. Med. Wchnsr.*, 1925, *51*, 1562.
45. Bell and Trethowan, 1961, Op. Cit.
46. Goode, E., "Marijuana and Sex," *Evergreen Review*, 1969, *66*, 19–21.
47. As stated in, for instance, Gallant, D. M., "The effect of alcohol and drug abuse on sexual behavior," *Med. Aspects Human Sexuality*, 1968, 30–36.

CHAPTER 13

TRAFFICKING IN COCAINE: GETTING IT HERE

Officials of U.S. Customs and the Drug Enforcement Administration (DEA) report . . . that the traffic in cocaine—up more than 700 percent in the last five years—has reached "epidemic proportions." . . . One veteran DEA officer estimates that as many as 300 couriers daily, some carrying as much as several kilos of cocaine, slip into the country.

—N. M. Adams, "Cocaine Takes Over"

Of all the topics covered with our cocaine-using and cocaine-dealing interviewees, the subject of trafficking—how cocaine is brought into this country and distributed—generated the most consternation. The subject generally showed either outright fear or a suspicion that we were, after all, working in some capacity for the police or the "narcs." One series of interviews with a purported dealer had to be prearranged with a third party and conducted via public telephone. He was under indictment for selling nearly a kilogram (2.2 pounds) to an undercover agent, and we were eager to learn how such a large quantity was brought in. For obvious reasons, he was reluctant to discuss the topic with outsiders before his court appearance. We never did get his story, in fact. However, from our interviews and from the limited—and very recent—literature, we felt we obtained a good picture of current cocaine-dealing practices in this country.

The trafficking of cocaine consists of two very different sets of operations. The first involves procuring the drug, usually in Colombia or Peru, and smuggling it into the

United States. The second involves its local distribution. Often, two very different groups of people are responsible for these tasks.

Increasingly, however, the cocaine trade is seeing free-lance amateurs, who both smuggle and then distribute small amounts themselves. In this regard, the cocaine trade differs markedly from the heroin trade, which is highly stratified, with importers, backers, dealers, and users, a structure largely due to heroin's control by organized crime. With the exception of the Vietnam War era, when American servicemen had ready access to Asian heroin, there have been few reported cases of young Americans attempting to smuggle heroin into the States for their personal use and distribution.

An example of the workings of an unusually structured and formal cocaine operation was described by an agent of the Bureau of Narcotics and Dangerous Drugs (BNDD, the predecessor of DEA):

> There are two principal partners, one controlling operations in South and Central America and the other in Miami. The syndicate boss abroad, through a number of subordinates, buys coca leaves, sets up laboratories, maintains contact with local officials, arranges for payoffs, and recruits and dispatches local couriers with cocaine to the United States, mostly by plane.
>
> The Miami boss, like a head of a large commercial corporation, has deputies in charge of travel, transportation, personnel, security, accounting and quality control—"cutting" pure cocaine for wholesale and retail trade.[1]

Typically, however, there are two separate groups involved, and they are not formally linked. One group of people is involved in bringing cocaine into the United States, while a second group is involved in distributing the cocaine. In this chapter, we examine how it gets here.

THE SOUTH AMERICAN CONNECTION

In all likelihood the cocaine inhaled by a user anywhere in the United States had its beginning as bundled coca on the backs of llamas, being led out of the Andean highlands to "eagerly waiting brokers."[2] These brokers, with contacts in organized crime in the major Latin countries, process the leaf into *coca bruta*—a coca paste that is the product of the first extraction procedure (see Chapter 8 for a detailed account of the step-by-step extraction process). This crude cocaine paste (sulfate base) is usually sold in 2-kilogram lots for the equivalent of a few hundred dollars.[3] Because of the tremendous quantities needed to produce cocaine paste, the laboratories are usually located near the coca-growing fields or terraces (which are typically in either Bolivia or Peru).

According to one set of DEA figures, approximately 110 kilos of leaves are needed to produce 1 kilo of cocaine paste.[4] The conversion ratio from cocaine paste to the finished product, cocaine hydrochloride, is somewhat higher than 1:1.[5] One kilo of coca leaves yields 7 grams of cocaine paste (143:1 ratio); 100 grams of cocaine paste yield 81 grams of cocaine hydrochloride.

Considerable amounts of cocaine paste are smuggled from initial processing points in Bolivia into Brazil and Chile,[6] where it is refined at a more sophisticated laboratory into cocaine hydrochloride. After this second processing, it is packaged in "clear, thick plastic pouches" and is then ready for wholesale delivery and exportation.[7]

In Chile, particularly in and around Arica, there are many clandestine laboratories that convert the raw products into cocaine hydrochloride. Then, according to the DEA:

> After refining, the drug is shipped south to consumption and distribution centers such as Santiago, Concepcion, Valparaiso . . . only a small part of the illicit production goes to Chilean addicts; traffickers prefer the external market, particularly Europe and the United States, where higher profits can be obtained.[8]

A considerable amount of paste is produced in Peru as well. Large amounts of this paste are smuggled out of Peru into Ecuador for conversion into refined cocaine. The refined product is then shipped to the United States via Colombia.

According to the Drug Enforcement Administration, there are several routes by which cocaine enters the United States:

- One route originates in Peru, then travels through Ecuador, Panama, then Mexico, from which it enters the

United States via air, land, or sea. Texas port cities such as Houston and Galveston are the destination.

- A second route starts in Chile and extends through other Latin American countries to various ports on the U.S. Pacific Coast, probably most often in California.
- A third route starts in Bolivia and proceeds to the West Indies and then the United States, with Miami and New York City being the major ports of entry.

The profits along this cocaine trail are extraordinary:

- A South American farmer makes $2 a kilo for his coca leaves or $350 for a kilo of paste (and the price for a kilo of paste can be as high as $1,000, according to Sabbag[9]).
- Delivered in South America, a kilo of cocaine that is 90–98% pure will cost anywhere from $4,000 to $8,500. "A dealer with a mobile lab can turn $350 raw material investment into a $6,000 product. A good lab can process one hundred pounds of cocaine a week."[10]
- In New York, in 1976, a kilo of cocaine sold for over $30,000. However, that is for a relatively pure product. It is usually "hit" with an adulterant, and the 1 kilo becomes 2, worth $30,000 each. Thus the smuggler parlays a $6,000 investment into $60,000.[11] Cocaine prices, along with everything else, have gone up since Sabbag wrote his book, but the multiplier effect seems to be about the same.

Inflation in cocaine prices has been rapid in the past few years in both foreign and domestic cities. Fooner quotes 1973 prices of cocaine as $1,600 to $1,800 a pound (or $3,500 to $4,000 a kilo) in Bogota and Guayaquil, Ecuador, and about $650 a pound (or $1,300 a kilo) when delivered to a wholesaler.[12] Two years earlier, in 1971, *The New York Times* reported that a kilo sold for about $900 in Chile.[13]

Recent information indicates the early 1978 price for quality cocaine in Bogota to be $12,000 to $15,000 per kilo,[14] while a reported $16,000 was paid over two years earlier in Mexico City for a "short" (underweight) kilo of mediocre cocaine.[15]

The literature on cocaine dealing in South America has been sparse. The gap has been well filled, however, with the recent publication of Robert Sabbag's entertaining book *Snow Blind: A Brief Career in the Cocaine Trade,* which recounts the exploits of a cocaine smuggler, one Zachary Swan. The book covers the mechanics of making a South American connection and initiating and consummating a cocaine purchase, as well as the details of a variety of smuggling techniques. For instance, on making cocaine connections:

> Connections in the cocaine trade are made very much as they are made in the legitimate business world. The difference is one of direction rather than degree. Where a legitimate businessman makes money selling his customers to a wholesaler—by way of a mailing list, for example—a cocaine smuggler makes money selling the wholesaler to the potential customer.[16]

In many ways, Swan's efforts in establishing a cocaine connection followed a pattern encountered by many small-time smugglers, according to our interviewees. Although he left for South America with the names of a couple of individuals who were supposed to help him—one eventually did—his initial purchase was arranged through a contact he established on his own shortly after arriving in Santa Marta, Colombia. In this case his newfound friend, Blackie, made money for putting Swan in contact with a cocaine connection. It is in this manner that the drug-buying cycle is most often perpetuated: would-be buyers are put in touch, via a middleman, with sellers, often for a price. It is also how many young Americans end up in jail, broke, or in even worse predicaments. In many cases, the friendly "hip local" with the drug connection also has police connections. Swan is fortunate, however. Blackie is not a police informer and Swan's cocaine connection is complete. Later, Swan would be arrested for cocaine trafficking, but it would be under different circumstances.

The book illuminates some other pitfalls in establishing a South American connection:

- Rip-offs—One individual Swan meets wants $1,000 down before consummating an $8,000 kilo deal. It turns out that this dealer has a reputation for disappearing after taking the money.
- Poor knowledge of cocaine—Early in his career, Swan

mistakenly concludes that 10 grams of cocaine he has purchased are of poor quality, because the cocaine failed to give him a "speed rush." He doesn't buy that kilo, instead getting one that produces a more instant reaction. It turns out that the initial cocaine was of excellent quality, while the one he ultimately bought was, by South American standards, of poor, heavily diluted quality.

CONTROL OVER THE MARKET

Over the last ten years there has been a realignment of the cocaine smuggling setup, in particular, a shift from the traffic center. According to Fooner:

> In the 1950s Miami became the center because it was easy for Spanish-speaking smugglers to use the Cuban community as a cover. Miami-based Cuban traffickers serviced New York and other markets around the country. Now the center seems to have shifted to New York, with Colombian smugglers in the ascendancy.[17]

Most narcotics experts attribute the growth in cocaine traffic to the activities of some of the Cuban exiles, who brought both the "habit and traffickers with them."[18] The Cuban involvement in cocaine is an old one. When he was commissioner of narcotics, Anslinger said that "ninety per cent of all illegal cocaine is taken in Cuba."[19]

Because of cocaine's growing popularity (and increasing profits), Latin and South American nationals have become interested in the "cocaine connection." According to federal experts the Chileans, possessing a source of cocaine in their mountains, moved into the trade about 1971. Two years later, apparently, the Chilean dealers stopped selling cocaine "directly to U.S. recipients and started working through Colombian criminal groups, using Colombian rather than Chilean couriers."[20]

The impact of the cocaine trade has been especially great in Colombia and Bolivia. Although the lion's share of the illicit cocaine profits goes to North America, enough is left over to have a significant impact on the economies and politics of these relatively poor countries. Cocaine smuggling from Colombia, for instance, with the United States the main destination, has become so important that it rivals coffee as the country's largest export, law-enforcement officials say. Some estimates put the 1977 value of drug smuggling out of Colombia at $1.5 billion, equal to the coffee earnings. Some economists believe the record 29% inflation during 1977 in Colombia was due as much to the influx of drug money as to the skyrocketing coffee prices.[21] And there have been widespread effects.

It has been charged, for instance, that cocaine money influenced the 1978 Colombian campaign for Parliament, in which votes were allegedly bought for $10 apiece, especially in the Atlantic Coast smuggling areas. A variety of production-control efforts instituted in both countries have failed, for a number of reasons, including purported official corruption. It has proved virtually impossible to control coca-leaf collection in either Peru or Bolivia, the major growing regions, and thus channel production toward the legitimate market. Bolivian authorities estimate that 80% of the 30,000 to 35,000 metric tons of coca leaves produced in that country each year go to the illicit market. Further, a Colombian police official estimated that of every ten ships leaving the harbor in Cartegena, the country's major port, nine leave with some cocaine on board. "We cannot even think in terms of stopping the trade," a pessimistic Colombia official said, "but we can keep the pressure up in the hope that the price will stay high and fewer people can get it."[22]

However, the cocaine trade is not the prerogative of any one organized crime syndicate, unlike the situation that has traditionally characterized the heroin network. Plate quoted Captain Aaron Rosenthal of the New York City Police Department's Narcotic Division:

> You can't go into heroin yourself. Were you to go to Marseilles, where heroin is refined and shipped out, you'd wind up in one of three states. First, dead. Second, ripped off. Third, with a batch of communion wafers and no money. But my feeling is that if you went to Colombia you could make a buy even without a prior connection.[23]

With cocaine, Rosenthal went on to say, "we now see for the first time the emergence of major drug entrepreneurs who would appear to have no formal status in the criminal community." Latin American jails and prisons are filled with young American entrepreneurs who (quite successfully) sought their fortune in cocaine.

By all accounts—and we interviewed two individuals who spent time in a Colombian prison—the experience in Latin American prisons is frightful. In Mexico alone, over 125 U.S. citizens were arrested in 1974 on smuggling charges. Almost all of these were cocaine-related, and the sentence for those found guilty was a mandatory six years.[24] As of early 1978, there were thirty-nine Americans in Colombian jails, mostly on cocaine-dealing changes.[25]

The final monopolistic control of the cocaine trade has not been resolved. It may never be. But, as Ianni suggested in his book *Black Mafia*, the new route of drugs from South America should have an important impact on the American drug scene:

> The most important effect will be continued displacement of Italian-American syndicates from the international drug traffic as this new section replaces the older one which came through Europe. The street implications are enormous. It not only means that new patterns of wholesaling will be established, changing the ethnic balance of power in organized crime. It also means that cocaine may very well displace heroin as the "street drug."[26]

A short history of cocaine trafficking

Jerry Strickler, at one time chief of the Latin American Section, International Operations Division of the Drug Enforcement Administration, and currently deputy chief of operations for Europe and the Far East, Operations Division, has long been considered one of the leading experts on cocaine trafficking. He provided us some insights into the involvement of various South American nations in the smuggling of cocaine into the United States. In an excellent article about cocaine smugglers and their techniques, Plate presents a lengthy interview with Mr. Strickler that amplifies some of these points.[27]

Until the middle 1960s, according to Mr. Strickler, Cubans served as intermediaries between the Latin American supply sources and the U.S. dealers. In the early 1970s, however, Chilean criminals first surfaced as couriers to the

States. These Chileans had extensive records, often with involvement in both the heroin and cocaine trades. Within a very few years, there was a marked decrease in the number of Chileans apprehended and an increase in the number of Colombians being arrested as couriers. These Colombians also had criminal records, but often for such relatively minor offenses as picking pockets. The DEA conclusion, according to Mr. Strickler, was that the Chileans were "layering" themselves, selling the drugs to the Colombians rather than continuing themselves to be the direct importers.

More recently, there is evidence that at least some of the Colombians who had been serving as importers (couriers, or mules) have gained contact with the clandestine cocaine laboratories and are now running their own couriers and handling all aspects of the shipments from the source to the American dealers.

Cocaine trafficking, then, is very dynamic, with relative positions in the chain from production to dealing subject to fairly rapid change.

COCAINE COURIERS—THE "MULES"

> A smuggling courier tries to get from South America to Miami by way of Australia, but is caught in Hawaii.
>
> Two Columbian couriers, bound for New York, detour through Hamburg, Germany.
>
> Other couriers leapfrog through the Caribbean Islands on their way to the states.
>
> Still others fly from South America to Vancouver or Montreal and enter the states from the North.[28]

They are referred to as "mules," their tactic is evasion, and their cargo is cocaine. Their intricate routing patterns are devised to mask the telltale origin point, which is usually Colombia.

According to a federal intelligence report, a cocaine ring operating out of Santiago, Chile, reportedly used up to forty couriers at one time, each courier responsible for bringing in 2.5 kilos of cocaine.[29]

The courier system operates on the principle that there is less risk involved if large numbers of people carry relatively small amounts of cocaine. These South American couriers tend to be "simple folk—housewives, cab drivers, pickpockets, day laborers."[30]

There is no identifiable "type" of courier. In the past (pre-1970), Latin American women were often used, pretending to be pregnant as a cover for the cocaine that was bound to their stomachs. With increasing surveillance and apprehension of these "modest women" couriers, the smugglers began assuming the guise of "businessmen and tourists." A more recent trend has been the recruiting and use of "young United States girls and students who are usually offered $1,000 plus an airline ticket for bringing back several packages of cocaine."[31]

Apparently, the courier system has been so successful that many of the couriers have started their own small cocaine smuggling operations. The entire structure of the smuggling operation, therefore, is characterized by a lack of centralized organization.

Zachary Swan, Sabbag's smuggler, gives several elaborate examples of the use of couriers. Careful precautions were taken to ensure that the courier, if apprehended, could walk away free. A relatively unsophisticated example of Swan's many smuggling scams involves two identical suitcases. If a custom's inspector discovers cocaine in a woman's suitcase, she simply denies ownership. After all, the clothes are the wrong size, and there on the luggage rack is her *real* suitcase, identical and containing both her clothes and identification. This fools no one, but in a court of law where rules of evidence apply, the woman cannot be convicted.

Conversations with a courier who was apprehended at the Bogotá airport and served two years of a six-year sentence revealed the following generalities about "mules":

- The average amount smuggled was over 1 kilo. However, one woman, a Las Vegas dancer, was apprehended with over 10 kilos in her suitcase.
- Smuggling techniques were often simple, even primitive. Sometimes they consisted of nothing more elaborate than hiding cocaine on the body or in a suitcase.
- With the exception of our interviewee, all other American women arrested for serving as mules (and they numbered over twenty during the time she was imprisoned) had successfully smuggled cocaine out of

Colombia at least once before. One woman was arrested with 2 kilos in her possession on her thirteenth trip out.

- None of the twenty women imprisoned in Colombia had any ties to organized crime. Most, in fact, were genuine free lancers.
- All couriers were booked on scheduled airlines and planned to make a legitimate reentry to the States.

SMUGGLING TECHNIQUES

Throughout cocaine's long history of illicit use, smugglers have never lacked for ingenuity in devising smuggling schemes. For example, the June 21, 1925, *New York Times* reported on the use of carrier pigeons to smuggle cocaine "into Great Britain from the Continent." A February 2, 1930, *New York Times* article provided greater detail on the "Rio Grande Pigeon Connection." Apparently during this period many animals (dogs, donkeys, and even cattle) were utilized as "dumb smugglers" of narcotics and cocaine. The smuggling mission cost them their lives, as they were killed upon arrival at their destination to permit extraction of the large quantities of drugs "fed to the animal in a large metal capsule." Though carrier pigeons carried less (the amount was said to be "$5 to $10 worth of cocaine"), they could be used many times, and were almost impossible to stop. Preventive action in this case consisted of watching the border for shipments of pigeons from Texas to Mexico, and registering all pigeon sales.

An unknown quantity of cocaine is smuggled through U.S. border checkpoints—both Mexican and Canadian. Some is carried in by South American seamen who jump ship in New York and other American ports of entry. There are increasing reports of private airplanes and pleasure boats being used to smuggle the cocaine into this country.[32]

The methods for concealing the cocaine from customs officials are often ingenious, sometimes clumsy, and in more than a few cases fatal. It must be stressed that *none* of the following are unique. Both DEA agents and U.S. Customs inspectors are familiar with *all* of the following techniques here as well:

- Hiding the drug in a baby's "personal" clothing. One of our sources told a story of how five pounds of cocaine were allegedly slipped in with a baby's diaper supply.

- Tied to a baby. Two of our sources indicated personal knowledge of the success of this method.
- Hiding it in children's toys, or regional gifts such as South American Indian dolls.
- Hiding in on the body. This method ranges from simple concealment in a pocket, purse, etc. to use of an elaborate vest consisting of a series of small pouches, each filled with cocaine. A DEA official showed us a photograph of such a vest. It consisted of twenty-six individual compartments, each of which held plastic bags of approximately 31 grams of cocaine—the total amount seized in this case was 829.11 grams. The smuggler even had his initials neatly stitched on this vest!

A method perfected by Zachary Swan—referred to as "Swan's Mail Moves"—consists of reducing the bulk of the cocaine by half by squeezing it in a printing press, placing the pressed cocaine in carved-out wooden Colombian souvenirs, and mailing them to the States.[33]

The International Criminal and Police Review noted that the more flat-chested women are particularily well suited to smuggling, they can wear special brassieres containing the drug."[34]

Another popular technique is "heavy seaming used to decorate the shoulders of men's jackets removed and replaced by bags of cocaine."[35] Changes in men's styles have resulted in less frequent use of this method, however. Another change in fashion has resulted in yet a new hiding place for cocaine. They are in the big soles and chunky heels of the currently fashionable shoes.[36]

"Funny" walk reveals cocaine smuggler

Customs agents in Miami noticed something "*funny*" in the way a man walked upon his arrival from a flight originating in Peru. The agents asked the 26 year old American male to remove his shoes and socks. One half pound of cocaine was found taped to his soles. (*Washington Star-News*, March 31, 1975)

Many of our contacts mentioned that the safest and easiest way to get cocaine into this country is to pack it in rubber containers and then swallow it. Easy it may be, safe it definitely is not!

> The temptation of such profits [from the sale of cocaine] apparently caused the death of two young Americans in a La Paz hotel in December when a technique for smuggling cocaine proved fatal. The youths swallowed sizable quantities of cocaine packed in rubber contraceptives several hours before boarding a flight for New York, hoping to pass it through the digestive system. But the containers broke, apparently from the effect of the gastric juices, and both died from cocaine intoxication.[37]

The *Washington Star-News* reported on the death of a twenty-six-year-old Texan who attempted the same smuggling technique. In this case the man "swallowed 10 small plastic bags containing about 12 ounces of cocaine. . . . [the] stomach acids dissolved the plastic on the flight from La Paz to Lima . . . and the heavy dose of drugs sent him into convulsions aboard the jet and in the airport.[38] Attempting this method, a DEA official warned, "is worse than playing Russian roulette with your life."

There are still other approaches. In 1974, customs officials in Miami arrested a seventy-four-year-old woman who had brought over three quarters of a pound of cocaine in a hundred small plastic tubes woven into a wool rug.[39] The same month, agents broke up an operation based in Seattle, Washington, in which the smugglers brought cocaine into the United States in hollowed-out water skis.[40]

A recent smuggling case demonstrated a practical understanding of cocaine's chemical properties, particularly its solubility in water and/or alcohol. A twenty-five-year-old artist was arrested while attempting to smuggle an estimated half-pound of cocaine in a 6-quart wine jug.[41] And, more recently, the man who earlier had played Timmy on the TV series *Lassie* was convicted of smuggling a liquid suspension of cocaine into the States from Peru, in a liqueur bottle.

A sampling of the "Cocaine Confidential" column in 1976–77 issues of *High Times* magazine reveals even more ingenious techniques:

- Concealed in an airplane engine sent to the States for repairs (October 1976)
- In hollowed-out wooden coat hangers (November 1976)
- In a cage containing a live dog (November 1976)
- In the middle of LP records which had been sliced in half, spread with cocaine, and put back together again (December 1976)
- Mixed into cans of lard (January 1977)

REFERENCES

1. Volsky, G., "Illicit Traffic of Cocaine, Growing by Leaps and Bounds in Miami," *The New York Times*, February 1, 1970.
2. Plate, T., "Cocaine: New Jackpot for a New Mafia," *Qui*, August, 1974, 38.
3. Ibid.
4. "Drug Traffic in South America," (Washington, D.C.: Bureau of Narcotics and Dangerous Drugs, 1970).
5. Drug Enforcement Administration, "Report of the Cocaine Policy Task Force," (unpublished), (Washington, D.C.: DEA, July, 1974).
6. "Drug Traffic in South America," 1970, Op. Cit.
7. Plate, 1974, Op. Cit.
8. "Drug Traffic in South America," 1970, Op. Cit.
9. Sabbag, R., *Snowblind: A Brief Career in the Cocaine Trade*, (New York: Bobbs-Merrill, 1976; reprinted by Avon Books, New York, 1978).
10. Ibid.
11. Ibid.
12. Fooner, M., "Cocaine: The South American Connection," *World*, 1973, *2*(5), 22–25.
13. "U.S. Agents Try, But Fail, to Stop the Flow of Cocaine from Latin Countries," *The New York Times*, January 25, 1971.
14. Chardy, A., "Columbia to Attack Traffic in Cocaine," *The Washington Post*, March 11, 1978, A20.
15. Waldorf, D., Murphy, S., Reinarman, C., and Joyce, B., *Doing Coke: Ethnography of Cocaine Users and Dealers*, (Washington, D.C.: Drug Abuse Council, 1977).
16. Sabbag, 1976, Op. Cit.
17. Fooner, 1973, Op. Cit.
18. Ottenberg, M., "Cocaine: The New No. 1. Drug," *Washington Star-News*, August 5, 1974(a), A1, A6.

19. Kober, B., "Cuba Called Leading Illicit Cocaine User," *Baltimore News Post*, June 9, 1961, A4.
20. Ottenberg, 1974(a), Op. Cit.
21. Chardy, A., 1978, Op. Cit.
22. Vidal, D., "Colombia is Still the Chief Generator of Cocaine Traffic, The U.S. is Both Chief Consumer and Principal Worrier," *The New York Times*, March 19, 1978, 2.
23. Plate, T., "Coke, The Big New Easy-Entry Business," *The New York Times Magazine*, October, 1973, 63–75.
24. Adams, W. M., "Cocaine Takes Over," *Reader's Digest*, 1975, 83–87.
25. Chardy, A., 1978, Op. Cit.
26. Ianni, F. A., *Black Mafia: Ethnic Succession in Organized Crime*, (New York: Simon and Schuster, 1974).
27. Plate, 1974, Op. Cit.
28. Ottenberg, M., "Cocaine 'Mules'—Sophisticated Smugglers," *Washington Star-News*, August 6, 1974(b), A3.
29. Plate, 1973, Op. Cit.
30. Ibid.
31. Volsky, 1970, Op. Cit.
32. Fooner, 1973, Op. Cit.
33. Sabbag, 1976, Op. Cit.
34. "Cocaine—Illicit Manufacture and Traffic," *Intl. Crim. Pol. Review*, 1969, 227, 97–102.
35. Ibid.
36. Fooner, 1973, Op. Cit.
37. De Onis, J., "Cocaine a Way of Life for Many in Bolivia," *The New York Times*, February 22, 1972, 22.
38. "Drug Scheme Fatal to Texan," *Washington Star-News*, August 21, 1974, 2.
39. "Drugs in Rug Bring Arrest of 74 Year-Old," *Washington Star-News*, August 8, 1974.
40. "Cocaine Smuggled in Water Skis," *Washington Post*, August 26, 1974.
41. "Agents Say Artist Smuggled Cocaine in 6 Quart Wine Jug," *The New York Times*, February 12, 1975.

CHAPTER 14

THE DOMESTIC NETWORK AND THE CONSEQUENCES OF TRAFFICKING

In New York City, for example, 50 per cent of the upper echelon cocaine dealers arrested by Drug Enforcement Administration agents were Colombians. And between 50 and 75 per cent of the cocaine seized can be traced to Colombia sources of supply.

—M. Ottenberg, "Cocaine: The New No. 1 Drug."

In this chapter, we examine the "who" and the "how" of domestic cocaine distribution and provide an overview of law-enforcement activities—both domestic and international—aimed at the cocaine trade.

DEALERS AND DEALING: A QUASI-FICTIONAL ACCOUNT BY WOODLEY (1971)

To the best of our knowledge, the only formal study yet published on cocaine dealers—who they are and how they do it—is the 1977 Waldorf et al. monograph on the distribution of a kilo of cocaine through a West Coast network (which is discussed later in this chapter).[1] Another and very interesting view of cocaine dealing is provided in a quasi-fictional book, *Dealer—Portrait of a Cocaine Merchant*, by R. Woodley, an account of a black cocaine dealer at work in New York City.[2]

Woodley's hero is Jimmy, apparently a middle-level cocaine dealer (dealing in grams and ounces rather than pounds) who buys his cocaine from an individual higher

First law of cocaine dealing

The purity of cocaine is usually inversely proportional to the distance (and number of dealers) between the importer and the small-time (1 gram or less) user.[3] By purchasing larger amounts (pounds and more), the dealer not only gets a better price, but obtains better-quality cocaine. It also means that the dealer does business with fewer and more responsible people. Jimmy explains how one moves up the ladder in the cocaine-dealing network:

> What happens is that if you been doing it long enough [dealing cocaine] and you sound reliable enough—cause people get checked out, you get to hear things and whatnot—you get to know the dudes involved. You feel your way, and eventually—well, in my case he finally said to bring me by, he'd like to meet me. So he cut me into him directly. So now this dude that I used to buy from, for a while he and I were on the same level, buying from the same man. Now he's still where he was and occasionally when he can't get in touch with that man he comes to me for product, so actually I have moved above him.
>
> You see, the whole thing is getting yourself in a position to cop big. Now, I got three or four levels of guys between me and the street, for safety. Trying to get further away from it, the further the better. And the guy below me, he has to want to be a small me. . . . And as I move up it creates a void that he can fill, if he's got the ambition, if he really wants the cash, and unless he takes a fall. It's a constant struggle, you know, until you get there. The trouble is, you get to a level and something goes wrong and you go tooosh, and you got to start all over again. But once you get there—aaaaah!

up in the cocaine network. "I stopped by to cop [buy] today, and my man's got eleven keys [kilograms] lined up. I've seen him with sixteen keys. And he's not the biggest there is." Various parts of a kilogram (2.2 pounds) of cocaine have names, "eights," "quarters," "halves," up to whole "keys" of cocaine, which in New York, according to Woodley, cost anywhere from $14,000 to $20,000 (and more recently, over $30,000[4]). As the dealer rises up the ladder of underworld drug connections, he buys larger and larger amounts.

Jimmy sells cocaine in a number of different quantities, each with a specific name. The smallest units of adulterated "cut" cocaine he sells are $10 and $20 "caps." A $20 capsule is enough cocaine for a "three and three" up to a "six and six" depending on the snort. In Woodley's terminology, a "three and three" refers to three lines of cocaine for each nostril. (This terminology is either unique to the group of people about whom Woodley wrote or is now out of fashion. We neither have read about or heard anyone else referring to "lines" or "rails" as "two and two," "three and three," etc.) Jimmy also sells a "tablespoon" amount, called a "quarter." Four quarters compose a "piece," which is approximately one ounce.

Jimmy keeps his cocaine, other drugs, his cutting agents, and guns at his "stash," which is the heart of his operation. It is kept seperate from his normal living quarters. In Jimmy's case it is located in a "white, respectable, high-priced neighborhood where cops don't go bustin' down the door because they feel like it." Jimmy generally keeps his records in his head, on slips of paper and in a pocket notebook. Only first names are listed, with dollar figures beside each name indicating the amount owed him. He has a strong arm assistant to "collect" on delinquent accounts.

DEALERS AND DEALING: EMPIRICAL DATA

The following discussion owes much to the help provided by Dan Waldorf and Sheigla Murphy of San Francisco, who have examined all aspects of a small West Coast cocaine-distribution network. Waldorf and Murphy very kindly put us in touch with a number of San Francisco Bay area cocaine dealers and users whom we were able to interview at some length. The two researchers also provided us with considerable information from their own extensive knowledge of the illicit drug scene.[5]

From these interviews we developed the following picture of the distribution pattern for a kilogram of cocaine purchased in Mexico:

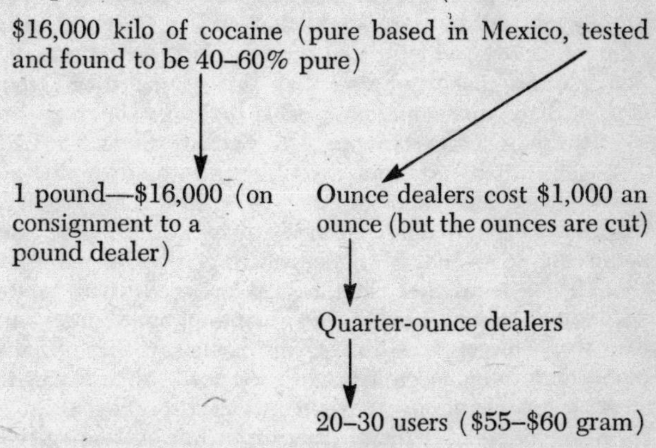

The West Coast dealers and users we interviewed indicated that in their experience the cocaine operation was controlled by young (late 20s, early 30s) white males. The quantities dealt in, typical prices, and degree of purity were (in 1975) in the one "deal" described previously:

- Keys—kilograms of cocaine in Mexico, tested out to be roughly 40% to 60% pure
- Pounds—$16,000, not cut with any adulterants
- Ounces—$1,000. Most of the ounces sold were cut with two grams of mannite. Some of the ounce dealers then cut the cocaine even more, but as one interviewee told us, "not all these dealers cut it . . . not because they were altruistic . . . [but] it just couldn't stand the cut."
- Grams—$55–$60. These were bought from the ounce dealers. Depending on the individual dealer, these could be cut further with an adulterant.

The cocaine "deal" described in detail in the Waldorf et al. study is useful for the firsthand information it sheds on cocaine dealing. Based on the Waldorf study and our own personal observations and conversations with dealers, we arrived at several conclusions concerning cocaine-dealing practices:

1. Smuggling efforts are often ineptly planned and executed. Apparently, in most cases no contingency plans are developed to deal with the situations when initial plans go awry—which often happens. Conversations with dealers/smugglers indicate that this seems to be more typical of cocaine-smuggling deals than the elaborate precautionary schemes practiced by Zachary Swan.[6]

2. "Fronting"—the practice of getting the drug first and paying the seller later, similar to establishing credit in legitimate commercial businesses—is an accepted procedure only at the middle level of cocaine dealing. Although the "smuggler" in the Waldorf study was fronted a kilo of cocaine by his Mexican contact, our sources indicate that purchases on that level, particularly if they take place in a foreign country, are paid for with cash on the spot. More common, according to our sources, is to be fronted "ounces," "three-quarters," "halves," and especially quarter ounces. Grams or less are never fronted.

3. Waldorf et al. describe a five-level cocaine-dealing hierarchy:

- Smugglers, who buy in largest quantities and also deal in bulk
- Ounce dealers, who deal in half pounds, sometimes "moving" pounds, but generally restricted to ounces
- Gram dealers, who buy ounces, and sell in half ounces, quarter ounces, and grams. To maximize their profits they often further adulterate the quality of the cocaine.
- "Stash" dealers, the most common dealers on the drug scene, who typically sell small amounts—grams or less—to minimize the cost of keeping their personal supply of cocaine. Often, like gram dealers, they will buy quarter or half ounces and sell the grams to their friends. Sales at this level are characteristically low-key, friendly transactions. There is no big sales hype and dilution of the cocaine is minimal.

- Middleman. This role from time to time is played by most members of the drug scene. The middleman utilizes his knowledge of a cocaine source to get either cocaine or cash. The situation arises when an individual is approached by a friend seeking cocaine. The middleman has two options—he can either introduce the potential buyer to the seller or act as the go-between, purchasing the cocaine with the buyer's money. Often, depending on the relationship, the middleman will either charge a small fee or accept some cocaine for the favor. Waldorf et al. quote a middleman describing his role in cocaine dealing:

  > Well, I always call it that [middleman] because I don't have the funds to lay out for a large sale, a large amount of dope. It's somebody I know has access to it or has the things [drugs] somebody else wants. You know, well, I'll bring them together, or if they don't want to be brought together I'll do the trip, buy the drugs and pass it on. I get in a lot of these middleman trips because, like, people trust me. . . . I don't deal with people I don't know. It's usually like there's a friendship between us and I know that . . . the chances of being burnt or busted are very slim. . . .

Zachary Swan himself acted as a middleman in a cocaine transaction involving Rene, a buyer, and Armando, a seller:

> . . . Swan introduced Rene to Armando, who, under instruction from Swan, charged Rene six dollars for coke offered at five and half (price per gram for quantity purchases). The $500 average kilo went to Swan and until Armando and Rene became friends or mutually trusted business associates, and the price was altered, Swan would collect $1,500 on every kilo Armando sold Rene. It was an understood and accepted business practice. . . .[7]

4. Our observations concur with the Waldorf et al. findings that drug dealing at the lower end of the distribution network is seldom a full-time occupation. At that end of the cocaine-dealing spectrum cocaine sales are not seen as a means to make money but rather as a way to ob-

tain and use cocaine, otherwise unaffordable. In fact, a majority of the individual users in the Waldorf et al. group expressed a strong dislike of becoming either a big-time or full-time cocaine dealer. Somewhat surprisingly, the reason most gave for not wanting to become a big-time dealer was that they felt cocaine was too high-priced, and they didn't want to participate in "ripping off" their friends.

5. Lastly, Waldorf et al.'s study reveals that prices charged for cocaine followed, in many ways, normal business practices. That is, they were contingent on prevailing market prices, the price paid for cocaine, the quality, the buyer-seller relationship, and the length of time the seller had the drug, and how much he had used.

Prices for cocaine, by all accounts—from users, PharmChem statistics, DEA statistics–have gone up over the past few years. According to Ashley, in 1971, a pure "gram" of Bolivian flake, the best illicit cocaine available, "could be had for from $40–$50. . . . A quarter ounce (7 grams) went for $200–225; and an ounce brought $600–$700."[8] A look at the prices reported in the 1975 *PharmChem Newsletter* reveals price increases across the board: up to $100 for a gram, $425 for one quarter of an ounce, and ounces ranging between $1,100 to $2,000. The majority of the ounce prices were $1,500 and up.[9] As indicated earlier, mid-1979 prices range up to $150 a gram.

We include the following letter, dated July 18, 1974, in its entirety. From follow-up calls we made to other sources in the Boston area, the prices the letter writer quotes seem accurate. We, of course, had no way to substantiate the veracity of the information contained in the letter. But as the writer says, "Why should I lie"?

> Cocaine stories? Here's some of my basically limited experience with the good C. I've never bought any, but one of my close friends at a large university in Boston this school year was a gram/¼ ounce dealer and knew several pound-plus dealers. One other guy dealt on occasion, also on the same intermediate level. Based on my association with them, I at least know something about the Boston scene. I'll call my friend Tom and the other person Jack.

Tom could get two kinds of C, white flake and brown Bolivian rock. He'd sell the white flake for $60/gram, $285/¼ ounce and the brown rock for $75/gram and $350/¼ ounce. The white flake would be about 60%–70% pure and the brown rock 80%–90%, so it was probably better to buy the higher grade. The flake came in almost 100% pure, but Tom would cut it with crushed aspirin to 50%–60%, and the rock he sold unadulterated. (He took pride in selling fine rock.) As a chemistry major, he was able to conduct spectroscopic analysis to determine purity. His cost per ¼ ounce was $225 and $275 for flake and rock respectively and per ounce was $700 and $800 respectively. His supplier was a friend, also a chem. major, who started out rich and handled so much that he'd give free lines to almost anyone present at a small gathering. Meeting ships in Boston Harbor, his cost was $5,000/lb. for flake, $5500 for rock, as I recall hearing once. On the docks is also a good place to pick up good hash cheap. I saw this guy dickering with another dealer over a ½ lb. of flake and let him have it for $3000. My friend Tom cut this ½ lb. into ounces and picked up two grams gratis for his head, which six of us did later that night.

The first time I did C was last November when Jack was dealing grams of same description. I did two lines up each nostril and only got my head numbed. I did the same thing two days later and did I get high. By high on C, I mean feeling extremely self-confident with a self-satisfied smile on the face and increased powers of concentration, without feeling physically wasted. If one does too much, you can feel overkeyed, taut, nervously hypered. I've never pointed it, but people I've talked to who have say it's the closest thing to pure uncaring bliss they can imagine, but there is a physical aftereffect of feeling ragged-out (as in a burned-out nervous system?) By the last line of those aforementioned two grams, I was feeling overkeyed, but only at the very end and soon mellowed out into a pleasant high for an hour and a half. I've only done C about fifteen times, all for free, because at prevailing prices, it's too expensive for such a relatively brief high, at least for working-class heroes, like myself. Dealing and doing coke is a game for rich college kids. You get to meet other people in your peer group and your friendship is cemented through common defiance of the all-embracing "man." One thing I've noticed—almost all dealers I know are counted by society as bright, promising young scholars "above" drugs. What is more important, the perception or the reality? Hope I've helped, all of the above is God's own truth. Why should I lie?

FORMS IN WHICH ILLICIT COCAINE IS AVAILABLE

The potential buyer of cocaine, whether on the retail or wholesale level, is confronted by several forms of cocaine, in which the texture, physical state, and color differ. Illicit cocaine comes in three forms: rock, flake, and powder. When *The Gourmet Cokebook* came out in 1972, the situation was that:

> The rock is more readily available, while the flake is considered a delicacy for connoisseurs of cocaine. The powder is actually dilute.[10]

Today, the powdered form is the only one the majority of cocaine users ever see, the other two forms representing purer and thus more costly cocaine. However, these forms are also available. In fact, powdered cocaine can be, and often is, reconstituted into flake or rock form. A discussion of this process can be found in the next chapter.

The flake state is the 99–100% pure pharmaceutical-quality form of the drug. In the flake state, cocaine resembles small snow crystals and has a shiny, almost transparent appearance. "Rock" cocaine consists of irregularly shaped small rocks. It also has a shiny, transparent look, but is not considered as pure as flake cocaine. Once adulterants or cuts are added, the cocaine becomes less shiny.

Advertising purity

There are some interesting differences in the ways in which cocaine dealers advertise the quality of their "product." Throughout Woodley's book, Jimmy mentions the number of "cuts" that can be administered to the cocaine in which he deals:

> But when I'm milling up, I always put in a little extra [cocaine], just give a little extra. That keeps the quality up, that keeps business up, that keeps your reputation up . . . they want quality, like the very best superfine coke can take a four. But mostly the good stuff can take a three for the street. Now when I say my stuff can take a three, I mean it can *take a three.*[11]

To "take a three" means to add three times the weight, in adulterants, to the initial amount of cocaine. The impression is that Jimmy makes a big thing of the strength of his "product." As a rule, none of the dealers we met (and this included dealers on both coasts, mostly white) publicly advertised the number of cuts their cocaine could take. That it was cut and would in all probability be cut again was known and accepted, both by dealers below them in the dealing hierarchy and by sophisticated users. But the facts were never broadcast as such.

One small-time West Coast cocaine dealer we interviewed felt that publicly advertising the number of cuts the cocaine could still take was a practice carried over from the selling of heroin, where dealers are particularly concerned with letting their customers know how many more times the heroin can be adulterated. Most of the cocaine dealers that we interviewed stressed the purity of their product, and let it go at that.

TIPS ON DEALING FROM A (FORMER) DEALER

We asked one of the dealers interviewed in this study to provide us with a list of factors to consider when dealing in cocaine. Although he is now permanently out of this activity, he did provide us with a number of insights. First, this dealer, all the others we interviewed, and the literature on the subject clearly suggest that the risks far outweigh the gains, particularly at the low end of the dealing spectrum (e.g., at the gram and ounce level). As this dealer said, "for those of you who wish to indulge in cocaine in a materialistic manner—don't—there are already too many bummed-out coke dealers around. But if that doesn't deter you, read on":

1. Be informed. Get whatever answers you can through either a more knowledgeable friend or the literature.

2. Buy and learn how to use the more sophisticated devices for testing. Learn some basic chemistry, particularly as it applies to cocaine testing.

3. Start out small and slowly build—never cutting. Follow your sixth sense.

4. Get a good powder scale.

5. Put out quality (high price if necessary) over quantity and only to trusted competent friends. Cash only, little or no fronts. Don't allow yourself or your friends to overextend themselves.

6. Know who your friends are and in turn their friends (discreetly, of course). Be aware of the entire situation and exercise extreme caution without paranoia, and believe in yourself. If you are not doing something that you understand and believe in—don't do it! Don't get overconfident or paranoid—either can sink you. Keep it sensible and mellow.

LAW ENFORCEMENT AND LEGAL ACTION

So far, in these two chapters, we have discussed a variety of illegal activities. These all have consequences, however, which the law-enforcement sector is eager to mete out. Although state-level penalties vary widely for the use, possession, or sale of cocaine, most are severe. As a former dealer just recently out of a state penitentiary after serving three years of a five-year sentence for cocaine-sales conviction told us:

> At the most, you can work sixteen to eighteen hours a day, and at that only for a few months at a time. The police–ah, the police—on the other hand work twenty-four hours a day, and for seven days a week at that. The math just isn't in your favor. Eventually, they will catch you . . . and nothing, man, and I mean nothing, not the greatest high in the world or all the money, is worth three years in prison. . . .

In 1961, domestic seizures of cocaine by the Federal Bureau of Narcotics (DEA's predecessor) totaled only 6 pounds. As late as 1969 only 52 pounds were seized. This began to change dramatically in 1970, however, when 354 pounds were seized.[12] Table 15 indicates the amounts of cocaine (in pounds) removed from the domestic market, either through sales to undercover agents or through seizure, over the past six years.

TABLE 15
Total Cocaine (in pounds) Removed from the Illicit Market (FY71–FY79)*

Source: *Year:/*	*FY71*	*FY72*	*FY73*	*FY74*
DEA federal drug removals, delivered and seized	427	443	239	413
DEA-initiated state/local removals	†	†	152	124
Ports and borders (Customs and Immigration and Naturalization Service)	360	379	734	923
Totals:	787	828	1125	1492

Source: *Year:/*	*FY75*	*FY76*	*FY77*	*FY78*	*FY79*
DEA federal drug removals, delivered and seized	507	430	434	663	751
DEA-initiated state/local removals	193	82	58	80	128
Ports and borders (Customs and Immigration and Naturalization Service)	767	1069	977	1463	1170
Totals:	1467	1581	1469	2206	2049

* FY = Federal Fiscal Year; up to FY77 this meant July 1—June 30. Since then, it covers Oct. 1–Sept. 30. FY79 data through June 30, 1979 only.

† Data not collected until 1973.

Source: *Drug Enforcement Statistical Report*, 1974 and 1978.

For the past few years, the Drug Enforcement Administration has employed approximately 2,000 special agents (see Table 16), a gradually increasing proportion of whom are assigned to foreign countries and are often instrumental in arrests and seizures involving cocaine. As shown in Table 17, there have been striking increases in the amounts these foreign-stationed agents have seized over the past few years (in cooperation with the governments of the countries in which they are stationed).

The amount of time and money spent on these international control efforts has been great. Since 1974, for instance, we have invested $600 million in Colombia to combat the drug trade, and as much as $600 million more may be added in 1979–80, according to interviews with Colombian officials.[13] And foreign authorities have not been idle, either. Colombian officials said they arrested

TABLE 16

Cocaine-Related Arrests by Domestic and Foreign-Stationed DEA Agents (1972–79)

Year	*No. DEA special agents†*	*Cocaine-related arrests*	*DEA-initiated state/ local arrests*	*No. agents assigned to foreign countries*	*Arrests by these agents*
FY73*	1423	1443	N.A.‡	113	N.A.
FY74	2069	1725	2249	151	397
FY75	2059	2056	1262	171	471
FY76	2037	1799	790	174	608
FY77	1968	1216	364	165	522
FY78	1945	1416	622	159	586
FY79	1909	1335	634	166	513

* See Table 15 for definition. FY79 data through June 30, 1979 only.

† Agents with authority to make arrests. DEA has other types of agents.

‡ 1973 was the first year of a cooperative federal/state/local narcotics task force. Arrest data were not reported by type of drug involved.

Source: *Drug Enforcement Statistical Report*, 1974, 1978 and 1979.

TABLE 17

DEA/Foreign Cooperative Seizures of Cocaine

Year:	*FY70*	*FY71*	*FY72*	*FY73*	*FY74*
Pounds seized:	78	261	246	1011	1115

Source: *Drug Enforcement Statistical Report*, 1974 and 1978.

Year:	*FY75*	*FY76*	*FY77*	*FY78*	*FY79*
Pounds seized:	1077	3315	3857	6198	6417*

* FY79 data through June 30, 1979 only.
Source: *Drug Enforcement Statistical Report*, 1974 and 1978.

7,342 persons on drug charges in 1977 and confiscated 15,604 pounds of cocaine and 529,491 pounds of marijuana. They also said there are thirty-nine Americans in Colombian jails (as of March 1978), mostly on charges of dealing in cocaine.[14]

In the past, unsophisticated or crude methods might have been employed or at least considered for the detection of cocaine users. In 1923, Dr. W. Kohler, a German physician, was reported as advocating coloration of commercial cocaine to prevent errors in mistaking it for other substances and as an aid to detect cocaine abusers:

> The cocaine addict snuffs cocaine by the nose in heavy doses. Cocaine that has been colored blue causes marked coloration of the nostrils.[15]

Thus, police work in this area would be a matter of apprehending all people displaying blue noses! And in 1912, Owens suggested a method of detection based on looking for people with damaged nasal septums—a sure sign of chronic cocaine abuse.[16]

Current technology, however has provided both the law-enforcement agencies and customs officials with the very latest instruments and techniques to detect and arrest cocaine smugglers, dealers, and users.

After the arrest: recent legal actions

Nearly 8,000 individuals were arrested for cocaine-related charges in 1977 in the United States. In most of these cases, the defendants were arrested while actually in possession of the drug, which usually leads to a conviction. However, since 1973, defense attorneys have increasingly sidestepped the issue of their clients' possession, use, or trafficking in cocaine and instead have concentrated their efforts on attacking the legal classification of cocaine as a narcotic. The premise used to challenge various state laws governing cocaine use has been the same in all cases. Defense attorneys have attempted to demonstrate that because cocaine has been erroneously classified as a narcotic, defendants sentenced under existing statutes have been deprived of the protection of both the 5th and 14th amendments; they have been deprived of liberty without due process of law (5th Amendment), and they have not been accorded equal protection under the law (14th Amendment).

As outlined by Ashley, the keystone of the defense argument is the 5th Amendment's guarantee of a fundamental protection against unreasonable or arbitrary laws.[17] The argument is that a law designating cocaine as a narcotic cannot be a reasonable and just interpretation of the facts. If the law makes an extreme distinction between narcotic and non-narcotic drugs, which it clearly does in its sentencing sanctions, then it becomes reasonable to assume that cocaine's misclassification as a narcotic affects due-process guarantees to persons charged with narcotic-crimes involving the use of cocaine.

According to Ashley's review of the fight for legalization of cocaine, the equal-protection clause of the 14th Amendment is relevant in the defense of cocaine violations.[18] More widely known for civil-rights application, the 14th Amendment guarantees that individuals in similar circumstances should be treated similarly. However, in the case of the cocaine statutes, there are certain inequities present. In particular, state statutes provide for harsher sanctions for persons convicted of cocaine offenses than they do for persons charged with offenses involving similar central nervous system stimulants, such as amphetamines.

Consequently, it seems clear that the law fails to treat these persons equally.

Recent court cases involving cocaine

During 1977 and 1978, trial courts for the first time ruled against the legal classification of cocaine as a narcotic. Trial courts in Alaska, Illinois, and Massachusetts ruled against the state laws, while challenges to the Florida, California, and Colorado laws were defeated. The initial rulings in the former states, however, were reversed upon appeal.

In the Superior Court of California, Chief Judge Allen refused to rule California's cocaine law unconstitutional, arguing that the issue was one for the state legislature. According to Judge Allen, classification of cocaine as a narcotic was "not a denial of equal protection." "Cocaine is a unique chemical substance with effects and social problems different from other drugs or controlled substances."[19]

In Illinois, Judge Coutrakon of the Sangamon County Circuit Court ruled that cocaine is a harmless substance and that the Illinois law classifying it as a narcotic was unconstitutional. Judge Coutrakon said, "I call them as I see them, and the evidence here was uncontradicted that cocaine is no more harmful than coffee or alcohol."[20] His decision was based on expert testimony provided by Dr. Birhari, assistant health commissioner of New York City, and the chief of the New York State Hospital Center for Drug Addiction and Detoxification.

In Colorado, Denver District Judge Rovira upheld the constitutionality of the state law. The challenge brought forth by Verna Fugett concentrated on the unconstitutionality of the state's classification. Rovira, however, ruled that the scientific jury was still out on cocaine, stating that "the evidence and the scientific literature available to the court leads to the conclusion that cocaine does possess harmful attributes, that cocaine is not a benign drug, that scientific knowledge of cocaine and its effects is not adequate, and much research and study must still be done."[21] Judge Rovira concurred with the district attorney's office in arguing that the legislature had intended that certain substances considered harmful be put in a classification regardless of the pharmacological properties. In that light, the judge was bound by precedent to interpret "narcotic" in a way that made the Colorado law constitutional.

In a precedent-setting decision, the Alaska Supreme Court reversed a December 1976 ruling by Anchorage Judge Carlson which held the state cocaine laws unconstitutional. The Supreme Court stated, "We find that there is a sufficiently close and substantial relationship between the means chosen to regulate cocaine and the legislative purpose of preventing harm to health and welfare to justify the prohibition of use of cocaine, even in the home." In his initial decision, Judge Carlson had dismissed cocaine charges against seven individuals, indicating that state laws had wrongly classified the drug as a narcotic. The state appealed and Carlson was overruled. As to the classification issue, the State Supreme Court said:

> We conclude that the legislature specifically intended to regulate the use and possession of cocaine, regardless of its pharmacological status, and that the purpose of the statute is to regulate drugs that have a potential for harm to health and welfare.[22]

The court indicated that it doubted whether the legislature was concerned whether cocaine was a stimulant or depressant, but rather was more concerned with the potential for harm it posed to Alaskan society.

Synthetic cocaine: not illegal?

Individuals with a strong background in chemistry and an interest in cocaine should note that *The Journal* recently reported that a defendant in a Virginia trial was acquitted on three counts of cocaine distribution on the grounds that the cocaine he sold to an undercover agent was derived from a synthetic base and not from natural coca leaves.[23] All states have regulations prohibiting the use and distribution of cocaine derived from coca leaves. But synthetic cocaine is not mentioned in the statutes, and when the prosecution was unable to prove scientifically that the cocaine was natural, the county judge dismissed the charges.

According to an official of the Drug Enforcement Administration who was consulted, synthetic cocaine is rare and difficult to produce. However, he has no knowledge as the extent or prevalence of synthetic cocaine in the United States.

The future: legalization or decriminalization

A trend has been established. With increasing regularity the news media in 1979 reported on court cases involving the fight to decriminalize cocaine through the reclassification of the drug into a schedule with lesser penalties. Though legalization seems unlikely, according to all sources, decriminalization of cocaine is a possibility. However, decriminalization, or lessening of the penalties associated with cocaine's use, will come about as a consequence of development of a solid constituency, similar to the one that has developed around the issue of marijuana decriminalization. With cocaine currently selling at over $150 a gram, however, and with purity levels generally low, the development of such a broad-based constituency seems a bit remote. And this must come in the face of the well-developed prejudices and historical misconceptions that have surrounded cocaine's use since its introduction to this country in the late 1800s.

REFERENCES

1. Waldorf, D., Murphy, S., Reinarman, C. and Joyce B., *Doing Coke: Ethnography of Cocaine Users and Dealers*, (Washington, D.C.: Drug Abuse Council, 1977).
2. Woodley, R., *Dealer: Portrait of a Cocaine Merchant*, (New York: Holt, Rinehart and Winston, 1971).
3. Adapted from *The Gourmet Cokebook: A Complete Guide to Cocaine*, (New York: White Mountain Press, 1972; also published by D. C. Production Enterprises, Inc., New York).
4. Sabbag, R., *Snowblind: A Brief Career in the Cocaine Trade*, (New York: Bobbs-Merrill, 1976), reprinted by Avon Books, New York, 1978.
5. Waldorf et al., 1977, Op. Cit.
6. Sabbag, 1976, Op. Cit.
7. Ibid, p. 130–131.
8. Ashley, R., *Cocaine: Its History, Uses and Effects*, (New York: St. Martin's Press, 1975).
9. *PharmChem Newsletter*, "Annual statistical summaries of street drug analyses." *PharmChem Newsletter*, 1975, *4(4)*.

10. *The Gourmet Cokebook*, 1972, Op. Cit.
11. Woodley, 1971, Op. Cit.
12. Woods, J. H., and Downs, D. A., "The psychopharmacology of cocaine." In: *Drug Use in America: Problem in Perspective*, Appendix, Vol. I, (Washington, D.C.: U.S. Government Printing Office, 1973), 116–139.
13. Chardy, A., "Colombia to Attack Traffic in Cocaine," *The Washington Post*, March 11, 1978, A20.
14. Ibid.
15. Anonymous, "Cocainism," *Journal of the American Medical Assoc.*, 1923, *80*, 864–865.
16. Owens, W., "Signs and symptoms presented by those addicted to cocaine," *JAMA*, 1912, *58*, 329–330.
17. Ashley, R., "The fight for legal cocaine," *High Times*, June, Vol. 10 57–63 1976.
18. Ibid.
19. "Judge Won't Toss Out State's Cocaine Law," *San Jose Mercury News*, June 14, 1977.
20. Phillips, R., "Cocaine not narcotic? If so, it does not interfere with driving ability, as alcohol does," *Current Medicine for Attorneys*, 1977, *24*, 14–15.
21. *From the State Capitals*, Drug abuse control trends summarized, February 1, 1979, (Asbury Park, New Jersey: Bethune Jones).
22. *From the State Capitals*, March 1, 1978, Op. Cit.
23. "Synthetic Cocaine Not Illegal," *The Journal*, 1978, *7(6)*, 5.

CHAPTER 15

COCAINE ADULTERANTS AND CONSUMER-PROTECTION TECHNIQUES

Heroin and cocaine are two of the most extensively adulterated drugs on the present illicit market.

—D. C. Perry, "Heroin and Cocaine Adulteration"

Only the "manufacturer" of that street cocaine and an analytical chemist can know the composition of street cocaine with reasonable certainty. Therefore, if street cocaine must be consumed, the only reasonably safe route is as snuff since . . . mainlining is the equivalent to Russian roulette.

—M. H. Malone, "It's the Real Zing"

With the increase in street demand for cocaine, the quality or purity of cocaine has decreased in the last several years. The potential street buyer of cocaine is usually confronted with cocaine that has either been diluted or adulterated. No one knows this better than the dealer himself, as a passage from Woodley shows. Jimmy, on cutting his cocaine, says:

> "I add a little of another thing which makes my coke superfly."
>
> "What other thing?"
>
> He smiled again. "Call it mysterious. There are certain things you don't want *nobody* to know. Got to protect my formula. Let's leave it mysterious. What I do is, I buy lactose and dextrose by the case, twelve containers to a case, and I usually use them together as a cut. You can

get them in these plastic quart bottles." He picked up two opaque factory-labeled containers. "I mix them together. Then you got to sift them."[1]

ADULTERANTS USED WITH COCAINE

Adulterants fall into two broad categories:

- Inert cuts—pharmacologically inert substances used to make "weight" or dilute the cocaine, primarily because of their visual or textural similarity to cocaine, but which "add nothing to either the reality or the illusion of the cocaine experience."[2]
- Active cuts–substances that produce numbing or stimulating effects in some ways similar to cocaine. These include mood-altering substances, especially benzedrine, and some psychedelics, and a variety of local anesthetics, such as procaine and lidocaine.

The following discussion draws from our earlier work and from two recent and useful consumer-oriented books: Lee's *Cocaine Consumer's Handbook*[3] and Gottlieb's *The Pleasures of Cocaine.*[4] We also indicate which of the common "street" tests of cocaine purity are generally used to detect these adulterants. These tests themselves are discussed in some detail later in this chapter.

Inert cuts

Cocaine, as well as heroin, is often adulterated by many substances not clinically classified as drugs. Sugar is common, in the form of lactose or dextrose, as is inositol (Vitamin B) and, increasingly, mannitol (mannite, menite, or menita). Although regularly used in pharmaceutical preparations and therefore considered relatively safe, "medical knowledge of these substances is based on oral use."[5]

Mannitol. Used commercially principally as a filler for pills and as a baby laxative, its use as an adulterant has increased because of its cocainelike appearance, ready absorption by the mucous membranes, and lack of toxic or irritating effects. Popular with the more sophisticated dealers because the way it crystallizes is similar to the way cocaine does, mannitol is the preferred cutting agent when cocaine is to be reduced to a liquid state, then adulterated and reconstituted.[6] Gottlieb recommends use of a fine distilled-water spray on a mixture of mannitol and cocaine powder to form a crystal-like substance characteristic of high-quality cocaine.[7] Another reason for mannitol's popularity is that it passes the flame test (however, this test is not among the more accurate of the street tests).

Lactose and dextrose. On the positive side these sugars are relatively inexpensive, are widely available, and have no toxic effects. On the negative side, they readily absorb moisture from the air, resulting in the formation of sugar lumps in the cocaine, which can aggravate their relatively slow absorption through the nasal mucous membranes. They also tend to dull the effects of cocaine and have been reported as a cause of postnasal drip.[8]

Inositol (Vitamin B). Easily obtainable and currently very popular with dealers, Vitamin B compound is a white crystalline granular form with a slightly sweet taste.[9] Unfortunately, inositol may induce even greater nasal dripping than do the sugars.[10]

Other inert cuts. Among the most dangerous nondrug cuts are cornstarch, talc powder, and oven flour. Their greatest danger is that they are largely insoluble in blood, and therefore can clot up in the body. As Perry[11] reports, there have been numerous cases of people who have injected heroin or cocaine cut with talc or cornstarch and developed emboli (clots) in the lungs or eyes, which can lead to respiratory failure and blindness.

Quinine

Quinine sulfate, a bitter crystalline powder, has generally been considered a heroin rather than cocaine adulterant, and many heroin overdose deaths are purportedly principally due to the quinine.[12] Unlike the cuts described above, quinine is physiologically active independent of the cocaine, a fact that can have serious, even fatal consequences. Death attributable to quinine sulfate has resulted from amounts as low as half a gram, though the average reported lethal dose is eight grams.[13]

Quinine can cause such physical symptoms as ringing in the ears, visual impairment, nausea, and headaches.[14] Quinine-adulterated cocaine produces a variety of generally unpleasant side effects, depending on the route of administration. With frequent inhalation over the course of several hours, the nasal membranes tend to become quickly and very painfully abraded. Oral use can result in gastric disorders.

Local anesthetics

PharmChem statistics from 1973 to 1978 indicate that cocaine is most often cut with other local anesthetics such as procaine (novocaine) and lidocaine (xylocaine). The other local anesthetics, benzocaine and tetracaine, are used less frequently. With the addition of some of these adulterants it is possible for "street" cocaine to be far more lethal than pure cocaine, according to Malone.[15]

Although there are no valid data for the comparative intravenous toxicity of cocaine, procaine, and the other local anesthetics in humans, we do know that the degree of toxicity varies, as shown by studies performed on rats and rabbits. The Luduena et al. study cited by Malone[16] indicated that the toxicity levels (in mice) for the various local anesthetics were: procaine, 52 mg/kg; lidocaine, 20 mg/kg; cocaine, 19 mg/kg; and tetracaine, 7.3 mg/kg.[16] The difference in having a cocaine sample mixed with either tetracaine or procaine is that the tetracaine would be seven times as toxic as procaine, a potentially significant life-threatening difference.

Benzocaine, reported in 3% of the tested cocaine samples, poses a special problem not directly related to its toxicity. It is relatively insoluble and, therefore, "it should *never* be injected."[17] This lack of solubility increases the chance of blood clots and serious complications. All of the local anesthetics, with the exception of lidocaine, are detectable via the Clorox test.

Stimulant adulterants

Methamphetamine, benzedrine, and, more rarely, dexedrine, caffeine, and pemoline (also used as a memory and learning aid) have been used as adulterants, principally for their stimulating effects, by which some dealers hope to mislead potential buyers into thinking they are getting potent cocaine. They are also used at times to "restore the stimulating effect to cocaine that has been adulterated too much."[18]

Of the stimulant adulterants, methamphetamine, or methedrine, is the most common. Pharmaceutically it is a white, odorless, bitter-tasting, fine crystalline powder. A central nervous system stimulant, it produces a sense of alertness, restlessness, and euphoria. However, while similar to the euphoria induced by cocaine, these effects typically last much longer and are considerably more profound.

According to both the literature and our conversations with users, the principal physical and mental differences between cocaine and methedrine are that the latter:

- Has a sharply bitter taste
- Causes a pronounced grinding of the teeth
- Produces an intense and severe stinging in the nose when snorted
- Causes a tightening of the neck and facial muscles, particularly in the jaw

It has also been reported that some of cocaine's unpleasant side effects are accentuated by stimulants, including pronounced dizziness, increased anxiety and paranoia, insomnia, aggressive behavior, and cardiac stress.[19]

These stimulants, fortunately are generally easily identifiable via the Clorox test.[20]

Miscellaneous adulterants

Several other chemicals, some active, some inert, have on occasion been used as adulterants. These include the psychedelic phencyclidine hydrochloride (PCP or "angel dust"), which has been reported in 1% of the street samples analyzed in the past few years by PharmChem Labs.[21] Occasionally encountered inert cuts include epsom salts and ephedrine sulfate, used principally as a bronchial dilator for asthma sufferers.[22]

COSTS AND PURITY OF "STREET" COCAINE

Our reanalysis of the information from FY75 (July 1974–June 1975) through FY78 (June 30, 1978) from DEA worksheets summarizing results of both wholesale and retail "buys" of illicit cocaine by government undercover narcotics agents shows a definite relationship among purity levels, cost, and the amount of cocaine purchased, as shown in Table 18. The table clearly shows that purchasers on the wholesale level (defined by the DEA as any purchase of cocaine that is of at least 20% purity or a minimum weight of 20 grams) get a considerably better deal than do the smaller-time dealers on the retail level. The wholesale cocaine is less expensive overall, considerably more pure, and thus considerably cheaper per gram of pure cocaine. Overall, the undercover agents purchased more cocaine and of a better quality at the wholesale than at the retail level.

We obtained data from another source concerning purity (and thus quality) levels. PharmChem Laboratories of Palo Alto, Calif., has conducted analyses of a wide variety of street drugs since 1973. Samples are sent to them anonymously by drug users all over the country. Until a 1974 DEA ruling, they were able to print in their monthly newsletter quantitative data on purity levels. Since then, they can only print qualitative information (what, but not how much). The laboratories have published the results of all tests conducted from 1973 through the first two months of 1979, and included in these data are analyses of a total of 4,853 samples purported to be cocaine and nearly 8,000 other drug samples (see Table 19). If we assume that drug samples submitted to PharmChem reflect street drug activity in general, examining this large data base indicates some interesting facts concerning cocaine use during this period.

Basically, PharmChem data support the belief that cocaine use has gone up dramatically in the past few years. Between 1973 and 1976, cocaine samples represented approximately 30% of all drugs submitted to PharmChem for analysis. However, in 1977, nearly 43% of all samples involved cocaine, and in 1978, slightly more than 50%. This continued interest and apparent use of cocaine is even more dramatically reflected by the fact that purported cocaine samples accounted for approximately 70% of all drug samples submitted to PharmChem during the first two months of 1979.

The second fact that emerges in reviewing the PharmChem analysis concerns the validity factor or "truth in purchasing." The validity rate of cocaine samples has been high in comparison with other street drugs. Buyers can generally be *more* sure with cocaine that they are *getting at least some* of what they think they are buying than is the case with street drugs in general. For example, for the 1973–79 period, nearly 95% of the samples purported to be cocaine that were submitted to PharmChem for analysis actually contained some of the drug. This differed substantially from the results reported for the other drug samples—in which only 60% of drugs sent in for analysis actually contained some of the purported drug!

However, this supposedly high validity rate for cocaine bears further examination, since it is somewhat misleading. Between 1973–79, for the illicit drug market in general, there has been an increase in the proportion of drug samples submitted for analysis that contain at least some of the alleged drug. That is there are fewer total rip-offs. However, during this period, there has been a *decrease* in the proportion of samples containing *only* the purported drug, and an *increase* in the proportion of samples that are *adulterated* with drugs of which the buyers were unaware. For the potential buyer, then, the message is clear: you are more likely to get at least *some* of what you think you are buying, but also more likely to get an *adulterated* version of it.

This in general holds true for cocaine, but with a bit of a twist. Until 1975, PharmChem lumped together samples that contained "only cocaine" and those that contained "cocaine plus sugars" into a single category—"same as alleged." Since 1975, these categories have been reported separately. An analysis of them provides an interesting insight into the cocaine market. There has been a general *increase* in the proportion of "cocaine only" samples, and a *decrease* in the proportion of samples containing "coke plus inert sugars." Thus, during a period when the proportion of samples that actually contained cocaine and not some other drug has *decreased*, the proportion of samples containing *only* the real thing has actually *increased*. For example, the

TABLE 18

Cocaine Prices and Purity Information

	*FY75**		*FY76*	
	Wholesale	*Retail*	*Wholesale*	*Retail*
Gross grams bought	22,521	2,422	15,816	964
Total Cost	$1,142,329	$140,150	$856,829	$61,646
Cost/gross gram	$50.72	$57.87	$54.17	$63.95
Average purity	42.5%	11.2%	49.0%	13.0%
Net grams pure cocaine	9,701.41	2,703.0	7,747.0	125.71
Cost/net gram	$117.75	$518.50	$110.60	$490.38
No. of data points†	552	389	396	148

	FY 1977		*FY 1978*	
	Wholesale	*Retail*	*Wholesale*	*Retail*
Gross grams bought	9,691.3	603.4	12,679.3	798.7
Total Cost	$597,412	$45,008	$862,944	$61,007
Cost/gross gram	$61.65	$74.59	$68.06	$76.38
Average purity	42.9%	12.0%	45.0%	12.3%
Net grams pure cocaine	4,162.5	72.6	5,708.6	98.6
Cost/net gram	$143.52	$619.94	$151.17	$618.73
No. of data points†	251	100	330	124

* FY = Federal Fiscal Year. Up to FY77 this meant July 1–June 30. Since then, it covers Oct. 1–Sept. 30.

† Data point = a purchase by an undercover agent.

Source: DEA statistics, adapted

percentage of "coke only" samples has increased from 5.1% in 1975 to 28.2% in 1977.* The figures are still high —25.7% in 1978 and 18.1% for the first two months of 1979. However, this seeming "market honesty" may have peaked. Only time will tell.

* That is, 5.1% of the samples submitted for analysis during 1975 and purported to be cocaine, actually contained only cocaine, and no adulterants.

TABLE 19
Results of Analyses of 12,646 Street Drug Samples (1973–79)[a]

What purchasers actually got:	*What purchasers thought they were getting:* *Cocaine (4,853 samples)*	*All other drugs (7,793 samples)*
Same drugs they thought they bought	58.3%[b]	48.8%
Same drugs + others they were not aware of	36.5	11.2
Subtotal: Those samples with at least some of the alleged drugs	94.8	60.0
Drugs other than those they thought they bought	4.3	31.4
No identifiable drug or no drug detected	0.9	8.6
Subtotal: Those samples with none of the alleged drug	5.2	40.0
TOTALS:	100.0	100.0

[a] 1979 data cover January–February only

[b] Includes 1973–74 data in which no distinction was made between "cocaine only" and "cocaine + sugars"

Source: *PharmChem Newsletter*, 1974, *3(3)*; 1975, *4(4)*; 1976, *5(1)*; 1977, *6(2)*; 1978, *7(2)*; and 1979, *8(2)*.

The *Joint Effort Gazette*, a newsletter published jointly by the PharmChem Research Foundation and the Haight-Ashbury Free Medical Clinic, prints the weekly analysis of street samples sent to PharmChem Laboratories. An average of the quantitative analyses, conducted on cocaine samples, indicated that for the period Jan. 1, 1975, to Jan. 22, 1975, the 11 samples of cocaine averaged 47% in purity—ranging from a low of 14% to a high of 82% (the difference between the high and the low was only $10 a gram). Prices ranged from $50 to $60 for grams, and from $1300 to $1500 for ounces. For the period Feb. 15,

Second law of cocaine dealing

The price of illicit cocaine shows little or no correlation with purity level (based on PharmChem Lab statistics for a five year period, 1973–77). The *PharmChem Newsletter* reported that chemical analysis of a sample from an ounce of cocaine (alleged purchase price $1,900) showed *no* cocaine at all, only lidocaine and glucose.[23] Another example occurred at the Virginia Bureau of Forensic Science, Merryfield, Va. In interviewing a chemist at the laboratory about street tests to determine purity levels of cocaine, an undercover agent came in with a buy—an ounce of "cocaine," purchase price $1,500. A quick test by the chemist revealed the alleged cocaine to be nothing more than Bisquik! Hopkins quoted a Hollywood doctor: "If you don't know the drug, know the pusher."[24]

1975, to Feb. 22, 1975, cocaine (no number of samples tested is given) averaged 38% in purity, ranging from no cocaine at all to pure cocaine hydrochloride. Prices for grams varied from $45 to $65 and from $1,100 to $1,350 for ounces. One sample tested was pure lidocaine.

STREET TESTS FOR COCAINE PURITY

Because of the decreasing purity of street-level samples, both dealers and users are increasingly concerned about how to gauge the contents and purity of street cocaine. The most accurate quantitative testing procedures—telling both what and how much are in a sample—such as thin-layer or gas-liquid chromatography or mass spectrophotometry require sophisticated equipment.[25] Accordingly, there is increasing reliance on a number of largely informal and qualitative tests of sample purity. While these tests are in widespread use, very little data are available as to their accuracy in comparison to objective laboratory standards. We were able to generate some data on two of the more popular tests, however (see page 274). At best, most of these tests tell if there is any cocaine at all in a sample and, in some cases, the nature of the adulterants used as cutting agents. Below, we describe nine of these informal tests. In the next section, and at greater length, we describe a considerably more elaborate technique, the melting-point test, which, while not yet widely used, is within a nontechnician's grasp and provides a reasonably accurate picture of a sample's purity level. In fact, there is now commercially available equipment for conducting this test. The simpler tests to be described, arranged in order of increasing complexity, are:

- Visual test
- Taste test
- Water test
- Snorting test
- Burn or flame test
- Clorox or bleach test
- Methanol test
- Volume differentiation test
- Cobalt test (a variant of which is used routinely by undercover narcs)

Visual test. Pure cocaine crystals, as previously discussed, have an almost transparent appearance with an opalescent sparkle. However, so do the other local anesthetics that are often used as cutting agents (lidocaine, procaine, etc.). When cocaine is combined with most cuts, its sparkle is affected. Such cuts as lactose dull the sparkle considerably, while "dextrose has less of an effect, [and] amphetamine 'cut' [methamphetamine] dulls cocaine crystals less than most other cuts."[26] Although salts, such as quinine and epsom, also have crystalline structures, they are not so shiny as cocaine crystals. If cocaine comes in the rock form, then the "chances for purity are improved."[27] But the buyer can be fooled because cocaine is often cut and then reconstituted into rock form. "If, however, the rock is broken open and crystal layers are found within, the chances of purity are greatly improved."[28]

Taste test. Pure cocaine has a bitter, medicinal taste that is altered by most adulterants. Sugar cuts will sweeten the taste, dextrose more than lactose.[29] The salts have an after-taste, with epsom salts, in particular, being "a bit more sour in taste and sandy in texture."[30] Although various local anesthetics taste as bitter, they numb the tongue faster than cocaine and the numbness lasts longer. The taste and visual tests suffer the same drawbacks: they are subjective and not objectively verifiable with any set standard.

Water test. Mentioned by Castleman[31] and a few users, the test consists of putting small amounts of a cocaine sample in water. If it dissolves instantly, it is pure cocaine. We tested this out at the Virginia Bureau of Forensic Science. Our test showed that pure cocaine dissolved, not instantly, but before it hit the bottom of a small test tube filled with 3 milliliters of tap water. However, so did lidocaine, procaine, and fine sugar. In general, then, this is a most unreliable test.

Snorting test. Popular accounts hold this to be the "surest" but also the most "subjective" method.

> Timing the swiftness of the high and of the "freeze" or numbness is an important consideration. The strictest rule which the tester adheres to is to be sure he is straight when embarking upon this test.[32]

The "freeze" effect can also be caused by cuts of other local anesthetics. Apparently there are differences in the type of freeze caused by procaine, lidocaine, and cocaine. Both procaine and lidocaine produce a more instantaneous and longer-lasting freeze or numbing sensation than cocaine.

If the cocaine sample burns the nasal passage and makes the eyes tear, it "is a good educated guess that speed (either dextroamphetamine or methadrine) was the cut."[33] Another indicator of a speed cut would be continued restless and/or active behavior (continuing for two hours or more after snorting the cocaine). Sugar cuts and salt mixtures will often produce postnasal drip. A later effect of salt mixtures (epsom) or menita cuts is diarrhea.

> . . . to reliably ascertain the purity of cocaine by snorting requires a developed sensitivity, the cataloguing of

past experience, and a close attention to present details. In short one must be a connoisseur.[34]

Burn or flame test. The burn test consists of slowly burning a small amount of cocaine sample under a low flame. Aluminum foil is often used in this test. The manner in which the sample is burned is often indicative of the cut used. In particular, pure pharmaceutical cocaine burns clean, leaving no residue, while other cuts leaves residues of varying colors. Data we obtained when testing various adulterated samples against a laboratory standard can be found on pp. 274–275.

Clorox or bleach test. This popular test consists of sprinkling small amounts of cocaine in a clear glass of Clorox (or other liquid bleach). The expectation from the literature is that pure cocaine will spread out through the bleach in clear streamers, while adulterated samples will react differently, especially most local anesthetics and many stimulants.[35]

Methanol Test. Although more sophisticated than the preceding, this test has one major drawback—the results are the same for synthetic local anesthetics and amphetamines. The procedure is as follows:[36]

1. Measure two small equal portions of the sample drug to be tested and place them in two seperate teaspoons.
2. Add one quarter of a teaspoon of pure methanol (found in paint stores as methylated spirits) to one of the teaspoons.
3. Stir the methanol mixture with a toothpick. Any powder that remains is the adulterant (the "cut").
4. The amount of cut mixture left undissolved by the methanol is then compared with the unaltered amount of powder of the other teaspoon.

If, for example, twenty percent of the original amount did not dissolve, the substance tested could be no more than eighty percent pure.[37]

If procaine is the suspected adulterant, it can be extracted from the sample by replacing the methanol mixture with a solution of light petroleum mixed in with sodium bicarbonate. This dissolves out all the cocaine and leaves the cut behind.

Volume differentiation test. This unsophisticated test is used for larger (ounce or more) samples. The premise of the test is that pure cocaine weighs less than an equal volume of most adulterants. Therefore, the larger the volume for a given weight, the more pure is the cocaine.[38] A relatively pure ounce (86% pure) will measure approximately 50 level one-quarter measuring teaspoons. Thus, if the volume is substantially cut, the number of spoons would be less, although the weight would be the same.

The primary difficulty in interpreting the results is that different cuts have different weight-to-volume ratios. At best, therefore, the test indicates the presence of a cut, and a rough approximation of the amount of the cut.[39]

An analysis of two popular street tests

We had hoped to be able to arrange for an intensive laboratory examination of the adequacy of the various street tests currently employed by users/dealers of cocaine to test the purity (or presence) of cocaine. While this did not come about, we were able, with the help of Joe Phillips, a chemist at the Virginia Bureau of Forensic Science, to examine the adequacy of two major tests—the burn and Clorox tests. Both had drawbacks. The results:

BURN TEST. A small amount of the tested substance was placed on a lab spoon and heated over a low flame.

Substance	*Noticeable results*
Pure pharmaceutical cocaine	Burned instantly, leaving no trace; had a strong medicinal odor that lingered
Lidocaine	Same as cocaine—more bubbling but not the same strong smell
Sugars (dextrose and lactose)	Bubbled, left a brown residue; smelled of caramel
Caffeine	Burned quickly, leaving some crystals and brown residue that recrystallized, smelled
Quinine	Burned quickly, orange-brown smoke, left large black residue (Ashley 1975, Cortright 1974, and *The Gourmet Cokebook* state quinine burns cleanly)

Methadrine (Amphetamine)	Burned quickly (made popping sound) and cleanly, left no residue
Talcum powder	Nothing—does not burn
Starches	Turned brown, smelled of burned toast
Salts	Nothing—do not burn

Conclusion: At best this test might indicate the cut. It will not indicate purity of cocaine.

CLOROX TEST. A popular test among users is the Clorox test. To a small glass containing Clorox bleach is added a sprinkle of cocaine. Pure cocaine reportedly runs down in clear streamers.

Substance	*Noticeable results*
Pure pharmaceutical cocaine	Went down quickly, in streams, with whitish tinge
Cocaine (cut): 40% sugar, 25% lidocaine, 15% procaine, 10% cocaine	Streamed quickly; some white streams; overall streams brownish red
Lidocaine	Stayed on surface; yellow formation developed on surface
Procaine	Stayed on surface; brownish-red, bubbly formation developed on surface (Cortright 1974 states that the surface mass should be slightly pink)
Amphetamine (dextro)	Stayed on surface, stayed white (Cortright 1974 stated that it should have spread out in pink streamers)

Conclusion: Test will demonstrate presence of cocaine, but amount and purity of it are guesswork.

The cobalt or color test: the Scott specific field test

A standard test for determining cocaine's presence in a sample is known as the cobalt thiocynate test. This is the "cocaine test kit" advertised in youth-oriented news magazines and journals. The problem with the test is that other substances, such as lidocaine, procaine, tetracaine, benzocaine, and PCP, also react in the same manner as cocaine. An improvement of this standard test has been developed by L. J. Scott of the DEA South Central Regional Laboratory in Dallas, Texas.[40] According to a chemist at the Virginia Bureau of Forensic Science, this is the field test administered whenever possible by undercover agents.

Three reagents are used in this test:

Solution 1. 2% solution of cobaltous thiocyanate is dissolved in water, which is then diluted 1:1 with a 96% USP Glycerine.
Solution 2. Concentrated hydrochloric acid
Solution 3. Chloroform

The procedure consists of three steps:

Step 1. A small amount of the alleged cocaine sample is placed in a test tube and 5 drops of Solution #1 are added to it. Shake. A blue color develops at once if cocaine is present. If the solution does not turn blue, add more sample; if a blue color still has not developed, there is *no* cocaine in the sample.
Step 2. Add *one* (1) drop of Solution #2. Shake. The blue disappears, to be replaced by a light-pink solution. (If all the blue does not disappear, add no more than one drop of solution #2.)
Step 3. Add 3–5 drops of Solution #3. Shake. If cocaine is present a blue color will appear in the lower chloroform layer. The intensity of the blue is indicative of the purity of the cocaine.

The following are some compounds that do not produce a blue color with Solution #1: the synthetic local anesthetics, quinine, methadone, heroin, sugars, and starches.

A more accurate measure—the melting-point test

For all practical purposes, the melting-point test is the "state of the art" in home identification and testing of adulterated cocaine.

For the tester who wishes more than a good estimate of their cocaine, the melting point test provides a percentage figure accurate to within approximately five percent.[41]

The test is premised on the fact that all solid substances have a melting point, a temperature (or, more accurately, a small range of temperatures) at which they change from a solid to a liquid state. For cocaine, the melting point range is 192–197°C. Further, below about 100°C. no mixtures containing cocaine crystals will melt. Therefore, as Lee points out:

> Where in this range it does melt is determined by the purity of the cocaine, the percentage by which it is cut, and the type of adulterant used. For example, a sample which melts at 160°C. will be approimately sixty percent cocaine.[42]

The melting-point range (the number of degrees between the point at which melting starts and is completed) is a good indicator of the purity of the cocaine sample:

> A spread of between three and five degrees indicates a very clean crystal. A longer spread of six to ten degrees indicates less care in the refining process. A range of more than ten degrees will usually be caused by an adulterant. The percentage can be approximated by splitting the difference between the start and finished temperatures . . . [if] the samples started [melting] at 183°C. and finished at 187°C., [it] would indicate purity of about 85%.[43]

A caution: the information given here is intended to be introductory, since analysis and interpretation of this test is difficult, given the number of variables that can affect the outcome. Serious readers are referred to Lee's text, which describes at length the melting-point reactions of variously adulterated cocaine. Here we outline the test procedures and provide a table of melting-point ranges for the principal adulterants of cocaine, adapted from pharmacological texts and consumer handbooks (see Table 20). Procedural information is adapted from Lee.[44]

The simple equipment needed is obtainable from any laboratory equipment supplier and includes:

- 250°C. melt-point thermometer with an immersion line
- Hard glass capillary tubes, closed at one end, 90–120

mm long, with an 0.8–1.2 mm inner diameter and walls 0.2–0.3 mm thick.

- Florence boiling flask, flat bottom, 250 milliliter and with a #5 stopper neck.
- Poppyseed oil (or clear silicone oil)
- Alcohol burner
- Device to hold the flask over the alcohol burner.

The procedure is as follows:

1. *Set up the apparatus.* Put oil in the flask up to half an inch below the neck. Attach the flask by a clamp to a lab-stand bar and situate the alcohol burner under it.

2. *Prepare the sample to be tested.* It should be chopped extremely fine and mixed well. Gottlieb suggests drying it in a desiccator over silicon gel for twenty-four hours to remove any residual moisture.[45]

3. *Place the sample, a bit at a time, in the capillary tube.* The amount to go in the tube should be equal to a "line" of cocaine, and should be approximately 2.5–3.5 mm high in the tube. It is important that the cocaine be well packed.

4. *Place the thermometer and capillary tube connecting tightly packed cocaine into flask of oil.* A three hole rubber stopper can be used to fit into the top of the flask. Lee recommends that twine be wrapped in a "criss-cross fashion until it fits snugly in the neck of the flask."[46] This is to prevent the thermometer from breaking while being forced into the rubber stopper. Note: Another capillary tube containing the suspected adulterant can also be included for comparison purposes.

5. *Heat the oil.* Care should be taken to keep the flame from getting too close. The temperature should rise at a rate of 10°C. per minute. Gottlieb suggests that the bath fluid be heated slowly within 10°C. of the expected melting point, at which time the heating should continue at a lower rate, between 1.1–1.5°C. per minute.[47] The capillary containing the adulterated cocaine should be carefully observed and all changes and corresponding temperatures noted. The results are then analyzed and interpreted. According to Lee, "after several tests made on different samples of cocaine, the tester should rapidly become adept."[48] As noted earlier, melting-point test kits are now available commercially.

TABLE 20
Melting-Point Range for Principal Cocaine Adulterants

Substance	*Melting point (°C.)*
Cocaine hydrochloride	192–197
Cocaine (free base)	96–98
Procaine hydrochloride	153–156
Procaine (free-base)	60–
Lidocaine hydrochloride	76–79
Lidocaine (free-base)	66–69
Benzocaine	88–90
Manitol	165–168
Lactose	222
Dextrose	150
Quinine sulfate	95
Pemoline	259
Methedrine	171–175
Caffeine	235–237
Inositol	224–227

Source: A. Gottlieb, *The Pleasures of Cocaine*

Purification of adulterated cocaine

Gottlieb's consumer-oriented handbook is the first to address the process by which adulterated cocaine can be purified.[49] The principle is straightforward—different adulterants can be removed by dissolving the cocaine mixture in appropriate solutions (solvents). There are five steps in the process:

1. *Determine which adulterant was used.*

2. *Choose an appropriate solvent to either dissolve out the cocaine and leave the adulterant in relatively solid form or vice versa.*

Table 20 lists the more common adulterants. Gottlieb provides a complete and very convenient summary of a great variety of adulterants and the general solvents in which they are soluble or insoluble (e.g., in which they will not dissolve). Readers can also consult any standard pharmacological text.[50] In describing each drug, these texts present solubility ratios and solvents.

3. *"Wash" the adulterated cocaine with the appropriate solvent.*

The equipment for this step is simple and rather like making filtered coffee: the required solvent, a funnel with filter paper in it, and a glass jar or beaker. The adulterated cocaine is placed on the filter paper and a small amount of the solvent carefully poured over it, dropping into the container. "Washing" should be done in a well-ventilated room using a fumehood if possible. These safe precautions are absolutely necessary to minimize the dangers inherent in several solvents, which include toxic fumes (from methanol) and the possibility of explosions with alcohol, and, especially, with ether.

4. *Evaporate the solvent containing the liquified cocaine (necessary only when the cocaine is dissolved out of the mixture).*

Evaporation will naturally occur, given enough time, but Gottlieb suggests speeding up the process by heating the jar or beaker containing the mixture in either an oil (cooking oil) or hot-water "bath." The beaker or jar should be placed in the top half of a double boiler, and the bottom half, containing the oil or water, heated on an electric hotplate. The choice of oil or water is determined by the boiling point of the solvent in which the cocaine is dissolved. As Gottlieb says:

> For example, when the contents of the beaker is ethanol (boiling point = 78.5°C.) or chloroform (boiling point = 61.2°C.), water (boiling point = 100°C.) is employed in the bath. This prevents the solvent in the beaker from going above that temperature. These measures help to avoid accidental fire from flammable solvent fumes and prevent scorching of the materials dissolved in the solvent during the last stages of evaporation. If water is the solvent, oil, which has a much higher boiling point, is used in the bath.[51]

5. *Remove remaining traces of solvents and water.* This should be done either by placing the cocaine in an oven set at 300°F. for thirty minutes, or by placing it in a desiccator (a special closed container) overnight.

An example of the process may be helpful. If the suspected adulterant is inositol:

1. An appropriate solubility table will show that inositol

is insoluble and cocaine soluble in absolute alcohol (ethanol) and also in chloroform.

2. The adulterated cocaine is put in a filter paper in a funnel over a beaker or jar.

3. The solvent is slowly poured over the cocaine. This procedure is repeated several times to insure that all the cocaine is "washed" out.

4. The filter paper containing the inositol is discarded. The jar or beaker containing the dissolved cocaine and solvent is placed in a hot-water bath.

5. The result of the hot-water-bath evaporation is a wettish white powder. This can be left to dry naturally, placed in an oven for thirty minutes, or left overnight in a desiccator.

In other situations, such as cocaine adulterated with benzocaine or free-base lidocaine, the reverse procedure will be used—the adulterant will be dissolved in the liquid and the cocaine hydrochloride will be left on the filter paper.

This process is only a rough test of purity. The purification process also serves as a rough test of the percentage of adulterant used to cut the cocaine. For example, if we started with 5 grams of adulterated cocaine, and, after purification, were left with only 3 grams of reasonably pure cocaine, we could assume the cocaine was cut approximately 40%.

A *caveat:* If you're used to using adulterated cocaine and should happen to go to the trouble of purifying some, be forewarned that you're likely to be dealing with powerful stuff. Take care.

At least one "purification system" is now available commercially. It follows a simpler procedure. As yet there is no scientific evidence that this system does what it claims to do.

REFERENCES

1. Woodley, R., *Dealer: Portrait of a Cocaine Merchant,* (New York: Holt, Rinehart and Winston, 1971).
2. Gottlieb, A., *The Pleasures of Cocaine,* (San Francisco: And/Or Press, 1976).

3. Lee, D., *Cocaine Consumer's Handbook*, (San Francisco: And/Or Press, 1976).
4. Gottlieb, 1976, Op. Cit.
5. Perry, D. C., "Heroin and cocaine adulteration," *PharmChem Newsletter*, 1974, *3(2)*, 1 & 4.
6. Lee, 1976, Op. Cit.
7. Gottlieb, 1976, Op. Cit.
8. Lee, 1976, Op. Cit.
9. Gottlieb, 1976, Op. Cit.
10. Lee, 1976, Op. Cit.
11. Perry, 1974, Op. Cit.
12. Ibid.
13. Gottlieb, 1976, Op. Cit.
14. Lee, 1976, Op. Cit.
15. Malone, M. H., "It's the real zing," *Pacific Information Service on Street Drugs*, 1973, *2(4)*, 24–27.
16. Ibid.
17. Ibid.
18. Lee, 1976, Op. Cit.
19. Gottlieb, 1976, Op. Cit.
20. Lee, 1976, Op. Cit.
21. *PharmChem Newsletter*, 1976, *5(1)*.
22. Gottlieb, 1976, Op. Cit.
23. *PharmChem Newsletter*, 1975.
24. Hopkins, J., "Cocaine: A flash in the pan, a pain in the nose," *Rolling Stone*, April 9, 1971, *81*, 1,6.
25. Wynne, R. D., "Consumer action to regulate the illicit drug market," *Drug Forum*, 1973, *2*, 79–90.
26. Cortright, B., "Dope Scoreboard," *Los Angeles Free Press*, Jan. 4, 1974, *11(1)*, 13.
27. Ibid.
28. *The Gourmet Cokebook: A Complete Guide to Cocaine*. (New York: White Mountain Press, 1972; also published by D. C. Production Enterprises, Inc., New York).
29. Cortright, 1978, Op. Cit.
30. *The Gourmet Cokebook*, 1972, Op. Cit.
31. Castelman, M., "Snows up the nose: A History of Cocaine," *Ann Arbor Sun Community News Service*, 1975, *3(1)*, 13–15, 18.
32. *The Gourmet Cokebook*, 1972, Op. Cit.
33. Ibid.
34. Ibid.
35. Cortright, 1978, Op. Cit.
36. Ashley, R., *Cocaine: Its History, Uses and Effects* (St. Martin's Press, 1975) and *The Gourmet Cokebook*, 1972, Op. Cit.
37. *The Gourmet Cokebook*, 1972, Ibid.

38. Ibid.
39. Ashley, 1975, Op. Cit.
40. Scott, L. J., "Specific field test for cocaine," *Microgram*, 1973, *6*, 11.
41. Lee, 1976, Op. Cit.
42. Ibid.
43. Ibid.
44. Ibid.
45. Gottlieb, 1976, Op. Cit.
46. Lee, 1976, Op. Cit.
47. Gottlieb, 1976, Op. Cit.
48. Lee, 1976, Op. Cit.
49. Gottlieb, 1976, Op. Cit.
50. Goodman, L. and Gilman, A. (eds.), *The Pharmacological Basis of Therapeutics*, (4th ed.) (New York: Macmillan Company, 1970).
51. Gottlieb, 1976, Op. Cit.

CHAPTER 16

CONCLUSIONS

Despite the fact that cocaine is back in wide use and no longer the object of mass hysteria, a number of myths still persist.

Much of the mystification has to do with the drug's effects on humans, and is in large measure due to the difficulties in describing the effects of any chemical substance that can substantially alter complex human functioning.

> Pharmacologists are concerned with the changing effects of drugs at different dosages. A drug such as alcohol can make people relax at one dose, sleepy at another, combative at another, and psychotic at another. Nor is every person affected in the same way by these changing dosages. The effects of the surrounding environment (setting) and of the psychological state and history of a subject profoundly modify the action of the drug. Effects seen after chronic use differ from those observed after a single dose—often they are the opposite. Effects seen after injecting the drug often can bear little relationship to those seen after swallowing the same substance.[1]

Much of the lingering mythology stems from the major information sources about the drug, both in the scientific and the law-enforcement sectors. Much of the data has come from atypical subjects, studied by researchers with little experience with or firsthand knowledge of the social-recreational uses of the drug. Other data has come from law-enforcement officials who often themselves have marked biases. The net result is a rather truncated and incomplete body of information about the drug and its effects.

Some of the difficulty in accurately describing effects of cocaine stems from an often-blurred distinction between primary and secondary effects. For example, we know cocaine's stimulant and anorexic properties have the primary effect of reducing the desire for both sleep and food. Both of these reduced desires can themselves be causal factors for additional (secondary) medical problems. For example, laboratory results indicate that sleep deprivation or disturbance has led to such psychological states as extreme irritability and increased anxiety, as well as such psychotic-like events as hallucinations and paranoid delusions. So, when the literature indicates that cocaine can induce psychotic-like episodes, it is necessary to know all the facts concerning an individual's usage pattern *and* his general health status as well.

Wesson and Smith present a case study of a man who escalated his *intravenous* use of cocaine over a several-month period to the point where he was injecting up to 2 grams per night, on a fifty-to-sixty minute schedule.[2] He would start injecting at ten p.m. and continue until seven a.m. the next morning. After several months, he developed symptoms of acute paranoia, including visual and auditory hallucinations. Given the extreme and unusual circumstances in this case–amounts consumed, method of administration, life-style habits—it seems misleading to cite it as an example of cocaine-induced psychosis without clearly placing this person in a context relative to other and more typical cocaine users as a group—those who do not inject cocaine, who do not use 2 grams per day, who do get their sleep, and so on.

The latter report is an example of a frequent occurrence in the drug literature—the idiosyncratic case study—which unfortunately has a more than adequate representation in the cocaine literature. Another good example of researchers choosing subjects who represent the extreme on the drug-use continuum is a recent NIDA-funded study of the life-styles of nine male cocaine users.[3] The majority of these individuals injected rather than snorted the drug, and one was a regular heroin user as well. Most of them were very heavily involved with drugs and the drug community (as opposed to being more casual social-recreational users), and all had been arrested at one time or another.

Cocaine mythology: from the law enforcement sectors

Law-enforcement officials as well as researchers have contributed to the cocaine mythology. For example, here are some quotes from *On the Trail of the Poppy,* the adventures of Charles Siragusa, a federal undercover narcotics agent:

> To understand just how bad cocaine is, here are some facts. . . .
>
> Under a microscope, the refined crystals look like snowflakes, hence the term "snow," and when a junkie inhales cocaine, his inhibitions melt like snow. A mere pinch of the drug, placed on the back of the hand, from where it can easily be sniffed, turns a docile thief into a killer. Then a pistol or switchblade becomes a source of awesome power in his deranged mind, and murder, instead of simple assault, is the easiest thing in the world. . . .
>
> . . . Heroin is a sedative and cocaine is an excitant, and the effect of this combination on an addict is like slamming his brain into a brick wall of violent psychological reaction. Habitual use of cocaine alone can cause an addict to become epileptic. It can also cause severe brain damage.[4]

A conversation with a DEA agent during preparation of this volume revealed his belief that cocaine causes any latent criminal potential to surface, and that it is not unusual for a "latino" male to go through a couple of *ounces* of cocaine in a weekend spent with his lover.

And users themselves, as has been noted throughout the book, are major contributors to the ongoing mythology about cocaine, and every other recreational drug.

Cocaine research—some methodological considerations

In addition to distinguishing between primary and secondary effects, there are other methodological considerations which should be taken into account in any discussion of cocaine research involving human reactions to the drug. They are:

- *Few studies involving humans.* Until very recently, with the exception of Freud's studies conducted in the late 1800s, there have been few controlled experiments involving humans and cocaine.
- *Controlled laboratory settings.* Controlled laboratory experiments present us with a set of facts, and a limited number at that, but they often do not tell us anything about the user's beliefs or attitudes concerning cocaine. Futhermore, a laboratory setting often inhibits replicating patterns of drug use typically found in society, especially drug-use rituals.
- *Street or user self-reporting information.* In order to determine user beliefs it is necessary to study cocaine users in their natural environment, This in turn produces its own set of methodological considerations and problems. A particular problem associated with studies to date that have involved illicit drugs is the fact that we can never be certain that the active substance taken is the purported drug. Certainly, both PharmChem statistics and the more quantitative reports from the Drug Enforcement Administration suggest that most individuals are doing poor rather than pure or even high-quality cocaine. This makes it difficult to put into perspective self-reports of cocaine use. A related problem confronting the researcher concerns the amount of cocaine that is done. There is no such thing as a standardized amount of cocaine or typical dosage; consequently when an individual talks about doing a line of cocaine not only is the purity or potency of the drug unknown but the actual amount is also questionable.

Let's see if we can sort out the facts from the myths, and sum up what we do and don't know about the drug.

SUMMARY OF THE FACTS AND MYTHS

First, in recognition of the research difficulties and the vastly uneven quality of the research literature, Byck and

TABLE 21
Summary Table of Beliefs and Facts Associated with Cocaine Use

Belief/myth	Fact
Effects	
All individuals react similarly to the same dose.	There are extreme individual reactions to the same amount of cocaine.
Cocaine is addictive.	It is not addictive in the accepted medical definition of addiction. That is, one does not develop a tolerance to cocaine and thus need ever-increasing amounts to maintain or achieve the same level of intensity. However, it can be psychologically addicting.
Cocaine is an aphrodisiac.	Although cocaine is not an aphrodisiac per se, it is often used in sexual encounters.
Cocaine is a stimulant in increasing creative and/or physical performance.	Cocaine is a stimulant, but there have been no studies conducted suggesting it increases or improves creative efforts. As to physical performance, Freud indicated that use of cocaine had a positive effect on increasing muscular strength, while more recently, Kestenbaum found that muscular strength diminished with cocaine ingestion.
There are no bad effects associated with cocaine use.	Excessive cocaine use can result in anxiety, nervousness, giddiness, excitability, and paranoid delusions up to and including hallucinations. It is possible to overdose on cocaine, and deaths have been reported with recreational as well as supervised medical use of cocaine.
Use	
The cost of cocaine is related to its purity.	There is no correlation between price and purity. Based on DEA statistics, cocaine sold in America contains an average of less than 10% of the drug.

Cocaine in "rocks" is indicative of its purity.

"Rocks" of cocaine can easily be reconstituted, and therefore this is a poor test for judging the quality of cocaine.

There are good street tests to determine the purity of cocaine.

Although there are tests available, most of those cited in the literature (burn, taste, Clorox, etc.) are oriented more for qualitative than quantitative results. There are sophisticated tests available that will result in quantitative analysis of the sample. However, these generally require some knowledge of chemistry.

Store cocaine in (a) a dark-amber glass jar (avoid plastic containers) and (b) in the refrigerator.

Cocaine need only be stored in an airtight container.

Adulterants destroy or affect cocaine potency.

Not so; the potency of cocaine is unaffected by the adulterant.

Cocaine combined with heroin/morphine (speedball) is a great high.

This is a potentially fatal way to take cocaine. Nearly two-thirds of the reported cocaine-related deaths involved this combination.

Treatment

To prevent potential side effects of a perforated nasal septum, do one of the following:

1. With a razor, cut cocaine until it is a very fine powder.
2. Rinse out the nose with a liquid solution.
3. Inhale a liquefied solution of cocaine.

Excessive inhalation of cocaine will result in an ulcerated nasal septum. This is the result of the vasoconstrictive properties of cocaine, and is not caused by cocaine particles remaining lodged in the nasal hairs.

The following are antidotes to be used in cases of cocaine intoxication:

1. Cold showers
2. Injecting a milk solution
3. Use of depressants (e.g., barbiturates, heroin, etc.)

All are false, dangerous practices that will not help. There are *no specific antidotes* for acute cocaine poisoning. Maintain breathing and get the individual to a hospital expeditiously.

Van Dyke attempted to categorize the major findings about cocaine over the years by type and reliability of the evidence.[5] The most reliable evidence would be findings demonstrated in controlled experimental situations in at least two independent laboratories. The least reliable would be single-case anecdotal information in which no information is provided as to the characteristics of the users, the dosage, the conditions of use, etc. Byck and Van Dyke stress that, ideally, the effects seen in nonlaboratory situations should in turn be reproducible in controlled laboratory situations.

Of the thirty-three reported effects that have been attributed to cocaine in the literature surveyed, only five were considered by these authors to be at the highest level of reliability:

1. Cocaine's value as a local anesthetic
2. Increases in pupillary size
3. Increases in heart rate
4. Increases in blood pressure
5. Cocaine's effects as a mood elevator in normal people

Three additional effects were gleaned from clinical reports that were both consistent and stated the cocaine dosage used (findings of lesser certainty than the five above):

6. Cocaine constricts the size of the blood vessels.
7. It both elevates and depresses the mood among depressed patients.
8. It acts as a reinforcing stimulus (in fact, intravenously administered cocaine has been shown to be one of the most powerful, if not the most powerful, of drug reinforcers in animal experiments).[6]

Following these stringent criteria, then, five, or at most eight, effects can be declared as "facts" associated with the use of cocaine.

One final word. Cocaine remains an illicit substance, and as such, the potential user is not protected by any consumer-oriented regulations or safeguards. The pleasant euphoria produced by cocaine should be tempered by the knowledge that it remains an expensive, often highly adulterated, potentially dangerous, and above all illegal drug.

REFERENCES

1. Byck R. and Van Dyke, C., "What are the effects of cocaine in man?" In: R. C. Petersen and R. C. Stillman (eds.), *Cocaine, 1977*, (Rockville, Maryland: National Institute on Drug Abuse, 1977), 97–118.
2. Wesson, D. R. and Smith, D. E., "Cocaine: Its Use for Central Nervous Stimulation—Including Recreational and Medical Uses." In: R. C. Petersen and R. C. Stillman (eds.), *Cocaine, 1977*, Op. Cit., 137–152.
3. Spotts, J. V. and Schontz, F. C., *The Life Styles of Nine American Cocaine Users: Trip to the Land of Cockaigne*, Research Issues Series No. 16, (Rockville, Maryland: NIDA, 1976).
4. Weidrich, R., "On the Trail of the Poppy," *Sunday Magazine, Chicago Trubune*, September 11, 1966.
5. Byck, R. and Van Dyke, C., 1977, Op. Cit.
6. Woods, J., "Behavioral effects of cocaine in animals." In: R. C. Petersen, and R. C. Stillman, (eds.), *Cocaine, 1977*, Op. Cit., 63–96.

APPENDIX A

COCAINE: A CHRONOLOGICAL OVERVIEW

?–9th century
Pre-Inca period. Ceramic evidence indicates that the Mochica (600–800 A.D.) used coca.

10th–12th century
Trephined skulls were found in Andean tombs of this period. It is speculated that the skulls were pretreated with cocaine-laden juice from chewed coca leaves. This likely was the first use of cocaine as a local anesthetic. Ceramic evidence depicts wounded soldiers with bulging cheeks, indicating coca's use as an analgesic.

13th–16th century
The Inca Empire period. Coca was declared the gift of the sun god—Manco Capac—and referred to as the "Divine Plant." Initially its use was limited to the upper ruling class. Later, with the breakdown of the social structure and agrarian-based economy, the use of coca became more widespread. But use of coca by the plebes—the lowest class—did not become prevalent until the conquest by Pizarro.

15th–16th century
Golden Age of Discovery. America was discovered and such products as coffee and tobacco were sent to Europe. The hope was that the New World would provide material wealth—gold and silver—as well.

1499
Thomas Ortiz, a Dominican missionary, is believed to be the first to report the usage of coca among the Indians of northern parts of South America.

1531–36
Pizarro and a small band of men determined to find the reported wealth of the Inca in Peru, and subsequently conquered the Incan people. The use of coca was initially prohibited by decrees from King Philip of Spain, based on an assumption that its use was symbolic of a pact made with the devil.

1540–50
Relaxation of the laws prohibiting the use of coca; the natives apparently worked harder in the mines with less food when they were allowed to chew coca. Also, church revenues amounting to a considerable sum of money were based on a tithe of the coca production.

1550
Pedro Cieza de Leon published *Chronica del Peru*, the first history of the South American Indians and their habits, observing that the Indians "always carried a small leaf of some sort in their mouth." He believed the effects to be either imaginary or the results of a pact with the devil.

1565
Nicolas Monardes published the first European book on coca. This was later translated and published in English in 1596, entitled: *Joyfull Newes out of the Newfound Worlde. Wherein are declared the rare and singular vertues of Herbes, trees, plantes, ovales and stones, with their application* . . . Much of this was based on de Leon's book.

1590
Joseph de Acosta published *Natural History of the Indies*. On the effects of coca, Father Acosta said: "They [the Indians] say it gives them great courage, and is very pleasing unto them. Many grave men hold this as a superstition and a mere imagination. For my part, and to speak the truth, I persuaded not myself that it is an imagination, but contrawise I think it works and gives force and courage to the Indians, for we see the effects which cannot be attributed to imagination. . . ."
(Mortimer 1901).

1609
Garcilasso (Inca) de la Vega published *Royal Commentaries of the Inca*, a detailed account of the entire process from cultivating to chewing the coca plant, a subject with which he was very familiar as the owner of a large *cocale* (coca plantation). His father was a Spanish nobleman who served with Pizarro, and his mother was related to the Inca leader deposed by the conquering Spaniards.

17th–mid-19th century
The lack of interest in Europe and North America over coca was probably due to the inability to cultivate the plant in Europe and the fact that the coca lost much of its potency during the long sea voyages.

1750
Joseph de Jussieu sent specimens of the coca plant to Paris, where they are preserved in the Herbarium of the Museum of Natural History. These still constitute the standards for the coca plant.

1783
Lamarck classified the plant as belonging to the family *Erythroxylaceae* and the genus *Erythroxylon.*

1855
Gaedecke isolated coca's chief alkaloid, naming it *erythroxyline.*

1859
Dr. Paolo Mantegazza, of Italy, published a song of praise of coca's many properties.

1859 (or 1860)
Albert Nieman, a student of Wöhler, isolated the chief alkaloid of coca and named it cocaine.

1862
Schraff, an Australian medical researcher, noted numbing (anesthetic) effects of cocaine on the tip of the tongue. He also was among the first experimenters to study the effects of cocaine on animals. He noted that in frogs, cocaine produced a soporific condition accompanied by paralysis of the voluntary muscles.

1863
Vin Mariani, a preparation of coca and wine, was introduced by Angelo Mariani. This became very popular in both Europe and America, and such advocates as Pope Leo XIII extolled the elixir's wonders.

1868
Thomás Moreno y Maiz, surgeon-general of the Peruvian army, conducted a study of the effects of cocaine acetate on frogs and asked, ". . . could not one utilize it [cocaine] as a local anesthetic?"

1878–82

Many American journals (in particular the *Detroit Therapeutic Gazetter* from 1880–1882) published stories on a variety of medicinal uses of cocaine, including W. R. Bentley's use of cocaine to cure morphine addicts (1878) and Searle's coca preparation for patients in sedentary occupations (1881). The majority of writers however, dealt with the use of cocaine in treating narcotic addictions.

1879

Vasili Konstantinovich von Anrep conducted the most exhaustive studies to date on the pharmacological effects of cocaine on animals. He described in detail the process of cocaine poisoning and established lethal doses for rabbits (0.01 gm/kg) and cats (0.02 gm/kg). He also suggested use of cocaine as a local anesthetic.

1883

Theodor Aschenbrant, a German army doctor, reported that troops who used cocaine while on their maneuvers exhibited more energy and less fatigue than those who did not.

1884

Sigmund Freud wrote his "song of praise" to cocaine, "Ueber Coca." Intrigued by Aschenbrant's and Bentley's reports, he conducted experiments with cocaine on himself and friends. He was enthusiastic about its stimulating properties and suggested several potential therapeutic uses: as a stimulant, an aphrodisiac, and a local anesthetic and to treat a variety of ills—cachexia, digestive problems, depression, morphine and alcohol addiction, and asthma. This was the most complete text yet written on cocaine. Between 1884 and 1887, Freud wrote another three papers on cocaine.

Fleischl, a contemporary and friend, was given cocaine by Freud to cure his morphine addiction. He became a heavy user of cocaine and within a year was using up to 1 gram a day and exhibited all the symptoms of cocaine poisoning, including visual hallucinations. He was the first recorded cocaine "addict" in Europe.

Carl Koller, in a short paper read on September 15 to the Heidelberg Ophthalmological Society, announced that cocaine was the long-sought-for local anesthetic for eye surgery.

William Stewart Halstead, "father of modern surgery," injected cocaine into nerve trunks which resulted in "nerve block" or "conduction" anesthesia. Through experimentation on himself, he developed a heavy use pattern that eventually was "cured" by the use of morphine.

1884–85
"The Great Cocaine Explosion." Following Koller's experiment, cocaine became an instant celebrity in the medical world. Merck Co. and Parke Davis and Co. commenced production, and its popular use increased.

1885
Dr. J. Leonard Corning of New York, a student of Halstead, suggested the use of cocaine for spinal anesthesia.

John Styth Pemberton of Atlanta, Ga., introduced an American competitor to Vin Mariani. It was called "French Wine Cola—Ideal Nerve and Tonic Stimulator."

1886
Pemberton introduced Coca-Cola, a soft-drink syrup containing cocaine. The soda fountain became a part of the American scene, and scores of imitators were introduced. (In 1888 Asa G. Chandler, a certified wholesaler, bought rights to Coca-Cola.)

1887
Freud published his last paper on cocaine—"Fear for and Craving of Cocaine." This was in response to Erlenmeyer, a leading specialist in treating narcotic addicts, who accused Freud of releasing the "third scourge of mankind" after alcohol and morphine. Freud concluded that "cocaine has claimed no victims on its own" and, if a patient is not a morphine addict, he will not become a cocaine addict. He then withdrew cocaine as a cure for morphine addiction.

1890
Sir Arthur Conan Doyle, the creator of Sherlock Holmes, published *The Sign of Four*, which had the famous detective using cocaine three times a day to avoid the "dull routine of existence."

1885–1906
The age of patent medicine. Cocaine-boosted tonics were sold throughout America as cures for hay fever, asthma, common colds, fatigue, and many other ailments.

1887–1914
During this period forty-six (of the forty-eight) states passed some form of legislation regulating the use, sale, and distribution of cocaine. During this same period only twenty-nine states enacted legislation to regulate narcotic drugs—the opiates.

1898–1914
First widespread publicity campaign directed against a drug. Cocaine use was linked "with blacks, the poor, and criminals" (Ashley, 1975).

1901
Mortimer published the 576-page *History of Coca—"The Divine Plant" of the Incas*, which attempted to dispel the ever-increasing fear of American physicians about using cocaine. "Cocaine," Mortimer insisted, is ". . . not only harmless, but usually phenomenally beneficial. . . ."

1902
Wittstatler synthesized cocaine.

A survey conducted by Crothers demonstrated that only 3–8% of cocaine sold in New York and other major metropolitan areas was actually used in legitimate medical or dental situations.

1903
Cocaine was removed as an ingredient in the Coca-Cola drink. (This was partly the result of the bad press that cocaine began to develop and also because of pressure by Southern politicans, fearing "cocainized" blacks.)

1906
The Pure Food and Drug Act was passed. The act required that all over-the-counter patent medicines and soft drinks have their contents listed on the label.

1914
Harrison (Narcotics) Act was passed. Cocaine was identified as a narcotic, and all transactions involving its use were required to be recorded and reported to the federal government.

1914–30
Despite the laws, more cocaine than ever before was used in America. Europe experienced a similar phenomenon.

1916
England became the first European country to pass laws controlling cocaine use and distribution. (This preceded any such legislation governing the opiates by four years.)

1921
Pitigrilli published *Cocaine* (in Italian—in 1933 it was translated into English), the story of the "cocaine-crazed demimonde of the Parisian 1920s."

1930–mid-1960s
Cocaine was underground. Its use was restricted to "special" populations (i.e., jazz musicians, pimps, etc.).

1966–68
The "flower people" became a major news item. Haight-Ashbury became synonymous with the hippie life-style. Drugs, particularly amphetamines, LSD, and marijuana, became popular.

Late 1960s
"Speed kills" became the slogan of the time. *Easy Rider* made its debut, and cocaine started on its return to the drug scene.

1970–72
Cocaine use became popular again. Cocaine paraphernalia—spoons, kits—became big sellers in head shops. Many songs were written about cocaine. It became the "in" drug of the affluent, such as rock stars, and in show business and the advertising world.

1972–74
Cocaine became big business for the Federal Drug Enforcement Agency (formerly BNDD). More cocaine was seized in 1974 than heroin; law-enforcement agencies placed increasing emphasis on combating the cocaine traffic. The South Americans became the illicit power in importing and distributing cocaine.

1974
NIDA contracted for several studies of cocaine and cocaine effects on human beings (including the study on which the present volume is based).

1975
Richard Ashley published *Cocaine: Its History, Uses and Effects* the most comprehensive treatment of the history and use of cocaine done to date (based largely on work he did during the early '70s).

1976–
The second great cocaine explosion—a constantly expanding plethora of books, studies, research articles, legal arguments, arrests of the famous and nefarious, and the like. Cocaine prices increased; cocaine quality decreased; and it became established in the popular culture as the drug of the '70s. Cocaine's classification as a narcotic came under increasing attack.

1979

First Inter-American Seminar about Medico-Sociological Aspects of Coca and Cocaine held in Lima, Peru, July 2–5. Cocaine goes officially international. Hearings by the House of Representatives' Select Committee on Narcotics Abuse and Control, focusing on cocaine's abuse potential and on paraphernalia associated with its use, October–November. Increasing government scrutiny.

APPENDIX B

A SELECTED ANNOTATED BIBLIOGRAPHY ON COCA AND COCAINE

Ashley, R., *Cocaine: Its history, uses and effects.* New York: St. Martin's Press, 1975.

A popularized but serious and generally accurate socio-historical account of the drug, with a marked anti-regulatory emphasis. A first-rate introduction into the world of cocaine.

Becker, H. K., Carl Koller and cocaine. *Psychoanalytic Quarterly,* 1963, *32*:309–73.

This article, written by Carl Koller's daughter, recounts the early history of cocaine use and the role her father played in discovering the local-anesthetic properties of cocaine. Interesting insights into the early history of the drug. Included in Freud's *Cocaine papers* (see below).

Bejerot, N., A Comparison of the effects of cocaine and synthetic central stimulants. *British Journal of Addiction,* 1969, *65*: 35–37.

A review of the literature on cocaine and synthetic central stimulants in order to compare their pharmacological effects and symptoms of use and abuse.

Blejer-Prieto, H., Coca leaf and cocaine addiction. Some historical notes. *Canadian Medical Association Journal,* 1965, *93*: 700–704.

This article reviews firsthand source literature of the past 350 years, indicating the historical, medical, and sociological use of coca/cocaine.

Crowley, A., *Cocaine.* Reprinted San Francisco: Level Press, 1973, 1914.

This is a reprint of Crowley's classic denunciation of the Harrison Act in 1914. To Crowley, cocaine was the greatest of all drugs, and the book is one continuous song of praise about it and its effects.

Eiswirth, N. A., Smith, D. E., and Wesson, D. R., Current perspectives on cocaine use in America. *Journal of Psychedelic Drugs*, 1972, *5*:153–57.

This represents one of the initial efforts at describing the rise in the use of cocaine in the United States during the early 1970s. The article explores the history of cocaine use, the development of the black market, the type of use found in North and South America, and the drug's pharmacology and toxicology.

Finkle, B., and McCloskey, L. The forensic toxicology of cocaine. In Petersen and Stillman 1977, 153–92.

This study sought to determine cocaine's role in the significant and growing number of sudden and unexplained drug-related deaths. Results indicate that cocaine is involved in a low incidence of deaths when compared to other drugs. Of the 111 deaths examined, most were due to the use of morphine in conjunction with cocaine.

Freud, S. *The cocaine papers*. Vienna: Dunquin Press, 1963. Also reprinted in *Cocaine Papers of Sigmund Freud*, ed. R. Byck. New York: Stonehill Publishing Co., 1974.

Must reading for anyone interested in the history of cocaine. Contains some of the most eloquent testimony on the effects associated with cocaine use. Byck's more accessible edition includes all four of Freud's articles on cocaine plus several related papers about his discoveries and the influence of his cocaine work on his subsequent work in psychoanalysis.

Gay, G., Sheppard, C., Inaba, D., and Newmeyer, J., Cocaine in perspective: "Gift from the Sun God" to "The Rich Man's Drug." *Drug Forum*, 1973, *2*:409–30.

Another early overview on cocaine use in the 1970s. A history of its use, its pharmacology and physiological effects, the development of laws regulating its use, and current epidemiologic trends are discussed. An appendix, "A Chronology of Cocaine," ninth century A.D. to the present, is included.

Goodman, L., and Gilman, A., eds., *The pharmacological basis of therapeutics*. 4th ed. New York: Macmillan, 1970.

A classic textbook of pharmacology, toxicology and therapeutics.

Gottlieb, A. *The pleasures of cocaine*. San Francisco: And/Or Press, 1976.

A consumer's guide with considerable information on how to test and determine the quality of cocaine.

The Gourmet Cokebook: A complete guide to cocaine. New York: White Mountain Press, 1972.

The first of the underground "users" guides. Includes a popularized but sometimes inaccurate history of cocaine use.

(The "consumer's handbook" list now includes the more thorough and accurate Lee 1976, and also Gottlieb 1976).

Grinspoon, L., and Bakalar, J. B., *Cocaine: a drug and its social evolution*. New York: Basic Books, 1976.

A thorough but dry, scientific, and technical coverage of the history and effects of cocaine.

Gutierrez-Noriega, C., and Von Hagen, V. W., The strange case of the coca leaf. *Sci. Monthly*, 1950, *70(2)*:81–89.

Any bibliography on cocaine should include at least one citation from the works of Gutierrez-Noriega, a South American researcher who wrote numerous articles on coca/cocaine during the 1950s.

Jones, E. *The life and work of Sigmund Freud*, Vol. 1. New York: Basic Books, 1961.

Besides being a fascinating portrait of one of the world's foremost thinkers, this book is indispensable in understanding Freud's role in cocaine's history.

Lee, D., *Cocaine consumer's handbook*. San Francisco: And/Or Press, 1976.

One of the best handbooks available, offering considerable information on testing and determining cocaine's quality.

Mariani, A., *Coca and its therapeutic application*. New York: J. N. Jaros, 1890.

This book is interesting not only for its historical account of the use of coca, but also for its unabashed promoting of numerous Mariani coca-based preparations (including Vin Mariani and Elixir Mariani) for medical purposes.

Martin, R. T., The Role of coca in the history, religion and medicine of South American Indians. *Economic Botany*, 1970, *24*:422–38.

This comprehensive article reviews the role of coca in the history, religion, and medicine of South American Indians. The "white man's" attempt to curtail the use of coca by the Indians is also discussed.

McLaughlin, G. T., Cocaine: The history and regulation of a dangerous drug. *Cornell Law Review*, 1973, *58*:537–72.

Presents an excellent legal history of the regulation and control of cocaine at both the state and federal level.

Mortimer, W. G., *Peru History of Coca, the Divine Plant of the Incas*. New York: J. H. Vail and Co. 1901. Reprinted as *History of Coca*. San Francisco: And/Or Press, 1974.

Although written in 1900, this remains the most thorough discussion of coca. It examines in detail the role of coca in the lives of the Incas, its subsequent spread and evolution into an article of commerce following the conquest, and the eventual extensive use of coca and cocaine in the latter part of the nineteenth century.

Mulé, S. J., ed., *Cocaine: Chemical, biological, clinical, social and treatment aspects*. Cleveland: CRC Press, 1976.

A comprehensive, although highly technical, book of specially commissioned readings on cocaine.

Musto, D. *The American disease: Origins of narcotic control.* New Haven: Yale University Press, 1973.

An excellent overview on the criminalization of drug use in America.

Musto, D. A study in cocaine: Sherlock Holmes and Sigmund Freud. *Journal of the American Medical Association*, 1966, *204*:27–32.

This interesting article examines the use of cocaine by Sigmund Freud and Sherlock Holmes. It illustrates how objective evaluation of this widely used drug could be submerged by personal enthusiasm.

Petersen, R. C., and Stillman, R. C., eds. *Cocaine: 1977*. Research Monograph Series No. 13, DHEW Publ. No. (ADM) 77–432. Rockville, Md.: National Institute on Drug Abuse, 1977.

A comprehensive book of specially commissioned review articles and studies on various aspects of cocaine use, effects, and history.

Post, M. Cocaine psychoses: A continuum model. *American Journal of Psychiatry*, 1975, *132*:225–31.

Post, R., Kotin, J., and Goodwin, F. The effects of cocaine on depressed patients. *American Journal of Psychiatry*, 1974, *131*:511–17.

Post is must reading, as he was the first scientist since Freud to conduct research on cocaine effects on humans.

Sabbag, R. *Snowblind: A brief career in the cocaine trade*. New York: Bobbs-Merrill. 1976. Reprinted New York, Avon, 1978.

The best presentation of the big-time cocaine dealer done to date.

Siegel, R. K. Cocaine: Recreational use and intoxication. In Petersen and Stillman 1977, 119–36.

One of the few examples of a scientific inquiry into the current recreational use of cocaine. A total of eighty-five users were interviewed concerning their use of cocaine and other drugs.

Waldorf, D., Murphy, S., Reinarman, C., and Bridget, J. *Doing coke: An ethnography of cocaine users and sellers*. Washington, D.C.: Drug Abuse Council, 1977.

An excellent account of a cocaine network operating in the San Francisco Bay area.

Winick, C. The use of drugs by jazz musicians. *Social Problems*, 1950, *7*:240–53.

A fascinating examination.

Woodley, R. *Dealer: Portrait of a cocaine merchant.* New York: Holt, Rinehart, and Winston, 1971.

The original profile of a cocaine dealer, in this case a small-scale Harlem dealer, that has since been bolstered by other works on trafficking, in particular, Sabbag 1976 and Waldorf et al. 1977. Remains a good reference piece.

Woods, J. H., and Downs, D. A. The psychopharmacology of cocaine. In *Drug use in America: Problem in perspective,* Appendix, vol. 1: Patterns and consequences of drug use, 116–39. Technical papers of the Second Report of the National Commission on Marijuana and Drug Abuse. Washington, D.C.: Government Printing Office, 1973.

A first-rate review article specially commissioned by the National Commission on Marijuana and Drug Abuse. This remains an excellent and a comprehensive article since bolstered by more recent scientific compendia, in particular, Mule 1976, Petersen and Stillman 1977, and Grinspoon and Bakalar 1977.

BIBLIOGRAPHY

Abelson, H., Cohen, R., Schrayer, D., and Rappaport, M. Drug experience, attitudes and related behavior among adolescents and adults. *In Drug use in America: Problem in perspective,* Appendix, vol. I: Second Report to the National Commission on Marijuana and Drug Abuse. Washington, D.C.,: U.S. Government Printing Office, 1973.

Adams, N. M. Cocaine takes over. *Reader's Digest,* 1975, *106* 83–87.

Adriani, J. *The chemistry and physics of anesthesia.* 2nd ed. Springfield, Ill.: Charles C. Thomas, 1962.

"Agents say artist smuggled cocaine in 6-quart wine jug." *New York Times,* Feb. 12, 1975.

Alcala, R. P. The coca question in Bolivia. *Bull. Narc.,* 1952, *4(2):*10–15.

Aldrich, M. R., and Barker, R. W. Historical aspects of cocaine use and abuse. In *Cocaine: Chemical, biological, clinical, social and treatment aspects,* ed. S. J. Mule, 1–12. Cleveland: CRC Press, Inc., 1976.

Andrews, G., and Solomon, D., eds. *The coca leaf and cocaine papers.* New York: Harcourt Brace Jovanovich, 1975.

Anonymous. The following articles appeared in the *Journal of the American Medical Association.* (*JAMA*). They are arranged chronologically.

1900. The cocaine habit. *34:*1967.

1913. Deaths from cocaine injections. *61:*1307.

1917. Cocaine and unqualified dentists. *68:*1196–97.

1922. The campaign against cocaine. *78:*667.

1923a. Photogenic properties of cocaine. *80:*640.

1923b. Cocainism in Vienna. *80:*710.

1923c. Cocainism. *80:*864–65.

1923d. Abolition of cocaine. *80:*1254.

1923e. International control of the sale of narcotics, more particularly cocaine. *81:*761.

1924. Statistical data on cocainism and morphinism in Austria. *83:*1936.
1929(a). Accidents with local anesthesia. *92:*1680–81.
1929(b). Movements to combat drug addiction. *92:*329–30.
1929(c). Barbital as antidote to cocaine used in tonsillectomy. *93:*476.
1938. Use of cocaine for medical purposes. *111:*1975.
1940. Methods used for improving athletic performance. *115:*1281.
1941. History of cocaine as a local anesthetic. *117:*1284.
1970. Opium and cocaine inebriety (75 years ago). *214:*2251.
1974. Otolaryngologists hear defense of medical use of cocaine. *230(5):*652–53.

Ashley, R. *Cocaine: Its history, uses and effects.* New York: St. Martin's Press, 1975.

———. 1976. The fight for legal cocaine. *High Times,* June 1976, *10*:57–59, 63.

Astron, A., and Persson, N. H. The toxicity of some local anesthetics after application on different mucous membranes and its relation to anesthetic action on the nasal mucosa of the rabbit. *J. Pharmacol. Exp. Ther.,* 1932, *132:*87–90.

Barash, P. Cocaine in clinical medicine. In *Cocaine: 1977,* ed. R. C. Petersen and R. C. Stillman, 193–200. Research Monograph Series No. 13, DHEW Publ. No. (ADM) 77–432. Rockville, Md: NIDA, 1977.

Beal, J. H. Report on pharmacy legislation. *Proc. A. Ph. A.* 1901, *49:*460–61.

Becker, H. K. Carl Koller and cocaine. *Psychoanal. Quart,* 1963, *32:*309–73.

Bejarano, J. Further considerations on the coca habit in Colombia. *Bull. Narc.,* 1952, *4(3):*3–19.

———. 1961. Present state of coca-leaf habit in Colombia. *Bull. Narc. 13(1):*1–5.

Bejerot, N. A. A comparison of the effects of cocaine and synthetic central stimulants. *British Journal of Addiction,* 1969, *65:*35–37.

Bell, D. S., and Trethowan, W. Amphetamine addiction and disturbed sexuality. *Arch. Gen. Psychiatry,* 1961, *4:*74–78.

Bennett, W. C. The Andean highlands: An introduction. In *The Andean Civilizations,* vol. 2 of *Handbook of South American Indians,* ed. J. H. Steward. Smithsonian Institution, Bureau of American Ethnology, Bulletin 143 (6 vols.). Washington, D.C., 1946–50.

Berg, D. F. Dangerous drugs in the United States. *Int. J. Addict.,* 1970, *5(4):*795–806.

Blejer-Prieto, H. Coca leaf and cocaine addictions, some historical notes. *Can. Med. Assoc. J.,* 1965, *93:*700–04.

Bomboy, R. Major newspaper coverage of drug issues. *Fellows Series Monographs*, FS-1. Washington, D.C.: Drug Abuse Council, 1974.

Bose, C. Cocaine poisoning. *Brit. Med. J.*, 1913, *1*:16–17.

Brecher, E. *Licit and illicit drugs*. New York: Little, Brown, 1972.

Brecher, E., and Zinberg, N. Affidavit to defendant's joint memorandum in support of their motions for correction or reduction of sentences (United States of America v. Foss and Coveney, U.S. District Court, District of Massachusetts: Criminal No. 73-24-6), 1974.

Buck, A. A., Sasaki, T. T., Hewitt, J. J., and Macrae, A. A. Coca chewing and health: An epidemiologic study among residents of a Peruvian village. *Am. J. Epidem.*, 1968, *88:* 159–77.

Burroughs, W. S. *Naked Lunch*. New York: Grove Press, 1966.

Byck, R., ed. *Cocaine papers by Sigmund Freud*. New York: Stonehill Publishing Co., 1974.

Byck, R., and Van Dyke, C., What are the effects of cocaine in man? In *Cocaine, 1977*, ed. R. C. Petersen and R. C. Stillman, 97–118. Research Monograph Series No. 13, DHEW Publ. No. (ADM) 77–432. Rockville, Md.: NIDA, 1977.

Campbell, D., and Adriani, J. Absorption of local anesthetics, 1958. *JAMA 168:*873–77.

Cardenas, M. Psychological aspects of coca addiction. *Bull. Narc.*, 1952, *4(2):*6–9.

Carroll, E. Coca: The plant and its use. In *Cocaine: 1977*, ed. R. C. Petersen and R. C. Stillman, 47–62. Research Monograph Series No. 13, DHEW Publ. No. (ADM) 77–432. Rockville, Md.: NIDA, 1977.

Castleman, M. "Snows up the Nose: A History of Cocaine." *Ann Arbor Sun Community News Service*, 1975, *3(1):* 13–15, 18.

Chambers, C., and Inciardi, J. *An assessment of drug use in the general population*. Special Report No. 2, New York State Narcotic Addiction Control Commission. Albany, N.Y.: NACC, 1971.

Chambers, C. D., Taylor, W. J. R., and Moffett, A. D. The incidence of cocaine abuse among methadone maintenance patients. *Int. J. Addict*, 1972, *7(3):*427–41.

Chapel, J. Emergency room treatment of drug-abusing patients. *Am. J. Psychiat.*, 1973, *130:*257–59.

Chardy, A. "Colombia to Attack Traffic in Cocaine." *Washington Post*, March 11, 1978, A 20.

Chopra, I. C., and Chopra, R. N. The cocaine problem in India. *Bull. Narc.*, 1958, *10:*12–24.

Christison, R. Observations on the effect of cuca, or coca, etc. *Brit. Med. J.*, April 29, 1876, 527–531.

Clark, T. Cocaine. *Tex. Med.* 1973, *69*:74–78.

Clarke, E. *Isolation and identification of drugs in pharmaceuticals, body fluids and post-mortem material.* 2 vols. London: Pharmaceutical Press, 1969, 1975.

Cocaine—Illicit manufacture and traffic. *Int. Criminal Pol. Rev.*, 1969, *227*:97–102.

"The Cocaine Scene." *Newsweek*, May 30, 1977, 20–22, 25.

"Cocaine Smuggled in Water Skis." *Washington Post,* Aug. 26, 1974.

"Cocaine Used Most by Drug Addicts." *New York Times*, April 15, 1926.

Cohen, L. "C.B.O.E. Lashes out at U.S. Drug Unit on Cocaine Arrests." *Wall Street Journal*, Feb. 9, 1979.

Cooper, P. *Poisoning by drugs and chemicals, an index of toxic effects and their treatment*. 3rd ed. Chicago: Year Book Medical Publishers, 1974.

Cortright, B. "Dope Scoreboard." *Los Angeles Free Press 11(1)* (January 4, 1974):13.

Courtois-Suffit, G., R. Traffic in cocaine. *Bull. Acad. Med.*, 1921, *85*:720 (Abs.: *JAMA 77*:494).

Cramp, A. S. The Indispensable Use of Narcotics, *JAMA*, 1931, *96*, 1050–52.

Crowely, A. *Cocaine*, 1918. Reprinted San Francisco: Level Press, 1973.

———. 1922. *The diary of a drug fiend.* Reprinted New York: Samuel Weisner, 1973.

De Onis, J. "Cocaine as a Way of Life in Bolivia." *New York Times*, August 22, 1972, 22.

De Vito, J. J. In "From the Medical Examiner's File," *Med. Times*, 1975, *103*:89.

Downs, A. W., and Eddy, N. B. The influence of barbital upon cocaine poisoning in the rat. *J. Pharmacol. Exp. Ther.*, 1932a, *45*:383–87.

———. 1932b. The effect of repeated doses of cocaine on the dog. *J. Pharmacol. Exp. Ther. 46*:195–98.

———. 1932c. The effect of repeated doses of cocaine on the rat. *J. Pharmacol. Exp. Ther. 46*:199–200.

Drug Abuse Warning Network (Project DAWN) Files. IMS America, Inc., Ambler, Pa.

Drug Enforcement Administration. Report on cocaine users (#BH-003), conducted by the DAWN scientific investigators for the Cocaine Policy Task Force. Unpublished. Washington, D.C.: DEA, July 1974.

———. Report of the Cocaine Policy Task Force. Unpublished. Washington, D.C.: DEA, July 1974.

———. Statistics compiled through September 1978: Drug Enforcement Statistical Report, Enforcement Activity, Drug Abuse Indicators, Organization and Training Dates. Washington, D.C.: DEA, 1978.

———. Statistics compiled through December 1974: Drug Enforcement Statistical Report, Federal Performance Measurements, State and Local Performance Measurements, National Drug Measurements. Unpublished. Washington, D.C.: DEA, 1974.

———. Statistics compiled through September 1978: Drug Enforcement Statistical Report, Enforcement Activity, Drug Abuse Indicators, Organization and Training Dates. Washington, D.C.: DEA, 1978.

"Drug Scheme Fatal to Texan." *Washington Star-News*, Aug. 21, 1974, 2.

"Drugs in Rug Bring Arrest of 74-Year-Old." *Washington Star-News*, Aug. 8, 1974.

"Drug Traffic in South America." Washington, D.C.: Bureau of Narcotics and Dangerous Drugs, 1970.

Duke, J. A., Aulik, D., Plowman, T. Nutritional value of coca. *Botanical Museum Leaflets, Harvard University*, 1975, *24:* 113–19.

Echerman, W. C., Bater, J. D., Rachel, J. V., and Poole, W. K. *Drug usage and arrest charges: A study of drug and arrest charges in six metropolitan areas of the United States.* Prepared for the Bureau of Narcotics and Dangerous Drugs, Contract No. J-70-35 (December 1971).

Eddy, N. B., Halbach, H., Isbell, H. and Seevers, M. H. Drug dependence: Its significance and characteristics. *Bull. WHO*, 1965. *32:*721–33.

Edmundson, W. F., Davies, J. E., Acker, J. D., and Myer, B. Patterns of drug abuse epidemiology in prisoners. *Indust. Med. Surg.*, 1972, *41:*15–19.

Eiswirth, N. A., Smith, D. E., and Wesson, D. R. Current perspectives on cocaine use in America. *J. Psychedelic Drugs*, 1972, *5:*153–57.

Elinson, J. *A study of teen-age drug behavior.* Summary progress report covering the period 9/1/71 through 6/30/72, prepared by the College of Physicians and Surgeons, Columbia University, for the National Institute of Mental Health, under Grant No. MH-17589-03, June 1972.

Ellinwood, E. H. Amphetamine psychosis: Individuals, settings, and sequences. In *Current concepts on amphetamine abuse.* ed. E. H. Ellinwood and S. Cohen, 143–158, Washington, D.C.: GPO, 1972.

Finkle, B. S., and McCloskey, K. L. The forensic toxicology of cocaine. In *Cocaine: 1977*, ed. R. C. Petersen and R. C. Stillman, 153–92. Research Monograph Series No. 13, DHEW Publ. No. (ADM) 77–432. Rockville, Md.: NIDA, 1977.

Fooner, M. Cocaine: The South American connection. *World,* 1973, *2(5):*22–25.

Freud, S. *An Autobiographical Study*, tr. J. Strachey. New York: Norton, 1952.

———. 1884. On coca. *Centra. Gesammte Ther.* (Wien) II, S. 289–314. Reprinted in *The cocaine papers*, tr. S. Edminster. Vienna: Dunquin Press, 1963.

———. 1885a. Contribution to the knowledge of the effect of cocaine. *Wien. Med. Wochenschr. 35(5):*129–33. Reprinted in *The cocaine papers*, tr. R. Potask. Vienna: Dunquin Press, 1963.

———1885b. On the general effect of cocaine. *Med. Chirurg. Centra. 20(32):*374–75. Reprinted in *The cocaine papers*, tr. S. Edminster. Vienna: Dunquin Press, 1963.

———. 1887. Craving for and fear of cocaine. *Wein. Med. Wochenschr. 28:*929–32. Reprinted in *The cocaine papers,* tr. W. Hammond. Vienna: Dunquin Press, 1963. This and the preceding three papers are also reprinted in R. Byck, ed., *Cocaine papers by Sigmund Freud.* New York: Stonehill Publishing Co., 1974.

From the State Capitals. Drug abuse control trends summarized, March 1, 1978, and Feb. 1, 1979. Asbury Park, N.J.: Bethune Jones.

"'Funny' Walk Reveals Cocaine." *Washington Star-News,* March 31, 1975.

Gagliano, J. A social history of coca in Peru. Doctoral dissertation (history), Georgetown University, Washington, D.C., 1961.

Gallant, D. M. The effect of alcohol and drug abuse on sexual behavior. *Med. Aspects Human Sexuality,* 1968, *11(1):*30–36.

Gay, G. R., and Sheppard, C. W. Sex-crazed dope fiends! Myth or reality? In *Drugs and youth: The challenge of today*, ed. E. Harms. New York: Pergamon Press, 1973.

Gay, G., Sheppard, C., Inaba, D., and Newmeyer, J. 1973a. Cocaine in perspective: "Gift from the Sun God" to "Rich Man's Drug." *Drug Forum, 2(4):*409–30.

———. 1973b. An old girl: Flyin' low, dyin' slow, blinded by snow: Cocaine in perspective. *Int. J. Addict. 8(6):* 1027–42.

Glenn, W. A. A compendium on recent studies of illegal drug use. Prepared for the National Institute of Mental Health under Contract No. HSM-42-72-169, March 1973.

Goode, E. "Marijuana and Sex." *Evergreen Review 66(1969):* 19–21.

Goodman, L., and Gilman, A., eds. *The pharmacological basis of therapeutics.* 4th ed. New York: Macmillan, 1970.

Gordon, A. Insanities caused by acute and chronic intoxication with opium and cocaine, A study of 171 cases, Suggestions for legislative and other measures, The question of responsibility. *JAMA*, 1908, *51*:97–101.

Gossett, J. T., Lewis, J. M., and Phillips, V. A. Extent and prevalence of illicit drug use as reported by 56,745 students. *JAMA*, 1971, *216*: 1464–70.

Gottlieb, A. *The pleasures of cocaine.* San Francisco: And/Or Press, 1976.

The gourmet cokebook: A complete guide to cocaine. New York: White Mountain Press, 1972. Also published New York: by D.C. Production Enterprises.

Green, E. M. Psychoses among negroes: A comparative study. *J. Nerv. Ment. Disorders*, 1914, *41*:697–708.

Grinspoon, L., and Bakalar, J. B. *Cocaine: A drug and its social evolution.* New York: Basic Books, 1976.

———. 1979. Cocaine. In *Handbook on drug abuse*, ed. R. Dupont, A. Goldstein, and J. O'Donnell, 241–47. Washington, D.C.: NIDA, Office of Drug Abuse Policy.

"The Growing Menace of the Use of Cocaine." *New York Times*, Aug. 2, 1968.

Gutierrez-Noriega, C., and Von Hagen, V. W. The strange case of the coca leaf. *Sci. Monthly*, 1950, *70(2)*:81–89.

Gutierrez-Noriega, C., and Zapata-Ortiz, V. Experimental cocainism: General toxicology, habituation and sensitization. *Rev. Med. Exp.* (Lima), 1944, *3*:279–306.

Hanna, J. M. Coca leaf use in Southern Peru: Some biosocial aspects. *Am. Anthropol.*, 1974, *76*:281–96.

"Happy Days in Hollywood." *Vanity Fair*, May 1922, 73.

Harmetz, A. "Cocaine in Hollywood." *New York Times*, July 11, 1978.

Hellman, L. *Pentimento*. New York: Signet, 1974.

Herzfeld, A. A. Prevention of cocaine intoxication by ethyl alcohol in surgery. *JAMA*, 1921, *77*:1594.

Heyerdahl, T. *Kon-Tiki, across the Pacific by raft.* Tr. F. H. Lyon. New York: Permabook, 1960.

Hodge, W. H. Coca. *National Hist.*, 1947, *56*:86–93.

Holmstedt, B., Lindgren, J., Rivier, L., and Plowman, T. Cocaine in the blood of coca chewers. *J. Ethnopharmacol.*, 1979, *1*:69–78.

Hopkins, J. "Cocaine: A Flash in the Pan, a Pain in the Nose," *Rolling Stone* (April 9, 1971), *81*:1, 6.

"Huge Narcotic Ring Smashed in Berlin." *New York Times*, Sept. 14, 1926.

Hughes, L. W. The curse of coca. *Int. American*, 1946, *42*:18–22.

Ianni, F. A. *Black Mafia: Ethnic succession in organized crime.* New York: Simon and Schuster, 1974.

"Influence of Cocaine on Contemporary Style in Literature." *Current Literature*, 1910, *48*:633.

Jaffe, J. H. 1970. Drug addiction and drug abuse. In *The pharmacological basis of therapeutics*, ed. L. S. Goodman and A. Gilman, 276–313. New York: Macmillan, 1970.

Joel, E., and Frankel, F. Cocainism and homosexuality. *Dtsch. Med. Wchnschr.*, 1925, *51*:1562 (Abs.: *JAMA 85*:1436).

Jones, E. *The life and work of Sigmund Freud*, vol. 1. New York: Basic Books, 1961.

"Judge Won't Toss Out State's Cocaine Law." *San Jose Mercury News*, June 14, 1977.

Kaye, S. *Handbook of emergency toxicology: A guide for the identification, diagnosis and treatment of poisoning.* 3rd ed. Springfield, Ill.: C. C. Thomas, 1970.

Kestenbaum, R. S., Resnick, R. B., and Schwartz, L. K. Acute systemic effects of cocaine in man: A controlled study by intranasal and intravenous routes of administration. Division of Drug Abuse Research and Treatment, Department of Psychiatry, New York Medical College, New York, 1975.

King, P. *Cocaine—A play in one act.* New York: Frank Shay, 1917.

King, R. *Drug hang-ups: America's fifty year folly.* New York: Norton, 1972.

Kober, B. "Cuba Called Leading Illicit Cocaine User." *Baltimore News-Post*, June 9, 1961, A4.

Kolb, R. *Drug addiction: A medical problem.* Springfield, Ill.: C. C. Thomas, 1962.

Lee, D. *Cocaine consumer's handbook.* San Francisco: And/Or Press, 1976.

Leehody, J. R. The action of coca. *Brit. Med. J.*, 1876, *1*:750–51.

Leon, L. A. The disappearance of cocaine in Ecuador. *Bull. Narc.*, 1952, *4*:21–25.

Leshure, J. Barbital as a preventive of cocaine toxicosis, *JAMA*, 1927, *88*:168–69.

"Life and Leisure: It's the Real Thing." *Newsweek*, Sept. 27, 1971, 124 ff.

Lingeman, R. R. *Drugs from A to Z: A dictionary*, New York: McGraw-Hill, 1969.

Little, M. A. Effects of alcohol and coca on foot temperature responses of Highland Peruvians during a localized cold exposure. *Amer. J. Physical Anthropol.*, 1970, *32*, 233–42.

Luduena, F. P., Toppe, T. O., and Borland, J. K. A statistical evaluation of the relationships among local anesthetic activity, irritancy, and systemic toxicity. *J. Pharmacol. Exp. Ther.*, 1958, *123*:269–77.

MacKenzie, G. W. Complications of nose operations, *JAMA*, 1961, 61:1200–01.

Maher, J. Coca—Erythroxylon coca. Unpublished BNDD document, 1968.

Malcolm X. *Autobiography*. New York: Grove Press, 1965.

Malone, M. H. Its the real zing. *Pacific Information Service on Street Drugs*, 1973, *2(4)*:24–27.

Mariani, A. *Coca and its therapeutic application*. New York: J. N. Jaros, 1890.

Marshall, E. "Uncle Sam Is the Worst Drug Fiend in the World." *New York Times*, March 12, 1911.

Martin, R. T. The role of coca in the history, religion and medicine of South American Indians. *Econ. Bot.*, 1970, *24*:422–38.

Mayer, E. The toxic effects following the use of local anesthetics. *JAMA*, 1924, *82*:876–85.

Mayer-Gross, W., Slater, E., and Roth, M. *Clinical Psychiatry*. Baltimore: Williams and Wilkins, 1960.

McLaughlin, G. T. Cocaine: The history and regulation of a dangerous drug. *Cornell Law Review*, 1973, *58*:537–72.

Melzack, R., Ofiesh, J. G., and Mount, B. M. The Brompton mixture: Effects on pain in cancer patients, *Can. Med. Assoc.*, 1976, *115*:125–29.

Meyer, N. *The Seven Per Cent Solution*. New York: Ballantine, 1976.

Moffett, C. Rx cocaine. *Hampton's Magazine*, 1911, *26*:595–606.

Monge, C. The need for studying the problem of coca-leaf chewing. *Bull. Narc.*, 1952, *4(4)*: 13–15.

Mortimer, W. G. *Peru history of coca, the divine plant of the Incas*. New York: J. H. Vail, 1961. Reprinted as *History of Coca*. San Francisco: And/Or Press, 1974.

Mulé, S. J., ed. *Cocaine: Chemical, biological, clinical, social and treatment aspects*. Cleveland: CRC Press, 1976.

Musto, D. F. A study of cocaine: Sherlock Holmes and Sigmund Freud, *JAMA*, 1968, *204(1)*:27–32.

———. *The American disease: Origins of narcotic control*. New Haven and London: Yale University Press, 1973.

Mutch, N. Cocaine. *Guy's Hospital Gazette*, 1932, *46*:425–29.

National Commission on Marijuana and Drug Abuse. *Drug use in America: Problem in perspective*. Washington, D.C.: G.P.O., 1973.

National Institute on Drug Abuse. *Annual Data, 1977, Data from CODAP*. NIDA Statistical Series, Series E, No. 9. Rockville, Md.: NIDA, 1978a.

———. 1978b. *SMSA Statistics, 1977, Data from CODAP*. NIDA Statistical Series, Series E, No. 9. Rockville, Md.: NIDA.

"Nations Uniting to Stamp Out the Use of Opium and Many Other Drugs." *New York Times*, July 25, 1909.

Negrete, J., and Murphy, H. Psychological deficit in chewers of coca leaf. *Bull. Narc.*, 1967, *19(4)*:11–17.

Nelson, H. "Cocaine for Medical Use Hard to Find." *Los Angeles Times*, July 30, 1978.

Nostrums and quackery, articles on the nostrum evil and quackery. Reprinted with additions and modifications from *JAMA*. Chicago: American Medical Association, 1912.

Noya, N. D. Coca and cocaine: A perspective from Bolivia. In *The International Challege of Drug Abuse*, ed. R. C. Petersen. Research Monograph Series 19, DHEW Publ. No. (ADM) 78-60498. Rockville, Md.: NIDA, 1978.

Office of Drug Abuse Policy. *Annual Report, 1978*. Washington, D.C.: ODAP, 1978.

Osborne, H. *Indians of the Andes, Aymaras and Quechuas*. London, 1952.

Ottenberg, M. "Cocaine: The New No. 1 Drug." *Washington Star-News*, Aug. 5, 1974, A1, A6, 1974a.

———. 1974b. "Cocaine 'Mules'—Sophisticated Smugglers." *Washington Star-News*, Aug. 6, 1974, A3.

———. 1974c. "Smugglers Beat Cocaine Laws." *Washington Star-News*, Aug. 7, 1974.

Owens, W. Signs and symptoms presented by those addicted to cocaine. *JAMA*, 1912, *58*:329–30.

"Patching Hollywood's 'Coke Noses,'" *Medical World News*, 1978, *19*:81–82.

Penfield, W. Halstead of John Hopkins, the man and his problem as described in the secret records of William Osler. *JAMA*, 1969, *210*:2214–18.

Perry, Charles. "The Star-Spangled Powder or Through History with Coke Spoon and Nasal Spray." *Rolling Stone*, Issue 115, Aug. 17, 1972.

Perry, D. C. edited by B. E. Radcliffe, Heroin and cocaine adulteration. *PharmChem Newsletter*, 1974, *3(2)*, 1, 4.

Petersen, R. C., and Stillman, R. D., eds. *Cocaine: 1977*. Research Monograph Series No. 13, DHEW Publ. No. (ADM) 77–432. Rockville, Md.: NIDA, 1977.

PharmChem Newsletter. Annual statistical summaries of street drug analyses. 1974, *3(3)*; 1975, *4(4)*; 1976, *5(1)*; 1977, *6(2)*; 1978, *2(2)*.

Phillips, J. L., and Wynne, R. D. *A cocaine bibliography—Nonannotated*. Research Issues Series No. 8, DHEW Publ. No. (ADM) 75–203. Rockville, Md.: NIDA, 1975.

———. 1976. Sociological aspects of cocaine use and abuse. In *Cocaine: Chemical, Biological, Clinical, Social and Treatment Aspects*, ed. S. J. Mulé, 229–42. Cleveland: CRC Press, 1976.

Phillips, R. Cocaine not narcotic? If so, it does not interfere with driving ability, as alcohol does. *Current Medicine for Attorneys*, 1977, *24:*14–15.

Pickett, R. D. Acute toxicity of heroin, alone and in combination with cocaine and quinine. *Brit. J. Pharmacol.*, 1970, *40:*145–46.

Pitigrilli [D. Segré]. *Cocaine*, 1921. Reprinted San Francisco: And/Or Press, 1975.

Plate, T. "Coke: The Big New Easy-Entry Business." *New York Magazine*, Nov. 5, 1973, *6(45)*, 63–75.

———. "Cocaine: New Jackpot for a New Mafia." *Oui*, Aug. 1974, 38ff.

Post, R. Cocaine psychoses: A continuum model. *Am. J. Psychiat.*, 1975, *132:*225–31.

Post, R., Kotin, J., and Goodwin, F. The effects of cocaine on depressed patients. *Am. J. Psychiat.*, 1974, *131:*511–17.

Proust, M. *The past recaptured.* New York: Modern Library, 1932.

Rappolt, R. T., Gay, G. R., and Inaba, D. S. Propranolol: A specific antagonist to cocaine. *Clinical Toxicology*, 1977, *10:* 265–71.

Report of Committee on Acquirement of the Drug Habit. *Proc. A. Ph. A.*, 1902, *50:*567–73.

Report of Committee on the Acquirement of the Drug Habit. *Proc. A. Ph. A.*, 1902, *51:*466–77.

Report of the President's Homes Commission. S. Doc. No. 644, 60th Congress, 2nd Session, 1/8/09, 254–55.

Resnick, R. B., Kestenbaum, R. S., and Schwartz, L. K. Acute systemic effects of cocaine in man: A controlled study by intranasal and intravenous routes. *Science*, 1977, *195:*696–98.

Rhode, J. [C. J. C. Street]. *The White Menace.* Chicago: White House, 1926.

Ritchie, J. M., Cohen, P. J., and Dripps, R. D. 1970. Cocaine, procaine and other synthetic local anesthetics. In *The Pharmacological Basis of Therapeutics*, ed. L. S. Goodman and A. Gilman, 371–401. New York: Macmillan.

Rosen, C. "The Great God Basketball Jones." *Crawdaddy*, January 1974, *34*, 34–38.

Rowe, J. H., Inca Culture at the Times of the Spanish Conquest. In *The Andean Civilizations*, vol. 2 of *Handbook of South American Indians*, ed. J. H. Steward. 6 vols. Smithsonian Institution, Bureau of American Ethnology, Bulletin 143. Washington, D.C., 1946–50.

Sabbag, R., *Snowblind: A Brief Career in the Cocaine Trade.* New York: Bobbs-Merrill, 1976. Reprinted New York: Avon, 1978.

Saenz, L. N. *La coca: Estudio medico-social de gran toxicomania Peruana*. Lima, 1938.

———. 1945. *El punto de vista medico en el problema indigena Peruana*. Lima.

Scheppegrell, W. The abuse and dangers of cocaine. *Med. News*, 1898, *75*:417–22.

Schultz, M. G. The "strange case" of Robert Louis Stevenson. JAMA, 1971, *216(1)*:90–94.

Scott, L. J. *Specific field test for cocaine microgram*. 1973, 6, 11.

Searle, *New form of nervous disease, together with Erythroxylon Coca*, New York, 1881.

Shrady, F. G. *General Grant's last days with a short biographical sketch of Dr. Shrady*. New York: 1908.

Siegel, R. K. Cocaine smoking *N. Engl. J. Med.*, 1979, *300(7)*: 373.

———. 1977. Recreational use and intoxication. In *Cocaine: 1977*, ed. R. C. Petersen and R. C. Stillman, 119–36. Research Monograph Series No. 13, DHEW Publ. No. (ADM) 77–432. Rockville, Md.: NIDA.

Siragusa, C., and Wiedrich, R. "Cocaine, Castro and Cuba." *Chicago Tribune Sunday Magazine*, Sept. 11, 1966.

Smith, R., "Compulsive methamphetamine abuse and violence in the Haight-Ashbury district." In: *Current concepts on amphetamine abuse*, ed. E. H. Ellinwood and S. Cohen, 205–216, Washington D.C.: 1972.

Snowbird. "The Nightmare of Cocaine." By a former "snowbird." *North American Review*, 1924, 227:419.

"Soldiers Smuggle Cocaine to French." *New York Times*, June 24, 1921.

Spotts, J. V., and Schontz, F. C. *The life style of nine American cocaine users: Trip to the land of cockaigne*. Research Issues Series No. 16, DHEW Publ. No. (ADM) 76–392. Rockville, Md.: NIDA, 1976.

"Spread of Drug Habit Alarms Berlin Police." *New York Times*, Aug. 16, 1925.

Spruce, R. *Notes of a botanist on the Amazon and Andes, being a record of travel . . . during the years 1849–1864*. Ed. and condensed Alfred R. Wallace. 2 vols. London, 1908.

Stahl, F. A. *In the land of the Incas*. Mountain View, Calif., 1920.

Stockwell, G. A. Erythroxylon coca. *Boston Med. Surg. J.*, 1877, *96*:402.

Street, J. P. The patent medicine situation. *Am. J. Pub. Health*, 1917, *7*:1037–42.

Suarez, C. A., Arango, A., and Lester III, J. L. Cocaine-condom ingestion, surgical treatment, *JAMA*, 1977, *238*:1391–92.

Sullivan, W. "U.N. seeking curbs on leaf chewing." *New York Times*, Sept. 20, 1964.

"Synthetic Cocaine Not Illegal." *The Journal*, 1978, *7(6)*:5.

Tatum, A. L., and Seevers, M. Y. Experimental cocaine addiction. *J. Pharmacol. Exp. Ther.*, 1929, *36*:401–10.

Trebach, A. "Heroin, the Helper." *Washington Star-News*, July 21, 1974, E3.

Tschirch, A. *Handbuch der pharmakognoise*. Vol. 3, *Coca leaves*, Leipzig: Chr. Herm. Tauchnitz, 1923, 309–26.

Tschudi, J. J. *Travels in Peru during the years 1838–1842, on the Coast, in the Sierra, across the Cordilleras and Andes, into the primeval forests*. Tr. T. Ross. New York, 1849.

U.N. Economic and Social Council, Commission on Narcotic Drugs. *Study on coca leaves*. Third Session, May 1948.

"U.S. Agents Try, but Fail, to Stop the Flow of Cocaine from Latin Countries." *New York Times*, Jan. 25, 1971.

U.S. Public Health Service. State Laws Relating to the Control of Narcotic Drugs and the Treatment of Drug Addiction, Part IV, 1931.

VanDyke, C., and Byck, R. Cocaine: 1884–1974. In *Cocaine and Other Stimulants*, ed. E. H. Ellinwood and M. M. Kilbey, New York: Plenum Press, 1977, 1–30.

Vidal, D. "Colombia Is Still the Chief Generator of Cocaine Traffic, the U.S. Is Both Chief Consumer and Principal Worrier." *New York Times*, March 19, 1978, 2.

Volsky, G. "Illicit Traffic of Cocaine 'Growing by Leaps and Bounds' in Miami." *New York Times*, Feb. 1, 1970.

Von Hoffman, N. "High Is How You Live It." *Washington Post*, April 21, 1975.

Von Oettingen, W. F. Earliest suggestion of use of cocaine for local anesthesia. *Ann. Med. History*, 1933, *5*:275–80.

Waldorf, D., Murphy, S., Reinarman, C., and Joyce, B. *Doing coke: Ethnography of cocaine users and dealers*. Washington, D.C.: Drug Abuse Council, 1977.

Watson, Col. J. W. Letter. *New York Tribune*, June 21, 1903.

Watson-Williams, E. Cocaine and its substitutes *Brit. Med. J.*, 1923, *2*:1018–21.

Wesson, D. R., and Smith, D. E. Cocaine: Its use for central nervous system stimulation including recreational and medical uses. *Cocaine: 1977*, eds. R. C. Petersen and R. C. Stillman, Research Monograph Series No. 13, DHEW Publ. No. (ADM) 77–432, Rockville, Md.: NIDA, 1977, 137–152.

Wiedrich, R. "On the Trail of the Poppy." *Chicago Tribune Sunday Magazine*, Sept. 11, 1966.

Williams, E. H. "Negro Cocaine 'Fiends' Are a New Southern Menace." *New York Times*, Feb. 8, 1914.

Wiley, H. W., and Pierce, A. L. The cocaine crime. *Good Housekeeping*, 1914, *58*:393–98.

Wilson, S. A. K. *Neurology*, ed. A. N. Bruce, Baltimore: Williams and Wilkins, 1955, 833.

Winick, C. The use of drugs by jazz musicians. *Soc. Prob.*, 1959, *7*:240–53.

———. 1962a. The taste of music: Alcohol, drugs, and jazz. *Jazz Monthly*, *8(8)*:8–12.

———. 1962b. The taste of music: Alcohol, drugs, and jazz. *Jazz Monthly* *8*:10–12.

Winick, C., and Kinsie, P. *The lively commerce: Prostitution in the United States.* Chicago: Quadrangle Books, 1971.

Woodley, R. *Dealer: Portrait of a cocaine merchant.* New York: Holt, Rinehart and Winston, 1971.

Woods, J. H., and Downs, D. A. The psychopharmacology of cocaine. In *Drug use in America: Problem in perspective,* Appendix, vol. 1: Patterns and consequences of drug use, 116–39. Technical papers of the Second Report of the National Commission on Marijuana and Drug Abuse. Washington, D.C.: G.P.O., 1973.

Wynne Associates, Greater Kansas City Mental Health Project, and Documentation Associates Information Services, Inc. *Cocaine—Summaries of psychosocial research.* Research Issues Series No. 15, DHEW Publ. No. (ADM) 77–391. Rockville, Md.: NIDA, 1976.

Wynne, R. D. Community action to regulate the illicit drug market. *Drug Forum*, 1973, *2*:79–90.

Zapata-Ortiz, V. The problems of the chewing of the coca-leaf in Peru. *Bull. Narc.*, 1952, *4*:26–33.

Zinberg, N. Affidavit to defendant's joint memorandum (see Brecher and Zinberg, 1974).